THE MASK OF SANITY

HERVEY CLECKLEY, M.D.

Clinical Professor of Psychiatry,
Medical College of Georgia,
Augusta, Ga.; author of The Caricature
of Love *and of* The Three Faces of Eve
(with Corbett H. Thigpen)

THE MASK OF SANITY

An attempt to clarify some issues about the so-called
psychopathic personality

Non teneas aurum totum quod splendet ut aurum.
Alanus de Insulis

Fourth edition

THE C. V. MOSBY COMPANY
Saint Louis 1964

Fourth edition

Copyright © 1964 by

THE C. V. MOSBY COMPANY

Previous editions copyrighted 1941, 1950, 1955

Printed in the United States of America

Library of Congress Catalog Card Number 64-22758

Distributed in Great Britain by Henry Kimpton, London

To L. M. C.

From chaos shaped, the Bios grows. In bone
And viscus broods the Id. And who can say
Whence Eros comes? Or chart his troubled way?
Nor bearded sage, nor science, yet has shown
How truth or love, when met, is straightly known;
Some phrases singing in our dust today
Have taunted logic through man's Odyssey:
Yet, strangely, man sometimes will find his own.
And even man has felt the arcane flow
Whence brims unchanged the very Attic wine,
Where lives that mute and death-eclipsing glow
That held the Lacedaemonian battle line:
And this, I think, may make what man is choose
The doom of joy he knows he can but lose.

Preface to fourth edition

The first edition of this book was based primarily on experience with adult male psychopaths hospitalized in a closed institution. Though a great many other psychopaths had come to my attention, most of the patients who were followed over years and from whom emerged the basic concepts presented in 1941 were from this group. During the next decade a much more diverse group became available. Female patients, adolescents, people who had never been admitted to a psychiatric hospital, all in large numbers, became available for study and afforded an opportunity to observe the disorder in a very wide range of variety and of degree.

This additional clinical experience, helpful comment in the reviews of the first edition, enlightening discussion with colleagues, and an improved acquaintance with the literature all contributed to modify concepts formulated approximately ten years earlier. In attempting to revise the book for the second edition (1950), I found it was impossible to do justice to the subject by minor additions, deletions, and modifications. It was necessary to write a new and much larger book.

For the third edition, published in 1955, fewer alterations and additions were necessary. But a number of important changes were made. Some reviewers led me to feel that in previous editions I failed to convey accurately or adequately the concept I had formed. It is not easy to convey this concept, that of a biologic organism outwardly intact, showing excellent peripheral function, but centrally deficient or disabled in such a way that abilities, excellent at the only levels where we can formally test them, cannot be utilized consistently for sane purposes or prevented from regularly working toward self-destructive and other seriously pathologic results. Impressed by its effectiveness as used by Henry Head to distinguish a complex, deep, and obscure type of aphasia, I chose the term *semantic* to indicate my concept of a personality disorder which appears to have, at least hypothetically, some important similarities. A few readers were misled by my use of the term *semantic* to believe I claimed that the basic pathology in this disorder, or its cause, is deficiency in the understanding of speech or some other linguistic difficulty. Some comments, on the other hand, gave me the impression that it was assumed I had found fault with the psychopath because he could not achieve a final and absolute understanding of life's meaning at levels more or less eschatological. I restated my concept with the aim of making it more explicit, with the hope of being more articulate.

In the third edition (1955) the revision of the official nomenclature of psychiatric illness was noted, particularly the replacement of the term *psychopathic personality* by *sociopathic personality*. The older informal term *psychopath* persists, and indeed seems still the popular choice in discussions among psychiatrists, though the newer term *sociopath* is also frequently heard. Here both terms will be used with the understanding that they are regarded as synonymous and that they designate the same pattern of disorder.

Although I spared no effort to make it plain that I did not have an effective therapy to offer, the earlier editions of this book led to contact with psychopaths of every type and from almost every section of the United States and Canada. Interest in the problem was almost never manifested by the patients themselves. The interest was desperate, however, among parents, wives, husbands, brothers, etc., who had struggled long and helplessly with a major disaster for which they found not only no cure and no social, medical, or legal facility for handling, but also no full or frank recognition that a reality so obvious existed.

Telephone calls from Chicago, Denver, Boston, and The West Indies and letters from Miami and Vancouver have convinced me that the psychopath is no rarity in any North American community but that his problem is, by what seems to be an almost universal conspiracy of evasion, ignored by those therapeutic forces in the human group that, reacting to what is biologically or socially morbid, have sensibly provided courts, operating rooms, tuberculosis sanatoriums, prisons, fire departments, psychiatric hospitals, police forces, and homes for the orphaned, the ill, the psychotic, and the infirm. The measures

8

taken by the community to deal with illness, crime, failure, contagion, etc. are, one might say, often far from perfect. It cannot, however, be said, except about the problem of the psychopath, that no measure at all is taken, that nothing exists specifically designed to meet a major and obvious pathologic situation. Communications from physicians, sociologists, psychologists, students, and others from Europe, some from countries behind the Iron Curtain, and also from India, Australia, and other distant parts of the world continue to arrive. They convince me that the psychopath presents an important and challenging enigma for which no adequate solution has yet been found.

Although still in the unspectacular and perforce modest position of one who can offer neither a cure nor a well-established explanation, I am encouraged by ever-increasing evidence that few medical or social problems have ever so richly deserved and urgently demanded a hearing. It is still my conviction that this particular problem, in a practical sense, has had no hearing.

Although I still have no cure to offer for the psychopath (sociopath), it has encouraged me to feel that this book has served a useful purpose in making clearer to the families of these patients the grave problems with which they must deal. Apparently many psychiatrists, and many other physicians, have, over the years, advised relatives of psychopaths to read this book. The response of these relatives has given me deep satisfaction and has helped me to feel that efforts to pursue this study are not in vain. Although we may still be far from the goal of offering a cure, perhaps something has already been done to focus general interest on the problem and to promote awareness of its tremendous importance. This must be accomplished, I believe, before any organized attempt can be made by society to deal adequately, or even cogently, with the psychopath. Even now, twenty-three years after the first edition of this book was published, I often receive several letters a week from wives, parents, brothers, or other kinsmen of sociopaths. Most of these letters help me to feel that this book has at least enabled many people to see more clearly and realistically the nature of the problem with which they have had to deal blindly and in a strange and almost unique confusion. These correspondents often tell me that this book has been of great value in helping them understand better the disorder of a husband, wife, child, or sibling and plan more realistically and effectively to deal with situations heretofore entirely unpredictable and incomprehensible. I am most grateful for these generous and gracious expressions of approval of this book. The many hundreds of letters thanking me for even such a modest achievement encourage me to feel that a fourth edition may be worth while and that it deserves my most serious thought and concern.

It is a privilege to thank friends, colleagues, and others who have given me help and encouragement in preparing the material for the fourth edition and for earlier versions of this work.

It is appropriate to express my appreciation to Dr. Marion Estes, Dr. Fred B. Thigpen, Dr. Lester Bowles, and Dr. Lou Woodward. Dr. Corbett H. Thigpen, Dr. W. P. Robison, and Dr. B. F. Moss, Jr., my medical associates over the years, have played a major part in the development and revision of this work. Their thought and observation, available to me during countless pleasant and stimulating hours of discussion, have assisted and influenced my own conclusions to a degree that amounts to real collaboration.

I would like to mention particularly my gratitude to Mrs. Cornelia C. Fulghum who worked with me wisely and generously in strenuous efforts to meet a difficult deadline in preparing this fourth edition. Her contribution has, indeed, been beyond the ordinary call of duty.

This book could not have been completed without the important assistance of my daughter, Mary Cleckley Dolan, and my wife, Louise Cleckley, who so generously devoted time and effort to the mundane tasks of typing, indexing, and proofreading and who also afforded me stimulus, encouragement, and a wisely critical collaboration. It is a pleasure to express appreciation for such generous and substantial help.

Hervey Cleckley

Preface to first edition

The present volume grew out of an old conviction which increased during several years while I sat at staff meetings in a large neuropsychiatric hospital. Many hundreds of such cases as those presented here were studied and discussed. The diversity of opinion among different psychiatrists concerning the status of these patients never grew less. Little agreement was found as to what was actually the matter with them. No satisfactory means of dealing with them was presented by any psychiatric authority, and meanwhile their status in the eyes of the law usually made it impossible to treat them at all. They continued, however, to constitute a most grave and a constant problem to the hospital and to the community.

Since assuming full-time teaching duties at the University of Georgia School of Medicine, I have found these patients similarly prevalent in the wards of the general hospital, in the outpatient neuropsychiatric clinic, and in consultation work with the various practitioners of the community and with the hospital staff. The overwhelming difficulty of finding facilities for their treatment has been no less urgent than the yet unanswered question of what measures to use in treatment. How to inform their relatives, the courts which handle them, the physicians who try to treat them, of the nature of their disorder has been no small problem. No definite or consistent attitude on the part of psychiatric authorities could be adduced in explanation; no useful legal precedent at all could be invoked, and no institutions found in which help might be sought by the community.

I should like here to express my appreciation for their encouragement and guidance about this and about other neuropsychiatric problems to Dr. R. T. O'Neil, Dr. William M. Dobson, Dr. M. K. Amdur, Dr. O. R. Yost, and Dr. M. M. Barship. To all of them as colleagues, and in varying degrees as teachers, during my years with the United States Veterans Administration, I am sincerely grateful.

Dr. John M. Caldwell, of the U. S. Army Medical Corps, Dr. Cecile Mettler, Dr. Phillip Mulherin, Dr. F. A. Mettler, Dr. Lane Allen, and Dr. Robert Greenblatt, all of the faculty of the University of Georgia School of Medicine, I should like to thank for their interest and helpful criticism in the preparation of this work. Nor can I fail to mention here the kindness and active cooperation of other departments in the School of Medicine which, though less directly related to the present study, have been a valuable and constant support to the Department of Neuropsychiatry. Though I name only a few, I should especially like to express appreciation to Dean G. L. Kelly, Dr. J. H. Sherman, Dr. C. G. Henry, Dr. E. E. Murphey, Dr. Perry Volpitto, Dr. R. F. Slaughter, Dr. R. H. Chaney, Dr. W. J. Cranston, Dr. H. T. Harper, Dr. Lansing Lee, and Dr. J. D. Gray. The interest and understanding shown by these and others in the problems of the newly organized full-time Department of Neuropsychiatry have been more helpful than they know.

To Dr. Lawrence Geeslin, Dr. C. M. Templeton, Dr. Joe Weaver, Dr. Alex Kelly, and Dr. DuBose Eggleston, all of the Resident Medical Staff at the University Hospital, I am grateful for their fine and wise efforts to make neuropsychiatry an effective influence on the wards of a general hospital.

It is hard to see how the present manuscript could have reached completion without the understanding and energy contributed to its making by my secretary, Miss Julia Littlejohn.

Mr. Berry Fleming and Mr. Donald Parson, one as a distinguished novelist and one as a poet, but both sharing the psychiatrist's interest in human personality, have kindly made available to me their valuable points of view.

This volume owes a large debt to Dr. W. R. Houston, formerly Clinical Professor of Medicine in the University of Georgia School of Medicine, now of Austin, Texas. As my first teacher in psychiatry and still as a bracingly honest critic and a skeptical but always heartening guide, Dr. Houston's uncommon learning in many fields and his kindness have been an important support.

Most of all it is my pleasure to thank Dr. V. P. Sydenstricker, Professor of Medicine in the University of Georgia School of Medicine, whose genuine human qualities no less than his specific achievements in medicine and his remarkable energy, have encouraged, year after year, scores of less seasoned and sometimes groping colleagues to do sounder work and to find joy that is the stuff of life in even those daily tasks that would in another's presence become mere routine. Real wisdom joined with real humor cannot fail to be expressed in a rare and discerning kindness. These qualities, all in full measure, have done more not only to deal with illness, but also to reintegrate at happier and more effective levels those who have worked with him than their possessor can realize. It is indeed difficult to express fairly the gratitude which informs this writer in mentioning the constant encouragement, generous help, and the major inspiration that have come from Dr. Sydenstricker to the Department of Neuropsychiatry.

Hervey Cleckley
Augusta, Georgia
1941

Contents

Part II

*Incomplete manifestations or
suggestions of the disorder*

Section three

Cataloging the material

Part I

Orientation

Part II

A comparison with other disorders

Part III

A clinical profile

Section four

Some questions still without adequate answers

Part I

What is wrong with these patients?

Part II

What can be done?

An outline of the problem

1

Sanity—a protean concept

A millionaire notable for his eccentricity had an older and better-balanced brother who, on numerous fitting occasions, exercised strong persuasion to bring him under psychiatric care. On receiving word that this wiser brother had been deserted immediately after the nuptial night by a famous lady of the theatre (on whom he had just settled a large fortune) and that the bride, furthermore, had, during the brief pseudoconnubial episode, remained stubbornly encased in tights, the younger hastened to dispatch this succinct and unanswerable telegram:

Who's looney now?

This, at any rate, is the story. I do not offer to answer for its authenticity. It may, however, be taken not precisely as an example but at least as a some-what flippant and arresting commentary on the confusion which still exists concerning *sanity*. Although most patients suffering from one of the classified types of mental disorder are promptly recognized by the psychiatrist, many of them being even to the layman plainly deranged, there remains a large body of people who, everyone will admit, are by no means adapted for normal life in the community and who, yet, have no official standing in the ranks of the insane. The word *insane*, of course, is not a medical term. It is employed here because to many people it conveys a more practical meaning than the medical term *psychotic*. Although the medical term with its greater vagueness presents a fairer idea of the present conception of severe mental disorder, the legal term better implies the criteria by which the personalities under discussion are judged in the courts.

Many of these people, legally judged as competent, are more dangerous to themselves and to others than are some patients whose psychiatric disability will necessitate their spending their entire lives in the state hospital. Though certified automatically as *sane* by the verbal definitions of law and of medicine, their behavior demonstrates an irrationality and incompetence that are gross and obvious.

MATERIAL TO DISTINGUISH FROM OUR SUBJECT

These people to whom I mean to call specific attention are not the borderline cases in whom the characteristics of some familiar mental disorder are only partially developed and the picture as a whole is still questionable. Many such cases exist, of course, and they are sometimes puzzling even to the experienced psychiatrist. Certain people, as everyone knows, may for many years show to a certain degree the reactions of schizophrenia (dementia praecox), of manic-depressive psychosis, or of paranoia without being sufficiently disabled or so generally irrational as to be recognized as psychotic. Many patients suffering from incipient disorders of this sort or from dementia paralytica, cerebral arteriosclerosis, and other organic conditions pass through a preliminary phase during which their thought and behavior are to a certain degree characteristic of the psychosis, while for the time being they remain able to function satisfactorily in the community.

Some people in the early stage of these familiar clinical disorders behave, on the whole, with what is regarded as mental competency, while showing, from time to time, symptoms typical of the psychosis toward which they are progressing. After the disability has at last become openly manifest, enough episodes of deviated conduct can often be noted in retrospect to make the observer wonder why the subject was not long ago recognized as psychotic. It would, however, sometimes be not only difficult but unfair to pronounce a person totally disabled while most of his conduct remains acceptable. Do we not, as a matter of fact, have to admit that all of us behave at times with something short of complete rationality and good judgment?

•   •   •

I recall a highly respected businessman who, after years of outstanding commercial success, began to send telegrams to the White House ordering the President to dispatch the Atlantic Fleet to Madagascar and to execute Roman Catholics. There was at this time no question, of course, about his disability. A careful study revealed that for several years he had occasionally made fantastic statements, displayed extraordinary behavior (for instance, once putting the lighted end of a cigar to his stenographer's neck by way of greeting), and squandered thousands of dollars buying up stamp collections, worthless atticfuls of old furniture, and sets of encyclopedias by the dozen. None of these purchases had he put to any particular use. When finally discovered to be incompetent from illness, an investigation of his status showed that he had thrown away the better part of a million dollars. For months he had been maintaining 138 bird dogs scattered over the countryside, forty-two horses, and fourteen women, to none of whom he resorted for the several types of pleasure in which such dependents sometimes play a part.

Aside from persons in the early stages of progressive illness, one finds throughout the nation, and probably over the world, a horde of citizens who stoutly maintain beliefs regarded as absurd and contrary to fact by society as a whole. Often these people indulge in conduct that to others seems unquestionably irrational.

For example, the daily newspapers continue to report current gatherings in many states where hundreds of people handle poisonous snakes, earnestly insisting that they are carrying out God's will.* Death from snakebite among these zealous worshippers does not apparently dampen their ardor. Small children, too young to arrive spontaneously at similar conclusions concerning the relationships between faith and venom, are not spared by their parents this intimate contact with the rattler and the copperhead.

It is, perhaps, not remarkable that prophets continually predict the end of the world, giving precise and authoritative details of what so far has proved no less fanciful than the delusions of patients confined in psychiatric hospitals. That scores and sometimes hundreds or even thousands of followers accept these prophecies might give the thoughtful more cause to wonder. Newspaper clippings and magazine articles before the writer at this moment describe numerous examples of such behavior.

In a small Georgia town twenty earnest disciples sit up with a pious lady who has convinced them that midnight will bring the millenium. An elderly clergyman in California, whose more numerous followers are likewise disappointed when the designated moment passes uneventfully, explains that there is no fault with his divine vision but only some minor error of calculation which arose from differences between the Biblical and the modern calendars. During the last century an even more vehement leader had thousands of people, in New England and in other states, out on the hillsides expecting to be caught up to glory as dawn broke. Indeed, conviction was so great that at sunrise many leaped from cliffs, roofs, and silos, one zealot having tied

---

*And these signs shall follow them that believe; in my name they shall cast out devils; they shall speak with new tongues; they shall . . . take up serpents and if they drink any deadly thing it shall not hurt them . . . Mark 16:17-18.

turkey wings to his arms the better to provide for flight. Those who had hoped to ascend found gravity unchanged, the earth still solid, and the inevitable contact jarring.[278,292]

Few, if any, who prophesy on the grounds of mystic insight or special revelation come to conclusions more extraordinary than those reached by some who profess, and often firmly believe, they are working within the methods of science. A notable example is furnished by Wilhelm Reich, who is listed in *American Men of Science* and whose earlier work in psychopathology is regarded by many as valuable.[26] Textbooks of high scientific standing still refer to his discoveries in this field.[88,130,193]

It is indeed startling when such a person as this announces the discovery of "orgone," a substance which, it is claimed, has much to do with sexual orgasm (as well as the blueness of the sky) and which can be accumulated in boxes lined with metal. Those who sit within the boxes are said to benefit in many marvelous ways. According to the *Journal of the American Medical Association,* the accumulation of this (to others) nonexistent material is by Reich and his followers promoted as a method for curing cancer.[59] A report of the Council of the American Medical Association lists the orgone accumulator with various quack nostrums under "Frauds and Fables." The presence of any such material as "orgone" impresses the physician as no less imaginary than its alleged therapeutic effects. The nature of such conclusions and the methods of arriving at them are scarcely more astonishing than the credulity of highly educated and intellectual people who are reported to give them earnest consideration.[26]

Even in the 1940's, crowds estimated as containing twenty-five thousand or more persons, some of them having travelled halfway across the United States, stood in the rain night after night to watch a 9-year-old boy in New York City who claimed to have seen a vision which he described as "an angel's head with butterfly wings."

A clergyman of the Church of England during World War II confirmed as a supernatural omen of good the reported appearance of a luminous cross in the sky near Ipswich. In our own generation a man of profound learning has expressed literal belief in witchcraft and approved the efforts of those who, following the Biblical injunction, put thousands to death for this activity.[313]

These headlines from a daily newspaper deserve consideration:

NOW IN MENTAL HOSPITAL,
ACCUSED OF TREASON, HELD INSANE,
EZRA POUND GIVEN TOP POETRY PRIZE

My interest in this news does not indicate that I hold it to be impossible for a person with serious psychiatric disorder sometimes to write good poetry or to achieve other worthwhile attainments.

The headlines nevertheless reflect a bewildering conflict of evaluation in which some of the paradoxical elements strongly suggest absurdity. They also bring to mind what sometimes seems to be a rapt predilection of small but influential cults of *intellectuals* or *esthetes* for what is generally regarded as perverse, dispirited, or distastefully unintelligible.[5,35,80,119] The award of a Nobel Prize in literature to André Gide, who in his work fervently and openly insists that pederasty is the superior and preferable way of life for adolescent boys, furnishes a memorable example of such judgments.[102,204] Renowned critics and some professors in our best universities[183,290] reverently acclaim as the superlative expression of genius James Joyce's *Finnegan's Wake,* a 628-page collection of erudite gibberish indistinguishable to most people from the familiar word salad produced by hebephrenic patients on the back wards of any state hospital.

Let us illustrate briefly with the initial page from this remarkable volume:

> riverrun, past Eve and Adam's, from swerve of shore to bend of bay, brings us by a commodius vicus of recirculation back to Howth Castle and Environs.
>
> Sir Tristram, violer d'amores, fr'over the short sea, had passencore rearrived from North Armorica on this side the scraggy isthmus of Europe Minor to wielderfight his penisolate war: nor had topsawyer's rocks by the stream Oconee exaggerated themselse to Laurens County's gorgios while they went doublin their mumper all the time: nor avoice from afire bellowsed mishe mishe to tauftauf thuartpeatrick: not yet, though venissoon after, had a kidscad buttened a bland old isaac: not yet, though all's fair in vanessy, were sosie sesthers wroth with twone nathandjoe. Rot a peck of pa's malt had Jhem or Shen brewed by arclight and rory end to the regginbrow was to be seen ringsome on the aquaface.
>
> The fall (bababadalgharaghtakamminarronnkonnbronntonnerronn-tuonnthunntrovarrhounawnskawntoohoohoordenenthurnuk!) of a once wallstrait oldparr is retaled early in bed and later on life down through all christian minstrelsy. The great fall of the offwall entailed at such short notice the pftjschute of Finnegan, erse solid man, that the humptyhillhead of humself promptly sends an unquiring one well to the west in quest of his tumptytumtoes: and their upturnpikepointand-place is at the knock out in the park where oranges have been laid to rust upon the green since devlinsfirst loved livvy.*

The adventurous reader will, I promise, find any of the other 627 pages equally illuminating. It is not for me to say dogmatically that *Finnegan's*

---

*From Joyce, James: Finnegan's wake, New York, 1945, The Viking Press.

Wake is a volume devoid of meaning. Nor could I with certainty make such a pronouncement about the chaotic verbal productions of the patient on the back ward of a state hospital.

Ezra Pound's continued eminence as a poet and the almost worshipful admiration with which some scholars acclaim *Finnegan's Wake* are likely to evoke wonder from the man of ordinary tastes and reactions if he gives these matters any consideration.

Graduates of our universities and successful businessmen join others to contribute testimonials announcing the prevention of hydrophobia and the healing of cancer, diphtheria, tuberculosis, wens, and broken legs, as well as the renting of rooms and the raising of salaries, by groups who reportedly work through "the formless, omnipresent God-substance" and by other metaphysical methods. One group publishes several magazines which are eagerly read in almost every town in the United States. Nearly 200 centers are listed where "prosperity bank drills" and respiratory rituals are advocated. Leaders solemnly write, "the physical body radiates an energy that can at times be seen as a light or aura surrounding the physical, especially about the heads of those who think much about Spirit."*

The following are typical testimonial letters, and these are but three among many hundreds:

> I wrote to you somewhat over a week ago asking for your prayers. My trouble was appendicitis, and it seemed that an operation was unavoidable. However, I had faith in the indwelling, healing Christ and decided to get in touch with you. Well, as you might expect, the healing that has taken place borders on the so-called miraculous. I spent an hour each day alone with God, and I claimed my rightful inheritance as a child of God. Naturally the adverse condition had to disappear with the advent of the powerful flow of Christ-like consciously directed towards this illness.

> . . .

> You will be interested to know that just about the time when my prosperity-bank period was up I went to work in a new position, which not only pays a substantially higher salary but . . . [etc.]. I should probably not have had sufficient faith and courage to trust Him had it not been for the Truth literature. . . .

> . . .

> Thank you for your beautiful and effective ministry. I have had five big demonstrations of prosperity since I had this particular pros-

*From Fillmore, C.: Health and prosperity, Unity **98**:1-5, 1943.

perity bank. Last week brought final settlement of a debt owed me for about seven years.*

Not a few citizens of our country read, apparently with conviction, material such as that published by the director of the Institute of Mental Physics, who is announced as the reincarnation of a Tibetan Lama. This leader reports, furthermore, that he has witnessed an eastern sage grow an orange tree from his palm and, on another occasion, die and rise in a new body, leaving the old one behind. Many other equally improbable feats of thaumaturgy are described in eye-witness accounts.[72]

The casual observer has been known to dismiss what many call superstition as the fruit of ignorance. Nevertheless, beliefs and practices of this sort are far from rare among the most learned in all generations. A recent ambassador to the United States, generally recognized as a distinguished scholar, died (according to the press) under the care of a practitioner of Christian Science.

Even a doctor of medicine has written a book in which he attests to the cure of acute inflammatory diseases and other disorders by similar methods. But let him speak directly:

> At another time I examined a girl upon whom I had operated for recurrent mastoiditis. At the time of my examination she was showing definite signs of another attack. . . . Absent treatments stopped her trouble in two days. To one who had never seen anything of the kind before, the rapidity with which the inflammation disappeared would have seemed almost a piece of magic.

> • • •

> A third case is that of a woman who carried a bad heart for years. About a year ago she experienced an acute attack accompanied by pain, nausea, and bloating caused by gas. Her daughter telephoned to a practitioner of spiritual healing and explained the trouble to her. The reply was that an immediate treatment would be given. In ten minutes the trouble was gone, and there has been no serious recurrence since.†

The more one considers such convictions and the sort of people who hold them, the more impressive becomes the old saying attributed[314] to Artemus Ward and indicating that our troubles arise not so much from ignorance as from knowing so much that is not so. Hundreds of other examples like those mentioned are available to demonstrate that many persons of high ability and

---

*From Prayers answered, Unity 98:73-76, 1943.
†From Southard, C. O.: Truth ideas of an M.D., Kansas City, Mo., 1943, Unity School of Christianity.

superior education sincerely cherish beliefs which seem to have little more real support from fact or reason than the ordinary textbook delusion. Such beliefs are held as persistently by respected persons and influential groups, despite evidence to the contrary, as by psychotic patients who are segregated in hospitals.

Let it be understood that I am not advancing an opinion that those who are persuaded by prophets that the world will end next Thursday or that those who appeal to faith healers to protect a child from the effects of meningitis should be pronounced as clinically psychotic and forcibly committed to hospitals. Despite the similarity between the way such beliefs are adopted and the way a schizoid or paranoid patient arrives at his delusions, and despite the similar lack of evidence for considering either true, people such as those now under discussion are usually capable of leading useful lives in harmony with the community and sometimes of benefit to society. Nothing, in my opinion, is more basic than the necessity for men to allow each other freedom to believe or not to believe; however sacred, or however false, different creeds may be held by different groups.

Convictions that the world is flat, that one must not begin a job on Friday, or that Mr. Arthur Bell of Mankind United[198] is omnipotent are apparently held by some in reverent identity with the deepest religious attitudes of which they are capable. In this basic sense, each man's religion, as contrasted with the dogma or illusion in which he may frame it, his basic attitude and emotional response to whatever meaning and purpose he has been able to find in his living, deserves respect and consideration. The Methodist, the Mormon, and the Catholic, as well as the man who cannot accept any literal creed as a final statement of these issues, can honor and value, in a fundamentally religious sense, the valid reverence and the ultimate subjective aims of a good Mohammedan. This is possible without the ability to share his pleasant convictions about the likelihood of houris in paradise.

26

2

Traditions that obscure our subject

In raising general questions about personality disorder, we have briefly considered (1) persons suffering from illnesses that progress to major mental disability and (2) the numerous citizens of our nation, many of them able and well educated, who hold beliefs generally regarded as unsupported by evidence and considered by many as irrational or even fantastic. Aside from these groups and aside from all types of patients recognized as psychotic, there remains for our consideration a large body of people who are incapable of leading normal lives and whose behavior causes great distress in every community.

This group, plainly marked off from the psychotic by current psychiatric standards, does not find a categorical haven among the psychoneurotic, who are distinguished by many medical characteristics from the people to be discussed in this volume. They are also distinguished practically by their ability to adjust without major difficulties in the social group.

Who, then, are these relatively unclassified people? And what is the nature of their disorder? The pages which follow will be devoted to an attempt to answer these questions. The answers are not easy to formulate. The very name by which such patients are informally referred to in mental hospitals or elsewhere among psychiatrists is in itself confusing. Every physician is familiar with the term psychopath, by which these people are most commonly designated.[49] Despite the plain etymologic inference of a *sick mind* or of *mental sickness,* this term is ordinarily used to indicate those who are considered free from psychosis and even from psychoneurosis. The definitions of psychopath found in medical dictionaries are not consistent nor do they regularly accord with the ordinary psychiatric use of this word.*

In a revision of the psychiatric nomenclature (1952), the term *psychopathic personality* was officially replaced by *sociopathic personality*. Since then the informal term, *sociopath,* has often been used along with the older and more familiar *psychopath* to designate a large group of seriously disabled people, listed with other dissimilar groups under the heading *personality disorder*. In this book I will use the older term *psychopath* and the newer and less familiar term *sociopath* interchangeably and to indicate the same disorder. The cumbersome and altogether vague diagnostic category, *personality disorder,* officially includes a wide variety of maladjusted people who cannot by the criteria of psychiatry be classed with the psychotic, the psychoneurotic, or the mentally defective. Until fairly recent years, it was by no means uncommon for the report of a detailed psychiatric examination made on a patient in a state or federal institution to end with this diagnostic conclusion:

1. No nervous or mental disease
2. Psychopathic personality

The broadness of the familiar diagnostic term and the conflicting attitudes of different psychiatrists toward those so labeled are reflected in the varying concepts it implies and in its plainly diverse referents.

Several decades ago, a large group of abnormalities, mental deficiency, various brain and body malformations and developmental defects, sexual perversions, delinquent behavior patterns, chronically mild schizoid disorder, etc. were all classed as *constitutional psychopathic inferiority*.[124] After the ordinary mental defectives and most of the cases with demonstrable brain damage or developmental anomalies were distinguished, a considerable residue of diverse conditions remained under the old classification.

As time passed and psychiatric study continued, an increasing number of observers felt that the term *constitutional* was scarcely justified for some of

---

*Stedman's Medical Dictionary (1961): *"Psychopath:* The subject of a psychoneurosis; especially one who is of apparently sound mind in the ordinary affairs of life but who is dominated by some abnormal sexual, criminal or passional instinct."

Dorland's American Illustrated Medical Dictionary (1957): "Psychopath: a person who has a psychopathic personality. *sexual* p., an individual whose sexual behavior is manifestly antisocial and criminal."

Blakiston's New Gould Medical Dictionary (1949) gives: "A morally irresponsible person: one who continually comes in conflict with accepted behavior and the law."

Curran and Mallinson (Curran, D., and Mallinson, P.: Recent progress in psychiatry; psychopathic personality, Journal of Mental Science **90:**266-286, 1944) in 1944 say: "The only conclusion that seems warrantable is that some time or other and by some reputable authority the term psychopathic personality has been used to designate every conceivable type of abnormal character."

the several disorders listed in the categories just mentioned. Eventually these were officially discarded in our country and *psychopathic personality* was adopted, not only for the type of patient to be discussed in this volume but for a good many others easily distinguished from him in life but only with difficulty in the nomenclature.

In the revised *Standard Nomenclature for Diseases of the Psychobiologic Unit,* published in 1952, the familiar *psychopathic personality* was discarded. In its place is now the category of *personality disorders.* These, distinguished in the revised nomenclature from psychotic disorders and psychoneurotic disorders, include, sometimes under slightly altered names, all the various pathologic states formerly placed in the category *psychopathic personality.*[69]

At present many believe that all the conditions until recently listed under psychopathic personality are hereditary deficiencies, whereas others disagree with this assumption.[251] During the last few decades, increasing attention has been paid to interpersonal and environmental factors or influences almost entirely ignored before the beginning of Freud's work, and the tendency to attribute personality disorder wholly and simply to inborn defect has been less prevalent.

Some time after the period during which it was generally assumed, by the physician as well as by the clergyman, that abnormal behavior resulted from devil possession or the influence of witches, it became customary to ascribe all or nearly all mental disorder to bad heredity. Even in the early part of the present century this practice was almost universal.[216] Before relatively recent developments in psychopathology and before any real attempt had been made to understand the meaning and purpose of symptomatology, the invocation of inborn deficiency or "hereditary taint" was, it would seem, grasped largely for the want of any other hypothesis.

Another factor contributing to the popularity of belief in hereditary causation lies, perhaps, in the fact that families of patients in state hospitals were investigated and all deviations recorded. Most of these histories revealed aberrant behavior, if not in a parent or grandparent, at least in some great uncle or distant cousin. It is surprising that some investigators gave such little consideration to the fact that few men stopped on the street could account for all relatives and antecedents without also disclosing one or more kinsmen whose behavior would attract psychiatric attention.* This is not to say that there is no possibility of genogenic factors playing a part, perhaps a major part, in the development of the psychopath. It is to say that one is not justified in

---

*The ease with which defective heredity may be found in any case in which one looks for it is well known. A study published in 1937 revealed that 57 per cent of a group of normal people showed a positive family history of "neuropathic taint."[217]

assuming such factors until real evidence of them is produced. If such evidence is produced, these factors must be weighed along with all others for which there may be evidence and not glibly assumed to be a full and final explanation.

In recent years a contrary tendency has become prominent in psychiatry, a tendency to make, on the basis of symbolism and theoretical postulates, sweeping and unverifiable assumptions and to insist that these prove the cause of obscure personality disorders to lie in specific infantile, or even intrauterine, experiences.[91,172,246] This practice has become exceedingly popular and has, in my opinion, led to many fanciful and absurd pseudoscientific explanations of the psychopath and of other psychiatric problems. Let us bear in mind that the currently prevalent psychodynamic theories are of such a nature that they can be glibly used to "demonstrate" (by inference) the truth of virtually any assumption, however implausible, that one might make about what is in the unconscious. Let us not mistake these easy inferences for actual evidence.

After many years of work in psychiatry as a member of the staff in a closed hospital devoted to the treatment of mental disorders, and after many other years in charge of the psychiatric service in a general hospital, I believe that these curious people referred to as sociopaths or psychopaths, in the vernacular of the ward and the staff room, offer a field of study in personality disorder more baffling and more facinating than any other. The present work has been attempted because of an ever-growing conviction that this type of disorder is far less clearly understood than either the well-defined psychoses or the neuroses and that this lack of understanding is, furthermore, not sufficiently recognized and admitted. Although I do not pretend to achieve a final explanation of so grave and perplexing a problem, it is hoped that a frank and detailed discussion may, at least, draw attention to the magnitude of the problem.[47]

The chief aim of this study is to bring before psychiatrists a few of these cases, typical of hundreds more, who have proved so interesting to the writer, so difficult to interpret by the customary standards of psychiatry, and all but impossible to deal with or to treat satisfactorily in the face of prevalent medicolegal viewpoints. Many of these cases have been classified consistently as sociopathic personality by not one but a number of expert observers, usually by several staffs of psychiatrists, and nearly always with unanimity. Others are so similar and so typical that few, if any, experts could find grounds to question their status. It is my belief, however, that this diagnosis, as it is authoritatively defined and as it is generally understood, fails to do justice to the kind of patients considered here.

30

It is hoped that such a presentation may be of interest to physicians in general practice and, perhaps, to medical students, as well as to those whose work is confined more specifically to personality disorders. It is, indeed, the physician in general practice who will most often be called on by society to interpret the behavior of such patients as these and to advise about their treatment and their disposition.

These people, whom I shall call psychopaths for want of a better word, are, as a matter of fact, the problem of juries, courts, relatives, the police, and the general public no less than of the psychiatrist. Referring to such patients, Henderson says:

> It is often much against his better judgment that the judge sentences a man whose conduct on the face of it indicates the action of an unsound mind to serve a term of imprisonment. But he is almost forced to do so because, according to our present statutes governing commitment, the doctor may not feel that he is justified in certifying the individual as suitable for care and treatment in a mental hospital.*

It is important that the average physician at least be aware that there is such a problem. According to the present standards of psychiatry, such patients are not eligible for admission to state hospitals for the psychotic or to the numerous hospitals of the same type maintained by the federal government for war veterans. They are classed as sane and competent and, theoretically at least, are held responsible for their conduct. Being so classed, none of the measures used to protect other psychiatric patients (and their families and the community) can be applied to bring them under any sort of treatment or restriction, even when they show themselves dangerously disordered. By many psychiatrists they are, in a technical sense, considered to be without nervous or mental disease. There are many arguments that can be brought forward in support of these beliefs, particularly if one adheres strictly to the traditional and currently accepted definitions of psychiatry and minimizes or evades what is demonstrated by the patient's behavior.

It is difficult, however, for society to hold these people to account for their damaging conduct or to apply any control that will prevent its continuing. Those who commit serious crimes have a history that any clever lawyer can exploit in such a way as to make his client appear to the average jury the victim of such madness as would make Bedlam itself tame by comparison. Under such circumstances they escape the legal consequences of their acts, are sent to mental hospitals where they prove to be "sane," and are released. On the other hand, when their relatives and their neighbors seek

*From Henderson, D. K.: Psychopathic states, New York, 1939, W. W. Norton & Co., Inc.

relief from them and take action to have "lunacy warrants" drawn against them, not wanting to be restricted, they are able to convince the courts that they are as competent as any man.

It is pertinent here to remind ourselves of the considerable change that has occurred during recent centuries in the legal attitude toward antisocial conduct and punishment. Formerly, all who broke the laws were considered fit subjects for trial, and penalties were inflicted without regard to questions of responsibility or competency. As Karl Menninger,[216,] among others,[285,313] has so effectively pointed out, not only were the irrational considered fully culpable, but also young children and idiots. At an earlier date, animals and even articles of furniture, a tree (or a stone) were brought to trial, fantastic as it seems to us now, and sentenced to legal penalties.

Today the murderer who hears what he believes is God's voice telling him to kill is not, as a rule, hanged. He is committed to a psychiatric hospital for the protection of society and for his own best interests, but not as a punishment. This legal attitude has become so axiomatic, so familiar to the man on the streets, that it is well for us to remember it is relatively new.

We might also bear in mind that once only obvious irrationality was regarded as personality disorder, as disability. Medically we recognize the fact that many less obvious disorders are more serious and incapacitating than those with gross superficial manifestations that can be readily demonstrated. In our attempts to appraise the psychopath and his disorder, it will be helpful to bear these facts in mind and not to forget that our present medicolegal criteria are based on knowledge that is far from complete.

These people called psychopaths present a problem which must be better understood by lawyers, social workers, schoolteachers, and by the general public if any satisfactory way of dealing with them is to be worked out. Before this understanding can come, the general body of physicians to whom the laity turn for advice must themselves have a clear picture of the situation. Much of the difficulty that mental institutions have in their relations with the psychopath springs from a lack of awareness in the public that he exists. The law in its practical application provides no means whereby the community can protect itself from such people. And no satisfactory facilities can be found for their treatment. It is with these thoughts especially in mind that I seek to present the material of this book in such a manner that the average physician who treats few frankly psychotic patients may see that our subject lies in his own field scarcely less than in the field of psychiatry. After all, psychiatry, though still a specialty, can no longer be regarded as circumscribed within the general scope of medicine.[34]

In nearly all the standard textbooks of psychiatry the psychopath is mentioned. Several recent textbooks have indeed made definite efforts to stress for the student the challenging and paradoxical features of our subject. Often, however, tucked away at the end of a large volume, an obscure chapter is found containing a few pages or paragraphs devoted to these strange people who take so much attention of the medical staffs in psychiatric hospitals and whose behavior, it is here maintained, probably causes more unhappiness and more perplexity to the public than all other mentally disordered patients combined. From some textbooks the medical student is likely to arrive at a conclusion that the psychopath is an unimportant figure, probably seldom encountered even in a psychiatric practice. Nor will he be led to believe that this type of disorder is particularly interesting. Not only is the chapter on psychopathic personalities often short and sometimes vague or halfhearted, but even this is nearly always involved with personality types or disorders which bear little or no resemblance to that with which we are now concerned. Although it is true that these other conditions are officially placed in the same category with the one discussed here, which we believe is a clinical entity, it is hard to see how any student unfamiliar with the latter will profit by encountering it vaguely placed in a company of assorted deficiencies and aberrations that are by no means basically similar.

It is my earnest conviction that, classified with a fairly heterogeneous group under a loose and variously understood term, a type of patient exists who could, without exaggeration, be called the *forgotten man of psychiatry*. If this patient can be presented as he has appeared so clearly during years of observation, if some idea can be given of his ubiquity, and, above all, if interest can be promoted in further study of his peculiar status among other human beings, I shall be abundantly satisfied. It is difficult to contemplate the enigma which he provokes without attempting to find some explanation, speculative though the attempt may be. Present efforts to explain or interpret are, however, tentative and secondary to the real purpose of this volume, which is to call attention to what may be observed about our subject.

3

Not as single spies but in battalions

An attempt to determine the incidence of this disorder in the population as a whole is opposed by serious difficulties. The vagueness of officially accepted criteria for diagnosis and the extreme variation of degree in such maladjustment constitute primary obstacles. Statistics from most psychiatric hospitals are necessarily misleading, since the psychopath is not technically eligible for admission and only those who behave in such an extremely abnormal manner as to appear orthodoxly psychotic (that is to say, as suffering from another and very different disorder) appear in the records. If legal and medical rules were regularly followed, statistics from state hospitals and from the federal psychiatric institutions would show no psychopaths at all. Let it also be noted that these institutions contain a vast majority of the patients hospitalized in the United States for mental disorder. Most statistical studies, therefore, cannot be regarded as even remotely suggesting the prevalence of this disability in the population.

These facts notwithstanding, it is still impressive to note what the records of a typical psychiatric institution reveal.* Over a period of twenty-nine months, 857 new patients were admitted to one federal hospital, where a staff of ten psychiatrists, including myself, classified them after careful examination and study. Of this group, 102 received the primary diagnosis of

---

*See Appendix, pp. 483 to 488 for details of this survey.

psychopathic personality, being considered free of any other mental disorder that could account for the difficulties that led to their admission. This group, comprising nearly one-eighth of all those admitted, indicates that the disorder is far from rare. The records also show 134 other patients classified under *alcoholism* or *drug addiction* who, I believe, for reasons brought out in the appendix, were nearly all fundamentally like those diagnosed as psychopaths, the addiction and other complications being secondary. If even one-half of these are considered as psychopaths, we arrive at a figure of 169, or almost one-fifth of the total.

These statistics from one psychiatric institution cannot, of course, be taken as proof that the disorder is so prevalent everywhere. One must not overlook the fact, however, that each of these patients was accepted despite rules specifically classifying him as ineligible and often as a result of conduct so abnormal or so difficult to cope with that he was considered a grave emergency. Another factor worth mentioning is the psychopath's almost uniform unwillingness to apply, like other ill people, for hospitalization or for any other medical service. The survey at least suggests that these patients are common and that they constitute a serious problem in the average community and a major issue in psychiatry.

I have been forced to the conviction that this particular behavior pattern is found among one's fellowmen far more frequently than might be surmised from reading the literature. If the nature of the disorder in question defines itself throughout the course of this work with sufficient sharpness and clarity to be recognizable as a pathologic entity, little doubt will remain that it presents a sociologic and psychiatric problem second to none.

The man who develops influenza or who breaks his arm nearly always thinks at once of calling his doctor. The unconscious victim of a head injury is promptly taken by his family, by his friends, or, lacking these, by casual bystanders to a hospital where medical attention is given. Persons who develop anxiety, phobia, or psychosomatic manifestations are likely to seek aid from a physician. Even those who demur and delay since they fear they will be called weak or silly because of symptoms commonly classed as psychoneurotic can be, and usually are, persuaded by their families after varying periods of reluctance to ask for help.

Children, of course, often seek to avoid both the pediatrician and the dentist, despite the advice of parents. But the parent seldom fails, when need of treatment is a serious matter, in getting the child, with or without his willingness, into the hands of the doctor. Many patients ill with the major personality disorders we classify as psychoses do not voluntarily seek treatment. Some do not recognize any such need and may bitterly oppose, sometimes by violent combat, all efforts to send them to psychiatric hospitals. Such patients, however, are well recognized. Medical facilities and legal instrumentalities exist for handling the problem, and institutions are provided to accept such patients and hold them, if necessary against their own volition, so long as it is advisable for the patient's welfare or for the protection of others.

When we consider on the other hand these sociopathic or psychopathic personalities, we find not one in one hundred who spontaneously goes to his physician to seek help. If relatives, alarmed by his disastrous conduct, recognize that treatment, or at least supervision, is an urgent need, they meet enormous obstacles. The public institutions to which they would turn for the care of a schizophrenic or a manic patient present closed doors. If they are sufficiently wealthy, they often consider a private psychiatric hospital. It should also be noted here that such private hospitals are necessarily expensive and that perhaps not more than 2 or 3 per cent of our population can afford such care for prolonged periods. No matter how wealthy his family may be, the psychopath, unlike all other serious psychiatric cases, can refuse to go to any hospital or to accept any other treatment or restraint. His refusal is regularly upheld by our courts of law, and grounds for this are consistent with the official appraisal of his condition by psychiatry.

Nearly always he does refuse and successfully oppose the efforts of his relatives to have him cared for. It is seldom that a psychopath accepts hospitalization or even outpatient treatment unless some strong means of coercion happens to be available. The threat of cutting off his financial support, of bringing legal action against him for forgery or theft, or of allowing him to remain in jail may move him to visit a physician's office or possibly to enter a hospital. Subsequent events often demonstrate that he is acting not seriously and with the understanding he professes but for the purpose of evasion, whether he himself realizes this or not. He usually breaks off treatment as soon as the evasion has been accomplished.

Since medical institutions refuse to accept the sociopath as a patient and since he does not voluntarily, except in rare instances, seek medical aid, it might be surmised that prison populations would furnish statistics useful in estimating the prevalence of his disorder. It is true that a considerable proportion of prison inmates show indications of such a disorder.[29,189,248] It is also true that only a small proportion of typical psychopaths are likely to be found in penal institutions, since the typical patient, as will be brought out in subsequent pages, is not likely to commit major crimes that result in long prison terms. He is distinguished by his ability to escape ordinary legal punishments and restraints. Though he regularly makes trouble for society, as well as for himself, and frequently is handled by the police, his characteristic behavior does not usually include committing felonies which would bring about permanent or adequate restriction of his activities. He is often arrested, perhaps one hundred times or more. But he nearly always regains his freedom and returns to his old patterns of maladjustment.

Although the incidence of this disorder is at present impossible to establish statistically or even to estimate accurately, I am willing to express the opinion that it is exceedingly high. On the basis of experience in psychiatric outpatient clinics and with psychiatric problems of private patients and in the community (as contrasted with committed patients), it does not seem an exaggeration to estimate the number of people seriously disabled by the disorder still listed under the ambiguous term sociopathic personality as greater than the number disabled by any recognized psychosis except schizophrenia. So far as I know, there are no provisions made in any public institution for the care of even one psychopath.*

---

*An exception must be made in the case of psychopaths convicted of major crimes and sentenced to imprisonment in federal institutions. At the Medical Center for Federal Prisoners at Springfield, Mo., provisions are made for sociopathic personalities, their problems are recognized, and genuine efforts are made to handle them psychiatrically.[200],[248] This admirable undertaking applies, however, only to a small fraction of those needing attention and leaves still ignored the ninety-nine out of one hundred patients who remain without attention or restriction.

4

Method of presentation

Before attempting to define or describe the psychopath (sociopath), to contrast him with other types of psychiatric patients, or to make any attempt to explain him, I would like to present some specimens of the group for consideration.

This procedure will be in accord with the principles of science in method at least, since, as Karl Pearson pointed out in *The Grammar of Science,* this method always consists of three steps:[121]

1. The observation and recording of facts
2. The grouping of these facts with proper correlation and with proper distinction from other facts
3. The effort to devise some summarizing or, if possible, explanatory statement which will enable one to grasp conveniently their significance

Long ago, keeping these steps clearly in mind, Bernard Hart gave an account in *The Psychology of Insanity*[121] of personality disorder that has, perhaps, never been surpassed for clarity and usefulness. Psychopathology has not been a static field, and many new concepts have arisen which make Hart's presentation in some respects archaic and unrepresentative of viewpoints prevalent today in psychiatry. This point notwithstanding, the method followed by Hart remains an example of how the problems of personality disorder can be approached with maximal practicality with minimal risks of mistaking hypothesis for proof or of falling into the schismatic polemics that, scarcely less than among medieval theologians, have confused issues and impeded common understanding in psychiatry. Without claims to comparable success in the effort to follow Hart's method, I acknowledge the debt owed one who set so excellent an example in the early years of this century.

The most satisfactory way in which such clinical material could be presented is, in my opinion, as a series of full-length biographic studies, preferably of several hundred pages each, written by one who has full access to the life of each subject. Only when the concrete details of environment are laid in, as, for instance, in an honest and discerning novel, can the significance of behavior be well appreciated. Certainly no brief case summary and probably no orthodox psychiatric history can succeed in portraying the character and the behavior of these people as they appear day after day and year after year in actual life.

It is not enough to set down that a certain patient stole his brother's watch, that another got drunk in a poolroom while his incipient bride waited at the altar, etc. To get the *feel* of the person whose behavior shows disorder, it is necessary to feel something of his surroundings. The psychopath's symptoms have for a long time been regarded as primarily sociopathic.[241,243,244] It is true that all, or nearly all, psychiatric disorder is in an important sense sociopathic, in that it affects adversely interpersonal relations. In most other disorders the manifestations of illness can, however, be more readily demonstrated in the isolated patient in the setting of a clinical examination. In contrast, it is all but impossible to demonstrate any of the fundamental symptoms in the psychopath under similar circumstances. The substance of the problem, real as it is in life, disappears, or at least escapes our specialized means of perception, when the patient is removed from the milieu in which he is to function. The newer term sociopath properly emphasizes this point.

All that surrounds and has ever surrounded the schizophrenic or the man with severe obsessive illness is, of course, important to us if we seek to understand why these people became disabled. Lacking all information except what might be gained from either of these patients (with whom one is, let us say, confined in an oxygen chamber on the moon), the observer will, nevertheless, have little trouble in discerning that there is disorder and in discovering a good deal about the general nature of the disorder.

Aside from questions of cause and effect, we have little opportunity even to realize the existence of the subject we must deal with unless the psychopath can be followed as he departs from the (essentially in vitro) situation of physician's office or hospital and takes up his activities in the community on a real and (socially) in vivo status.

It is with such convictions in mind that we shall often include detail of the environment, perhaps digress to the patient's husband or parents, report glimpses of the patient through the eyes of a lay observer, and at times attempt, from what material is available, a tentative reconstruction of situations that can be experienced adequately only at firsthand. It is regrettable that so much detail of this sort is difficult and often impossible to obtain. Without adequate knowledge of his specific surroundings in the community, there is no way for more than the insubstantial image of his being, like the picture projected from a lantern slide, to reach awareness. The real clinical entity is approachable only in the unstatic, actual process of the patient's life as he takes his specific course as a personal and sociologic unit.

The disorder can be demonstrated only when the patient's activity meshes with the problems of ordinary living. It cannot be even remotely apprehended if we do not pay particular attention to his responses in those interpersonal relations that to a normal man are the most profound.

If no schizophrenic had ever spoken, we would probably have little realization of what we understand (incomplete as this is) of auditory hallucinations. The schizophrenic can, by his verbal communication, give us some useful clues in our efforts to approach many of his problems. Little or nothing of this sort that is reliable can, by ordinary psychiatric examination, be obtained from the sociopath. Only when we observe him not through his speech but as he seeks his aims in behavior and demonstrates his disability in interaction with the social group can we begin to feel how genuine is his disorder. Studying the psychopath almost entirely in the orthodox clinical setting in which patients ordinarily appear is like examining the schizophrenic with our ears so muffled that his reiterated and quite honest claims of hearing voices of the dead talking to him from the sun (and from his intestines) fail to reach our perception.

If another analogy be permitted, let us say that a pair of copper wires carrying 2,000 volts of electricity, when we look at them, smell them, listen to them, or even touch them separately (while thoroughly insulated from the ground), may give no evidence of being in any respect different from other strands of copper. Let us, however, connect them to a motor (or have someone seize both of them at once) and we find out facts not to be perceived otherwise. The unmistakable evidence of electricity appears only when the circuit is made. So, too, the features that are most important in the behavior of the psychopath do not adequately emerge when this behavior is relatively isolated. The qualities of the psychopath become manifest only when he is connected into the circuits of full social life.

The sort of presentation our problem requires is, of course, impossible. However, in an effort to give at least a vivid glimpse of the material under consideration, I have made use of a somewhat different form of report than that customarily offered.

The impersonal and necessarily abstracted picture of these psychopaths in a purely clinical setting fails to show them as they appear in flesh and blood and in the process of living. In the restricted and arbitrary range of activities afforded by hospital life, their tendencies cannot be so truly and vividly demonstrated as in the larger world. To know them adequately, one must try to see them not merely with the physician's calm and relatively detached eye but also with the eye of the ordinary man on the streets, whom they confound and amaze. We must concern ourselves not only with their measurable intelligence, their symptomatology (or, rather, lack of symptomatology) in ordinary psychiatric terms, but also with the impression they make as total organisms in action among others and in all the nuances and complexities of deeply personal and specifically affective relationships. To see them properly in such a light, we must follow them from the wards out into the marketplace, the saloon, and the brothel, to the fireside, to church, and to their work.

In attempting this, however incompletely and inadequately, it is perhaps desirable for us not to trade our naiveté at once for the experienced clinician's discriminating viewpoint. Let us first watch them in their full conduct as human beings, not neglecting even the impression they make on Tom, Dick, and Harry, before trying to frame them in a scheme of psychopathology.

The terms I shall use to describe them may often imply that they are blamed for what they do or suggest an attitude of distaste or mockery for some of their behavior. Many psychiatrists regard such patients, unlike those suffering from ordinary psychoses, as competent and responsible for their misconduct and their difficulties. The faulty reactions in living which these patients show are indeed difficult to describe without sometimes using terms that come more readily to moralists or sociologists or laymen than to psychiatrists. The customary psychiatric terminology does not, I believe, offer a range of concepts into which we can fit these people successfully.

With other patients whose disorder is frankly recognized, we can, by our impersonal and specifically medical language, communicate fairly well to each other what we have observed. Some aspects of the sociopath which elude such language may be reflected, however imperfectly, in the simplest accounts of direct impression by those who have been closest to him and have felt the impact of his anomalous reactions. For these reasons, then, and with apology, reference may be made to some actions as outlandish, foolish, fantastic, buffonish, etc.

The chief aim of this book is to help, in however small a way, to bring patients with this type of disorder into clearer focus so that psychiatric efforts to deal with their problems can eventually be implemented. It has of course been necessary and in every way desirable to eliminate all details that might lead to the personal identification of any patient whose disorder has been studied and recorded. All patients referred to have been carefully shielded from recognition. It is nevertheless true that the psychopath engages in behavior so unlike that of others and so typical of his disorder that no act can be reported of a patient from Oregon seen ten years ago without strongly suggesting similar acts by hundreds of psychopaths carried out in dozens of communities last Saturday night. I can only express regret to the scores of people whose sons, brothers, husbands, or daughters I have never seen or heard of but who have, no doubt, reproduced many or perhaps all of the symptoms discussed in this volume. This disorder is so common that no one need feel that any specific act of a psychopath is likely to be distinguishable from acts carried out by hundreds of others.

In discussing the possible influence of environment on the development of this disability, I hope I will not promote unjustified regret or remorse in any parent. Hundreds of times fathers and mothers have discussed their fear that some error or inadequacy on their part caused a child to become a psychopath. Most parents of such patients personally studied impress me as having been conscientious and often very kind and discerning people. As will be brought out later, I do not believe obvious mistreatment or any simple egregious parental errors can justifiably be held as the regular cause of a child's developing this complex disorder. All parents, no doubt, make great as well as small mistakes in their role as parents. It has seemed at times that the very points about which some mothers and fathers feel most uneasiness are the opposite of those so regretted by others and assumed to be the crucial mistakes that have contributed to the maladjustment of a child. Less than in most other kinds of psychiatric disorder has it seemed to me that one could find and point out as causal influences gross failures on the part of the parents which people of ordinary wisdom and good will might have readily avoided.

During recent years it has become popular to blame parents in glib and sweeping terms for all, or nearly all, of the misconduct or inadequacy of their children. It has also become popular to insist that society and not the one who commits the crime should be held responsible for murder, rape, or armed robbery.[56] Sometimes these claims are made without any appeal to evidence at all but merely by repetition of the familiar cliché. Some psychiatrists have even attempted to account for antisocial behavior by assuming that the parents unconsciously want their sons or daughters to commit criminal or immoral acts and that the progeny carry out these wishes while remaining unconscious of their motives.[154,155,156] These conclusions, like many others that have been drawn in the attempt to give fundamental and *dynamic* explanations of things still unknown, rest chiefly on theoretical assumptions—assumptions made on the basis of analogy or arbitrarily interpreted symbolism about what is in the unconscious but what is never brought forth into consciousness or otherwise submitted or demonstrated. This, I maintain, does not constitute genuine evidence as it is known to science, law, or common sense. I hope that the great numbers of conscientious and honorable parents who to my knowledge have struggled courageously over the years, despite grief and frustration, to rehabilitate their sons and daughters (and to make restitution in their behalf to society) will not be led by such fanciful explanations to blame themselves unjustly.

Cruvant and Yochelson[62] have expressed the opinion that strong and inappropriate negative attitudes toward sociopaths are commonly aroused in psychiatrists who attempt to deal with them as patients. It is scarcely surprising if such reactions tend to occur, when one considers all the disappointments and the frustrations involved in treatment and the repeatedly demonstrated irresponsibility and callousness of these patients.

When there is an opportunity to follow the career of a typical psychopath, his pattern of behavior appears specific—something not to be confused with the life of an ordinary purposeful criminal or of a cold opportunist who, in pursuit of selfish ends, merely disregards ethical considerations and the rights of others.

This pattern, I believe, differs no less distinctly than the specific and idiomatic thought and verbal expressions of schizophrenia differ from those of the mentally defective and from other psychiatric conditions. Never in faults of logical reasoning, or in verbal confusion or technical delusion, but rather in the sharper reality of behavior, the psychopath seems often to produce something as strange and as obviously pathologic as the following statement taken from the letter of a patient with schizophrenia:

> Financial service senses worries of 35 whirlpools below sound 1846, 45, 44, A.D. Augusta City treasur, Richmond County treasur, United States Treasur of Mississippi River flood area. Gentlemen will you come to . . . and idenafy none minastrative body that receives the life generated by fourth patented generative below sound. Further arrange financial credit for same. Would like two bedrooms at up town Hotel and convenient to roof garden. Until you gentlemen decide further what my occupation is you may as well announce me as comforting 35 whirlpools below sound. May you gentlemen have gray

eyes and thick bones as the flat sense minastrated are very valuable in idenafying me.

Even such a relatively simple bit of word salad stands out at once as indicative of profound and specific disorder within the writer. As in the words of the schizophrenic, so in the behavior of the psychopath there seems to work a positive knack for producing situations which can be accounted for only in terms of psychiatric illness which is unique.

Section two

The material

5

Max

This patient first came to my attention years ago while I was serving my turn as officer of the day in a Veterans Administration psychiatric institution. His wife telephoned to the hospital for assistance, stating that Max had slipped away from her and had begun to make trouble again. With considerable urgency and apparent distress she explained that she was bringing him to be admitted as a patient and begged that a car with attendants be sent at once to her aid.

He was found in the custody of the police, against whom he had made some resistance but much more vocal uproar. The resistance actually was only a show of resistance consisting for the most part of dramatically aggressive gestures made while he was too securely held to fight and extravagant boasts of his physical prowess and savage temper. His general demeanor in this episode suggested the familiar picture of small boys, held fast by peacemakers, who wax ever more eloquently militant as the possibilities of actual conflict diminish.

He came quietly with the attendants and on arriving at the admission ward was alert, self-assured, and boastful. Extolling his own mettle as a prizefighter, as a salesman, and as general good fellow, he was nevertheless friendly and even flattering toward the examining physician and the hospital.

He was far from what could be called drunk. In fact, it would be stretching a point to say he was "under the influence." He had been drinking, it is true, but he knew well what he was doing, and only by an impracticable flight of fancy could one attribute his behavior primarily to liquor.

At the admitting ward of the hospital, accompanying papers promptly revealed that the patient's desire for treatment arose in consequence of some checks which he had forged in Spartanburg, S. C. He had been arrested and convicted, but an agreement was reached whereby, instead of being sent to jail, he might come to the hospital for psychiatric treatment.

His wife, his attorney, and representatives of a veterans' organization pointed out that he had frequently been in hospitals for the treatment of mental disorder and maintained that he was not responsible for his misconduct.

He seemed pleased to be at the hospital and was expansive and cordial but a little haughty despite his well-maintained air of camaraderie. Although a small man, only 5 feet, 6 inches tall, he made a rather striking impression. His glance was fresh and arresting. His movements were quick, and he had an air of liveliness vaguely suggestive of a chipmunk. Though preposterously boastful, he did not show any indications of a psychosis.

The hospital records showed that he had been a patient eight years previously for a period of two months. During this time of study he showed no evidence of a psychosis or a psychoneurosis and was discharged with a diagnosis of psychopathic personality. He was found to have tertiary syphilis, but neurologic examination and spinal fluid studies showed no evidence of neurosyphilis.

Though at first cooperative and agreeable on this previous admission, he soon became restless and expressed dissatisfaction with the hospital. He was granted parole, but on his first pass into town he got into an altercation in which words were more prominent than blows and was held by the police for disturbing the peace.

After losing parole, he became constantly unruly in petty ways, often insulted the nurses and attendants, and several times egged on mildly psychotic patients to fight each other or to resist the personnel on the ward. On being questioned about this conduct by physicians, he glibly denied all and showed little concern at being accused. Since he was not considered as suffering from a real nervous or mental disorder and since it was difficult to keep him on any ward except the closely supervised one among actively disturbed patients, he had been discharged.

Records show that he sought hospitalization on other occasions after having been fined a half-dozen or more times for brawling on the streets and for petty frauds. There is every reason to believe, from the evidence of careful reports by the Red Cross and by social service workers, that when his troubles with the civil authorities became too discomforting he sought the shelter of a psychiatric hospital.

Several months previously he had spent six weeks at a Veterans Administration hospital in Maryland after getting into similar trouble with the police in Wilmington, Delaware. He complained at the time of having spells during which he lost his temper and attacked people, often, according to his story, with disastrous results, since, again according to his story, he had at one time been featherweight boxing champion of England.

According to the psychiatric history at the Maryland hospital, he had, in describing these spells, mentioned some points that would suggest epilepsy. As soon as he came to the hospital and was relieved of responsibility for the trouble he had made, the so-called spells ceased. His description of them varied. Sometimes, when particularly expansive, he boasted of superconvulsions lasting as long as ten hours, during which he made windowpanes rattle and shook slats from the bed. After being in the hospital for several weeks and apparently beginning to grow bored, his talk of spells died down and he seemed to lose interest in the subject. He was discharged after the staff had agreed that the alleged seizures were entirely spurious and the patient himself had all but admitted it. The diagnosis of psychopathic personality was made.

Between his first visit to the present hospital and his recent return, he had been in five other psychiatric institutions, each time following conflicts with the law or pressing difficulties with private persons. In all the records accumulated during these examinations and investigations, no authentic symptom of an orthodox mental disorder is noted. True enough, there are statements by wives and other interested parties about spells and opinions by the laity, such as the following which was quoted by his attorney on one occasion to shield him from the consequences of theft:

> I had occasion to be in Dayton, Ohio, recently and talked to the people running the . . . Loan Company at . . . Street, having stopped there for about an hour between trains en route for Chicago. I was informed by these gentlemen that he had wheels in his head.

Statements such as the foregoing, opinions that he is "undoubtedly goofy," that he does not behave like a man in his proper senses, etc., abound in the ponderous stack of letters, medical histories, social service reports, records of court trials, and other material that has accumulated in this man's wake. One who reads his strange and prolix story and, even more, one who knows the hero personally is only too ready to fall into the vernacular and agree. Nevertheless, it was equally true on reviewing his record at the time of his new admission that no symptom impressing a psychiatrist had been manifested and that many groups of psychiatrists had, after careful study, continued to find him free of psychosis or psychoneurosis, in other words, sane and responsible for his conduct and even without the mitigating circumstance of a milder mental illness.

Once during this period he had been sent to prison in a southern state for forgeries a little more ambitious than his routine practice. At the instigation of his second and legal wife, who consistently flew to his aid (despite her chagrin at the patient's having meanwhile consummated two bigamous marriages), well-meaning officers of a veterans' organization became interested and took up the cudgels.

Wearying sharply of prison, the patient had for some time been talking on all occasions about a blow on the head which he had sustained while in service. This alleged incident, though absent from his military records, had cropped up frequently but not regularly during his hospitalizations. Sometimes the blow, which he had sustained accidentally from the butt of a gun that a companion was breaching, had merely left him dizzy for a moment. Again it had knocked him unconscious for a short period and necessitated several days' rest in his tent.

Max now became more specific about his wartime injury and explained that he had suffered a severe concussion, lying out stark and unconscious for some eight or nine hours. Attorneys pointed out his many periods of treatment in psychiatric hospitals. The governor soon agreed to parole him into the custody of a federal hospital in Mississippi.

During his present hospitalization he was for several weeks happily adjusted on the admission ward, busy doing small favors for the physician, congenial with all the personnel, and helpful and kindly toward psychotic patients. He was alert, quick-witted, nimble with his hands, and entirely free from delusions, hallucinations, or any of the broader personality changes associated with the ordinary psychoses. He was by no means "nervous," even in the lay sense, and showed no emotional instability or signs of ungovernable impulse. Rather than an excess of anxiety, he showed the reverse, apparently finding little or nothing in his present situation or in all his past difficulties to cause worry or uneasiness.

As the time passed, however, he began to grow restive. He became somewhat condescending toward the physician, frequently referring to himself as a man of superior education and culture and boasting that he had studied for years at Heidelberg.

Shortly before the time set for him to come before the staff, he demanded his discharge. This was denied. He now became involved in frequent altercations with attendants and sometimes fought desultorily with other patients. These fights always started over trifles, and Max's egotism and fractiousness raised the issue. He never attacked others suddenly or incomprehensibly as does a psychotic person motivated by delusions or prompted by hallucinations. The causes of his quarrels were readily understandable and were always found to be similar to those which move such types as the familiar schoolboy bully. Usually his adversaries were patients also disposed to quarrel. No signs of towering rage appeared or even of impulses too strong to be controlled by a very meager desire to refrain.

He always took care not to challenge an antagonist who might get the upper hand. During this period he talked much of his past glories as a pugilist, describing himself as former featherweight champion of all the army camps in the United States. The desire to show off appeared to be a strong motive behind many of his fights. As will be brought out later, he was indeed a skillful boxer. These stories were not delusion but the exaggeration and falsifying, sometimes unconscious or half-conscious, that are often seen in sane people and not infrequently in those who are able, intelligent, and highly successful.*

---

*This tendency is so common even in wise and reliable people that one is at a loss to choose from the wealth of examples in everyday life. A highly regarded and respected friend of mine, a doctor of philosophy, recently appointed professor of physics in a small but distinguished college, and the author of several useful and accurate contributions to scientific literature, is the first who comes to mind.

This distinguished man has often regaled groups of acquaintances, myself among them, with accounts of working his way through the university by playing professional ice hockey at night, later setting type on a newspaper for several hours, rising before daylight to stoke tugboats on the waterfront, riding thirty-four miles to a high school to teach one subject and thirty-four miles back, as well as keeping house in a three-room apartment shared with six aviators and relieving the janitor of the building one hour during each twenty-four. All these activities were spoken of as being carried out simultaneously and along with full-time work at the university. He described in great detail and with apparent familiarity the duties of these positions. His only studying, he said, was done on the subway en route to his various duties.

The same friend once came up from behind while another man and I were commenting on the height of a cliff on which we stood. The hazards of a dive from the position were being idly discussed. The newcomer at once estimated, probably with commendable accuracy, the height, the angle of landing, and all the technicalities of such a dive. He then launched into an astonishing description of a dive he had made in early youth from a bridge 167 feet above the Guadalquiver.

One of the students to whom this excellent scholar lectures stated that it is the custom for each succeeding class to tabulate his adventures and their duration in these pseudoreminiscences and therefrom compute his age. The top figure so far is 169 years. Several classes have bettered 150. The students have great respect for him and confidence in him, as a teacher and as a man. They are particularly devoted to him.

Let it be clearly understood that the person discussed in this footnote is not being brought forward as illustrative of the subject of this study. He is no part of a psychopath. He is, in fact, a character whose essential traits lie at the opposite extreme. The reminiscences here ascribed to him are not told boastfully or for the purpose of shielding himself or of gaining any material end. He is strikingly free of arrogance, kind to a remarkable degree, and altogether worthy of his strong reputation as a good and reliable man. His word in any practical matter is to be respected.

He was often caught sowing the seeds of discontent among other patients whom he encouraged to break rules, to oppose attendants, and to demand discharges. He made small thefts from time to time. This trend culminated in his kicking out an iron grill during the night and leaving the hospital. He took with him two psychotic patients, and numerous others testified that he had tried to persuade them to leave also.

The next afternoon he was returned to the hospital by the police after being arrested in the midst of a brawl that he had caused by cheating at a game of chance in a low dive. He had taken a few beers but was shrewd, alert, and well in command of his body and his faculties.

He now insisted on his discharge from the hospital against advice and was brought before the medical staff. The diagnosis of psychopathic personality was again made. In his demands to be released, he arrogantly maintained that he had been pardoned outright by the governor of the state which had imprisoned him, pointed out vehemently that he was sound in mind and body, and expressed strong indignation at being confined unjustly in what he referred to as a "nut house." It was then pointed out to him that he was not pardoned but merely paroled, and he was told that if discharged at present he would be returned to the penitentiary.

Here his wrath began to subside at once and marvelously. Hastily, but with some subtlety, his tone changed, and he began to find points in common with the advice he had been receiving from the staff. He left the room in a cordial frame of mind, tossing friendly and fairly clever quips back at the physicians, nearly all of whom he had known during some of his many admissions to various hospitals.

About ten days later he was pardoned outright by the governor and almost immediately took legal action which got him discharged against medical advice.

Many similar adventures had occupied his time prior to the recent admission. Some of these had resulted in his being sent, as in the episode just cited, to psychiatric hospitals from which he promptly obtained his release by legal action. Others had led him to jail and to the police barracks dozens of times for charges not sufficiently serious for him to utilize the expedient of psychiatric hospitalization as a means of escape.

A series of troubles had led to his reaching the hospital on this last occasion. As mentioned previously, he had many years ago divorced his first wife and remarried. The second legal spouse continued to play an important part in his career. As the proprietress or madame of a local brothel generally conceded to be the most orderly and, perhaps in a certain sense, the most respectable institution of its sort in the city, she was constantly embarrassed by the actions of her husband. Though enjoying a good part of the revenue from this ever-lucrative business, Max troubled himself little to maintain the dignity of the house.

In fact, it seemed that he went out of his way to complicate matters for his wife. If not through his daily and nightly brawls or uproars in various low grogshops, dancehalls, "juke joints," etc., then by putting slugs into slot machines or serving as fence in some petty thieving racket, he brought the police in search of him down on the "house of joy" which maintained him.

Though satisfactory understandings existed between this institution and the law, policemen suddenly appearing at the door and trooping through the hallways proved anything but conducive to that sense of security and dignity Mrs. _____ had long and justly boasted for her house.

Especially after a few drinks, Max also liked to go about the house bragging to clients and to entertainers alike of his prowess in various lines, intruding on parties still at the "downstairs stage" of the night's activities, minding everybody's business, and inevitably turning the conversation to his superiorities. Most of the time he was quite amiable in this role—a cordial, but an all too cordial, host under circumstances in which people are usually concerned more with definite and perhaps pressing aims of their own than with the glowing reminiscenses of another. Occasionally when crossed, he became threatening even with clients and, though open strife was usually avoided, hot, wild words and strenuous scenes sometimes followed, with Max exulting in the aftermath by pacing up and down the corridors of the house, shadowboxing, cursing, crying out his pugilistic titles and victories, and challenging all comers.

No one realized better than his wife, a woman of experience and good judgment in such matters, what an unhappy effect these antics had on her clientele quietly seeking pleasure behind doors before which Max roared and paraded. Naturally she sought to silence him and to lead him off to the quarters they shared. Usually, however, her appearance served merely as a focus for his ire, and the tumult she sought to quell redoubled through her efforts. More than once under such circumstances he pursued her into her room, the wrangle having moved on to open violence, and there beat her to his heart's content. Mrs. _____, a tall and heavy person, gave a casual impression of being twice as large as Max. Furthermore, she was a woman of considerable strength. She often fought back vigorously and, though she seldom succeeded in landing a telling blow that would discourage her marital opponent, her resistance made the fight much more lively and greatly augmented the uproar of thuds, slaps, crashes, oaths, grunts, and honest yells of pain.

Over several years this connubial life had been interrupted frequently by Max's departure, which he usually took in heat after quarrels such as those just described. Often he left voluntarily with obscene curses at his wife on his lips. Sometimes she called the police after he had covered her with minor bruises and abrasions from his practiced fists and had him forcibly ousted. Over the years he spent perhaps two-thirds of his time away, going from city to city and living by his wits, which are sharp indeed. When caught in his minor frauds, which he practiced not only on the public but also on those associated with him in his ventures, he quickly left town. Or, if retreat was not quick enough, he spent a few days in jail, from which he soon obtained release by telling of his imaginary head injury, of his "spells," or of anything else that occurred to his fertile mind as a means to make people believe he was incompetent because of "shell shock." When his situation turned out to be more serious, he telegraphed or telephoned to his wife, who at once flew to his aid, usually with some little money at her disposal.

He covered the entire eastern seaboard on these trips and made several expeditions into the Midwest. For a few weeks in Texas he lived well off of money he milked from slot machines by some ingenious device or contraption or maneuver. His inventions of this type are numerous and highly practical. He could, perhaps, make an excellent living indefinitely off such takings if he did not, when drinking, and often when sober, boast too widely of his cleverness or otherwise bring himself to the attention of the police.

It has been mentioned that earlier in his career, but after his second marriage, he had been wedded to other women bigamously. His wife learned of these episodes and legal action was taken by the deceived women. From these minor troubles he was extricated by his shrewdness, the aid of his wife, and the power of his familiar tactics of claiming incompetency and irresponsibility.

This gambit of moves seems to have gained rather than lost effectiveness by repetition. It has become virtually a joker in the deck, or rather up the sleeve, and it has never failed him yet. One cannot but wonder if the juries, the courts, and other authorities are not overwhelmed by precedent and, seeing that his grounds for impunity have been upheld so often in the past, fail to challenge them adequately. Precedent is, of course, freely admitted to weigh heavily in law. On the other hand, these nonmedical observers seem to weigh seriously the plain facts of the patient's conduct when they decide that he is not a normal man. Psychiatry, with its clear rules and definitions for the determination of psychosis, has not seemed to be as much concerned with these facts.

The immediate cause of Max's return to the hospital on this occasion was indirectly connected with a third bigamous marriage which he recently made while off on one of his tours from connubial security. With his new partner he tried his hand again at forgery on a somewhat larger scale than usual. He prospered for a while and, flushed with prosperity and bravado, brought his new bigamous partner home with him on a visit to the brothel where his legal wife was struggling to restore standards which had suffered during his presence.

As might well be imagined, quarreling broke out at once between the two wives. Max, still in character, did nothing to pour oil on these sorely troubled waters. In fact, his every move seemed designed to whip up the already lively doings to a crescendo. The dispute culminated in a vigorous and vociferous set-to during which both ladies were pretty thoroughly mauled, furniture was broken, and the brothel all but wrecked. Max's most important personal contribution to the fray was a broken jaw for his legal wife, the madame of the house.

It is interesting here to note that, despite his continual brawling with both men and women over so many years while drinking or while quite sober and despite his ferocious threats of violence and his pretty genuine ability as a pugilist, no serious bodily harm had before this come to anyone at his hands. I believe that the substantial injury was unintentional, an act of thoughtless exuberance committed in the heat of a situation eminently and subtly designed to bring out high enthusiasm in such a man as our hero.

Having succeeded in bringing off a scene that even in his career stands out as a little masterpiece, he took the bigamous partner and fled back to the nearby city where his forgeries were in progress. Almost on his arrival detection met him, and hard on its heels came prosecution from home in consequence of the jawbreaking. To these difficulties charges for his latest bigamy were added. As such disasters began to accumulate about Max, his legal wife, finally aroused, decided for the moment to lend her influence to the punitive forces.

In the court action that followed, the present and third bigamous wife received an adequate sentence to the state penitentiary, and for a while Max's own fortune seemed none too bright. Wrought upon by his protestations, however, and perhaps influenced as well by the disappearance of her rival from the scene, his old protector, the legal wife, was won over and began to work with her husband. Soon matters were arranged for him to escape the ordinary consequences of his deeds and be sent again to a psychiatric hospital. His last admission, with which this account began, was the result.

Safe in the familiar harbor of a psychiatric hospital, he was for a week or more friendly, cooperative, and apparently content. He was at all times shrewd, somewhat witty on low levels of humor, and entirely free from ideas or behavior suggesting any recognized psychosis.

He became very friendly with me during this period and talked entertainingly and with enthusiasm about his many adventures. He denied all misconduct on his part but admitted that he had often been in trouble because of his wife and others. It was not the denial of a man who is eager to show himself innocent but the casual tossing aside of matters considered irrelevant or bothersome to discuss. After briefly laughing off all his accusations, he at once shifted the subject to his many triumphs and attainments.

Telling of his early life in Vienna, his birthplace, he spoke of his excellent scholarship in the schools, of his preeminence at sports, and of the splendid figure in general he had cut as a youth in that gay and urbane city. In none of these statements did he lay in details such as might be expected of a man developing a delusional trend. No psychiatrist, and few laymen for that matter, would have had the least difficulty in recognizing all this as "tall talk" designed to deceive the listener and to put the talker in a good light. All the patient's reactions showed that he himself was far from being taken in.

His birth and upbringing in Vienna coincide with the facts as obtained from his army records. His alleged experiences at Heidelberg are recorded many times on his own testimony. He described himself as a distinguished student in that honorable university, referring to Kant and Schopenhauer and several of the Greek philosophers as special subjects of his study. He spoke also of a deep interest in Shakespeare during his student days and sought to give the idea that he was celebrated among his fellows for his knowledge of the Bard.

The shrewdness and agility of his mind were prettily demonstrated in these references to the picturesque and traditional gaieties of student life, and to the works of the philosophers and poets. No less vividly and convincingly did he reveal an utter lack of any real acquaintance with all the subjects in which he boasted himself learned.

He knew the names of a half-dozen Shakespearean plays, several catchpenny lines familiar to the man on the streets, a scattering of great names among the philosophers. He was totally ignorant not only of the systems of thought for which his philosophers are famous but also even of superficial and general facts about their lives and times that any person, however unintellectual, could not fail to remember if he ever had the interest to read of such matters. Of Shakespeare he knew practically nothing beyond the titles that rolled eloquently from his tongue and a few vague and jumbled conceptions that have crept into the ideologies of bootblacks, peasants, and street gamins the world over. Furthermore, he had no interest, as contrasted with knowledge, in any matter that could be called philosophic or poetic. He liked to rattle off his little round of fragmentary quotations, the connections and the connotations of which he realized only in the most superficial sense, to contribute a few pat and shallow saws of his own believed by him to be highly original, iconoclastic, and profound, to boast generally of his wisdom, and then to go on to descriptions of his other attainments and experiences.

To my surprise, he was several times taken by psychiatrists who studied him briefly and by social service workers as a man of some intellectual stature. His story of study at Heidelberg, though usually discounted, was, if the implication of the psychiatric histories is correctly read, sometimes taken as true or probably true.

Although my actual contact with Heidelberg is superficial enough, I had no difficulty in demonstrating in the patient a plain lack of acquaintance with the ways of life there. The general plan of study and the physical setup of the university, matters that would be familiar to anyone who had been an undergraduate there, however briefly and disinterestedly, were unknown to Max. He showed that he had probably passed through the town and that he had heard and still clearly remembered gossip and legend from the streets of Vienna about the university and its customs, but he had no more real understanding of it than a shrewd but unlettered cockney would have of Cambridge.

This phase of his examination provided, in my opinion, a striking example of the ambiguity inherent in our word *intelligence*. Here was a man of exceptional acumen. His versatile devices to defraud, his mechanical inventions to overcome safeguards which ordinarily protect slot machines and other depositories of cash, and his shrewd practical reasoning in the many difficulties of his career demonstrate beyond question the accuracy, quickness, and subtlety of his practical thinking. His memory is unusually sound; his cleverness at manipulating bits of information so as to appear learned is exceptional. He is not a man to be taken in by the scheming of others, though he himself takes in many. One can truthfully say about him that he is "bright as a dollar," "smart as a whip," that "his mind is like a steel trap," etc.

His ability to plan and execute schemes to provide money for himself, to escape legal consequences, and to give, when desirable, the impression that he is, in the ordinary sense, mentally deranged, could be matched by few, if any, people whom I have known. In such thinking he not only shows objective ingenuity but also remarkable knowledge of other people and their reactions (of *psychology* in the popular sense) at certain levels or, rather, in certain modes of personality reaction. He stands out for the swiftness and accuracy of his thinking at solving puzzles and at playing checkers. At any sort of contest based on a matching of wits, he is unlikely to come off second best.

To consider his intelligence (or should one say wisdom?) from another viewpoint, from that of the ordinary man's idea of what is good sense about working out a successful plan of life on a long-term basis, only the story of his career can speak adequately. Be it noted that the result of his conduct brings trouble not only to others but almost as regularly to himself.

To take still another point of view and consider him on a basis of those values somewhat vaguely implied by "intellectuality," "culture," or, in everyday speech, by "depth of mind," we find an appalling deficiency. These concepts in which meaning or emotional significance are considered along with the mechanically rational, if applied to this man, measure him as very small, or very defective. He appears not only ignorant in such modes of function but stupid as well. He is unfamiliar with the primary facts or data of what might be called personal values and is altogether incapable of understanding such matters. It is impossible for him to take even a slight interest in the tragedy or joy or the striving of humanity as presented in serious literature or art. He is also indifferent to all these matters in life itself. Beauty and ugliness, except in a very superficial sense, goodness, evil, love, horror, and humor have no actual meaning, no power to move him.

He is, furthermore, lacking in the ability to see that others are moved. It is as though he were colorblind, despite his sharp intelligence, to this aspect of human existence. It cannot be explained to him because there is nothing in his orbit of awareness that can bridge the gap with comparison. He can repeat the words and say glibly that he understands, and there is no way for him to realize that he does not understand.

I believe that this man has sufficient intelligence, in the ordinary sense, to acquire what often passes for learning in such fields as literature and philosophy. If he had more stability and persistence he could easily earn a Ph.D. or an M.D. degree from the average university in this country. If he had this stability and became a doctor of philosophy in literature, the plays of Shakespeare, the novels of Joseph Conrad or of Thomas Hardy would still have no power to move him. He could remember facts and he could learn to manipulate facts and even to devise rationalizations in such a field with skill comparable to that with which he now outthinks an opponent at checkers. If, for the sake of theory and speculation, such changes were granted to him, my contention that he would still be without this sort of understanding is, of course, impossible to prove. It is maintained, however, that this would be clear to all observers who have real interest in such aspects of life, however diverse might be their own formulated opinions on what is good, bad, true, or beautiful about art or about living.

But let us abandon speculation and return to the patient's conduct. He talked at length of his ability as a fencer, maintaining that he was the best swordsman, or one of the best, at Heidelberg during his student days and was also well known and feared in Vienna. He spoke of the championship he had won at boxing while in the army, boasting often of a belt which he still possessed symbolizing this achievement. On hearing that I had had a slight experience in amateur boxing, he offered to demonstrate his skill and to give me some points. Ostentatiously he insisted that I stand up and, pulling his punches, went through a number of sequences. He did this several times, always choosing a place on the ward where he could be observed by a large group of patients and attendants. He gave every indication of being a practiced boxer. This is borne out also by army records which indicate that he won some small prize as champion of his battalion or regiment.

Even before his presentation at the staff meeting, he again became dissatisfied, making complaints against the nurses and attendants, demanding special foods and privileges, bullying other patients, and inciting them to make trouble. At staff meeting the diagnosis of psychopathic personality was reaffirmed.

On failing to get his discharge at once, he became even more fretful and unruly and threatened to break out of the hospital. It became difficult to care for him on the ward for well-adjusted patients in which he had been placed, so he was transferred to the closely supervised ward, where he found himself surrounded by actively disturbed and egregiously psychotic companions.

He complained at once of this to his wife, who came to the hospital authorities in tears and with angry protestations, saying that it was an outrage to put her husband with all those crazy men who were violent and combative and who might hurt him. Earlier on the ward she made the same protest to an attendant, who saltily remarked on the inconsistency of such worries about a husband so well known for his boasts of might and ferocity and pugilistic skill. She made the matter so sharp an issue that Max, after promising to cooperate, was moved to a quieter ward.

Now, for a short while, he was more agreeably disposed. Boastfully he told me that he was, in addition to all his other parts, an artist of remarkable ability. He asked to be given a loaf of bread, stating that he would mold from it creations of great beauty and worth. On getting the bread, he broke off a large chunk, placed it in his mouth, and began to chew it assiduously, apparently relishing the confusion of his observers. After proceeding for a length of time and with thoroughness that once would have met with favor from advocates of Fletcherism, he at last disgorged the mess from his mouth and with considerable dexterity set about modeling it into the figure of a cross. Soon a human form was added in the customary representation. Rosettes, intertwining leaves, garlands, and an elaborate pedestal followed. The mixture of saliva and chewed bread rapidly hardened.

He now requested a pass to go into town, saying that he must obtain shellac and appropriate paints to complete his creation. He made it plain that he was molding this statuette for me, and it was clear that he regarded it as a most flattering favor. Since it was judged unwise to send him out alone, he was allowed to go in company of an attendant. He returned with his materials but also with the strong odor of whiskey on his breath.

The whiskey had been obtained in this manner: Pleading a call of nature which, judging by his frantic tone and impressive grimaces, the attendant deemed urgent, he hurriedly sequestered himself in a toilet. After waiting for what seemed like a most liberal interval, the attendant went to inquire into the delay. On receiving no response, he forced the door only to find that Max had made his escape through a small window near the top of the room, a feat which would have been extremely difficult for an ordinary man.

Guided by a happy instinct, the attendant hurried to a nearby dive where bootleg whiskey was sold and surprised our hero in the midst of his second or third potation. He was drinking to his own cleverness at outwitting the attendant and in loud, imperious tones commanded all present to drink with him and at his expense.

The attendant found him insolent and intractable at first but, with strong moral support from the proprietor and others, led him out after settling charges for drinks to all, which Max had grandly assumed without a cent in his pockets.

For the rest of the day he was surly and idle except for his efforts to promote quarrels, but on the morrow, extolling again his virtuosity as a sculptor, he settled down and finished his gift to me. It was indeed an uncommon production. The chewed bread had become as hard as baked clay. The whole piece was very skillfully and ingeniously shaped, dry, firm, and as neatly finished as if done by a machine. It was, furthermore, one of the most extravagant, florid, and unprepossessing articles that has ever met my glance. Max presented it with mixed pride and condescension, with an air of triumph and expectancy that seemed to demand expressions of wonder and gratitude beyond reach of the ordinary man. I did my best but felt none too satisfied with my efforts.

Max now asked for daily bread and for a room to be set apart as an atelier where he proposed to work regularly and without distracting influences.

In the hope that this activity would keep him out of trouble, all his requests were granted. He immediately demanded full parole also but agreed to wait a short while for this when it was denied.

For a week he worked steadily, his mouth crammed with the doughy mass, his jaws chewing deliberately, his hands nimbly shaping spewed-out hunks of the mess into various neatly finished and exact, but always garish, forms. His coloring of the flowers and garlands and imitation jewels, vivid red, pale purple, sickly pink, always struck a high level of the tawdry blended with the pretentious. The most gaudy atrocities of the dime store must give ground before such art.

He sent messages to the medical director of the hospital, to the supervisor of attendants and the chief nurse, and to many others whom he felt it well to ingratiate that *objets d'art* awaited them in his studio. He was visited by these people and by various prominent ladies of the city interested in welfare work and active in helping disabled veterans. To most of these he made presentations as well as moving speeches about his misfortunes, his gifts, and his ambitions. His demands for parole now became more vehement. Many influential citizens begged that he be given this chance to rehabilitate himself. As a matter of fact, he had been reasonably cooperative while at his new work. Parole was granted.

The police brought him back after a few hours. His left hand showed a painful laceration, the result of a severe bite inflicted in retreat by a barroom opponent who had resorted to this vaguely Parthian maneuver after finding Max's pugilistic skill too great to cope with in the ordinary manner. He showed some evidence of drink but was by no means sodden. Nor did he in any way give the impression of a man sufficiently influenced by liquor to have his judgment appreciably altered or any violent and extraordinary impulses released. In contrast with some of the other patients discussed here, Max, though a ready drinker, never or very rarely drank to the point of confusion. There is no record in all the saga of his being brought in senseless from the highways or fields. At the worst he could scarcely be classed as more than a moderate drinker.

He made no excuses for violating his parole but blamed others in full for the trouble he had started and felt grossly misused by the man he had attacked, by the police, and by the hospital which revoked his parole.

His wife at once pled for restoration of his parole, and a number of other influences supported her. Max reiterated the familiar argument: why deny liberty to a man classed as sane? Parole was restored after a week. Surprisingly, Max got through two days without difficulty but on the third burst into the office of the supervisor of attendants and vehemently demanded that a former attendant, dismissed for incompetence, be reinstated at once. He had brought this man with him into the office. Inspired by a couple of highballs but by no means drunk, he thundered and swaggered, threatening to use political influences to have the supervisor discharged if all his demands were not met forthwith. He named various political powers which he boasted that he could command. These influences, he very truly pointed out, had lent themselves to his efforts to get out of jail and out of hospitals in the past. He insisted, furthermore, that certain other attendants whom he disliked be discharged. Storming and cursing and threatening, he was removed to a closed ward.

Somewhat disgruntled, he ceased his modeling in postprandial bread and sulked, irritable and aggressive, among his psychotic companions. Soon, however, he became more agreeable and after a few days came swaggering into my office to display a new product of his ingenuity. Borrowing a dollar bill and a pair of scissors, he cut out five rectangles of plain paper identical in size and shape with the bill and poised himself with a faintly prestidigitatorial air.

"Watch this," he boasted.

As he cut up his models of the bank note and manipulated the pieces, he called for paste to be brought. Then, after a shrewd and tricky rearrangement, he pasted together his fragments.

"Count them," he ordered in the grand manner.

Not five but six paper models lay on the table, all plainly patched, but all defying the ordinary eye to detect any appreciable loss of substance.

Within a week his wife, after haunting the hospital and begging for his parole, insisting that she needed him at home, that she was in want, etc., succeeded in taking him out in her custody. Late that night local policemen brought him back. After giving his wife what might be called an average beating, he had caused considerable uproar at the bawdy house and fled to another dive where, after trying to get loans from a few idlers, he boasted and quarreled until the police intervened.

He remained then on a closed ward for about a week. After this time, legal charges against him having been dropped, he demanded release against medical advice. Since he was sane and competent in the eyes of law and science, he was discharged.

Two months later local newspapers carried small headlines calling attention to his being taken by federal agents after a protracted investigation in Texas. For weeks patched-up five-, ten-, and twenty-dollar bills circulated in several Texas cities, and Max, decked in flashy finery, drove about in his own car and splurged lavishly on food, drink, and women. The surprising volume of mutilated notes at last caused comment and finally suspicion. After skillful and persistent efforts, the federal agents finally worked out the puzzle and brought it to Max's feet.

My colleagues and I felt that perhaps our acquaintance with Max had ended. Federal justice is widely regarded as less relenting and less distractible than municipal and state justice. For most lawbreakers this is, indeed, true. Max's old play, however, had not lost its charm. Some months later he was in a psychiatric hospital and shortly afterward at large.

His career continued. The records show that once, while under a five-year sentence to a state penitentiary, he stressed his former syphilitic infection and boasted so vehemently in his old style that a physician who saw him in prison made a diagnosis of dementia paralytica. No neurologic or serologic findings supported this opinion, which was offered by a general practitioner after one interview. This was enough to start the familiar cycle of prison-to-hospital-to-freedom.

Once again, when anxious for shelter, he boasted that he could communicate with ancestors who had died thousands of years ago. His wife joined in and claimed that he had seen monkeys and baboons chasing him. At a general hospital a tentative diagnosis of schizophrenia was offered. Back at another psychiatric hospital he showed no evidence of an orthodox psychosis and after a short time got his discharge.

Again when pressed by a court verdict, he claimed amnesia for a period of two years, during which he had been active at defrauding. A suspicion of hysteria was expressed by some physicians. At the psychiatric hospital he stuck for a while to this story of amnesia, but, his vanity being aroused, he recalled in detail all his experiences. It was plain from his manner that he had not suffered from any true amnesia, and he no longer took pains to make anyone believe that he had.

A few years later he was brought to the hospital. This time his wife insisted that his beatings were too much to bear and stated that he had threatened to kill her with an axe, explaining that he could do so with impunity since he was a mentally disabled veteran and that, as she well knew, he had always succeeded in escaping the consequences of any crime. She soon recovered from her fears and asked for his parole. At the insistence of both man and wife, he was discharged after a few weeks.

Be it noted that despite his vigorous threats such as the one just mentioned, Max seldom, if ever, tried to do anyone serious physical injury. This fact has especial weight in view of his boasted and pretty satisfactorily demonstrated immunity from penal consequences. Max is not by inclination and has never been a violent or murderous person but in his conflicts with the law has appeared usually in the role of petty bully, sharper, thief, and braggart.

Some months later I, with other psychiatrists, testified at court when efforts were being made to have Max committed by law as "insane." Several citizens whom he had defrauded and seriously troubled in other ways, finding that he was not vulnerable to fines or sentences in the municipal courts, hoped to obtain relief and protection by getting him into a psychiatric hospital.

The psychiatrists could not avoid admitting that he did not show evidence of anything that is officially classed as a psychosis. I had to agree. In trying to explain briefly and comprehensively that I believed this man, although not suffering from a psychosis that could be named or from any of the technical symptoms of one, was entirely unsuited to be at large, the sense of futility was oppressive. Max, neat and well groomed, insouciant, witty, alert, and splendidly rational, rose, beaming, to hear again the verdict of freedom.

6

Roberta

This young woman, sitting now for the first time in my office, gave an impression that vaguely suggested—immaturity? The word is not entirely accurate for the impression. Immaturity might imply the guarded, withdrawn attitude often shown by children in the doctor's office. It was another, in fact, almost an opposite feeling that she gave. Something less than the average of self-consciousness, a sort of easy security that does not arise from effort or from pretense—some qualities of this nature seemed to enter into the impression.

Roberta was just 20 years of age, well developed, a little overweight, perhaps, but not greatly overweight. It was, as could be noticed on closer observation, a slight carelessness about dress, a laxness of posture more than any real obesity, that suggested an overnourished body. She was not pretty, but her looks were pleasant. Unlike most 20-year-old girls, she did not seem, with or without awareness, to be deliberately counting her feminine attractions into the equation that probably occurs in every personal contact between man and woman. This, perhaps, was what gave that first vague and complicated impression of an adult who, in some rather pleasant way, is still childlike.

It was a little surprising to hear her admit that she had resented being brought for the interview because she felt her mother and father were overdoing things to try to find something "wrong with her mind." There was nothing sullen about her and she soon expressed satisfaction at having come and a willingness to stay in the hospital as long as it might be deemed advisable.

She admitted without reluctance that she needed help of some sort and that she had "made a mess" of her life. She expressed interest in plans for a different future. In speaking of her need for psychiatric treatment, something suggested that her conviction of need was more like what a man feels who looks in the mirror and decides he needs a haircut than like the earnest and sometimes desperate need many people feel in their problems. The man who finds he needs the haircut is sincere in his conviction, despite the fact that convictions about such a trivial matter are also, and necessarily, trivial.

In this interview and during subsequent weeks, Roberta discussed in detail and at length hundreds of incidents in her life. Her history had been obtained from her parents, who accompanied her, and additional material was available in letters from her former girl scout leader, her Sunday school teacher, and others.

"I can't understand the girl, no matter how hard I try," said the father, shaking his head in genuine perplexity. "It's not that she seems bad or exactly that she means to do wrong. She can lie with the straightest face, and after she's found in the most outlandish lies she still seems perfectly easy in her own mind."

He had related, in a rambling but impressive account, how Roberta at 10 years of age stole her aunt's silver hairbursh, how she repeatedly made off with small articles from the dime store, the drug store, and from her own home.

"At first it seemed just the mischievous doings of a little girl," he said, "a sort of play—and her not realizing about its being serious. You know how children sometimes tell a lot of fanciful stories without thinking of it as lying."

Neither the father nor the mother seemed a severe parent. In the opinion of their pastor and others who knew them well, they had no unusual attitudes toward their children. Roberta's brother and two sisters were all well-behaved members of the community. The family was financially comfortable but not wealthy. There had been no black sheep in the group for the several generations during which they lived in a western North Carolina town with a population of 10,000.

"We didn't want to be too hard on Roberta when we first noticed these things," the mother continued. "I've heard that too much punishment sometimes confuses a child and makes matters worse. We talked it over with Mr. _____ (the pastor), with the superintendent of the school, and with all her teachers." There was nothing to suggest that this girl had been spoiled. The parents had, so far as could be determined, consistently let her find that lying and stealing and truancy brought censure and punishment.

"She never seemed sly or crafty," the mother said, a little puzzled about how to express the impression, "not like the sort of person you think of as stealing and being irresponsible. Roberta didn't seem wild and headstrong." Yet she often used remarkable ingenuity to conceal her misdeeds and to continue them.

As she grew into her teens, this girl began to buy dresses, cosmetics, candy, perfume, and other articles, charging them to her father. He had no warning that these bills would come. Roberta acted without saying a word to him, and, no matter what he said or did, she went on in the same way. For many of these things she had little or no use; some of them she distributed among her acquaintances. In serious conferences it was explained to the girl that the family budget had been badly unbalanced by these bills. As a matter of fact, the father, previously in comfortable circumstances, had at one time been forced to the verge of bankruptcy.

In school Roberta's work was mediocre. She studied little and her truancy was spectacular and persistent. No one regarded her as dull and she seemed to learn easily when she made any effort at all. (Her I.Q. was found to be 135.) She often expressed ambitions and talked of plans for the future. These included the study of medicine, dress designing, becoming an author, and teaching home economics in a nearby college. For short periods she sometimes applied herself and made excellent grades, but she would inevitably return to truancy, spending the school hours in cheap movie houses, in the drug store, or wandering through shops, stealing a few things for which she seemed to have neither need or specific desire. She did not seem to be activated by any "compulsive" desire emerging against a struggle to resist. On the contrary, she proceeded calmly and casually in these acts. She experienced no great thrill or consummation in a theft nor found in it relief from uncomfortable stress.

Twice in her early teens she alarmed her family by staying out all night, once after a Sunday school picnic, once after a small dancing party. With what seemed like disarming candor, she had told the girls at whose homes she stayed that her family knew all about her plans.

Such conduct of course suggests that she might have been deliberately trying to hurt her parents. If so, Roberta herself was quite unaware of such a motive. As with her thievery, her truancy, and her running up of bills, no conscious drive of real significance is found. Roberta insists that she loves her parents. "They've made some mistakes with me," she says, "but I've made a lot myself. I appreciate all they've done for me. Of course, I've learned my lesson now."

One of this girl's most appealing qualities is, perhaps, her friendly impulse to help others. In the hospital she showed tact and kindness in doing small favors for seriously troubled patients. This did not seem pretentious or in any way staged. At home she had for years shown similar traits. She often went to sit with an ill neighbor, watched the baby of her mother's friend, and rather patiently helped her younger sister with her studies. In none of these things was she consistent. She often promised her services and, with no explanation, failed to appear. An easy kindness seemed also to mark her attitude toward small animals. She would stop to pet a puppy, take crumbs out to the birds, and comfort a stray cat. Yet, when her own dog was killed by an automobile, she showed only the most fleeting and superficial signs of concern.

"She has such sweet feelings," Roberta's mother said, "but they don't amount to much. She's not hard or heartless, but she's all on the surface. I really believe she means to stop doing all those terrible things, but she doesn't mean it enough to matter."

"Lots of times we thought she'd got on the right track," the father said, referring to Roberta's brief period of interest in church work. When 17 years of age she had voluntarily assisted the director of religious education for a couple of months and had talked about making a career of such work. She had seemed sincere and her informal talks to small groups of younger children in Sunday school made a most favorable impression. Even while engaged in these activities, she was occasionally stealing and running up big bills which, by many subtleties, she concealed for a long time from her father.

"I wouldn't exactly say she's like a hypocrite," the father added. "When she's caught and confronted with her lies and other misbehavior, she doesn't seem to appreciate the inconsistency of her position. Her conscience seems still untouched. Even when she says how badly she's acted and promises to do better, her feelings just must not be what you take them for."

Having failed in many classes and her truancy becoming intolerable to the school, Roberta, after several more petty thefts from classmates and teachers, was expelled from the local high school. Her family sent her to a boarding school of her choice, from which she wrote enthusiastic letters. Despite this expressed satisfaction, she ran away from school and could not be located for several days.

After her return home it was found that she had cashed bad checks at school to obtain money with which she kept herself at a hotel in a town near the school and not far from her home. She knew several boys and girls there and had spent some time with them going to the movies and having dates. She had told a convincing story to the effect that her father was in town on business and that she had accompanied him. This explanation she made so blandly and with such casual laying in of detail that none of her friends or their parents suspected her of having run away. She borrowed sums of money from several people during this episode, telling them about all sorts of entirely unreal situations which made it necessary for her to have funds at once.

She seemed entirely unworried, never by word or gesture giving indication that she might have something to hide or to be seriously worried about. No adequate motive for her leaving school could be brought out. Sometimes she spoke of dislike for a teacher, again of some girl's having seemed snobbish, or, forgetting the other complaints, explained it all on the basis of having been so homesick. Such expressions she would later contradict thoughtlessly by praise of the school and statements to the effect that she had greatly enjoyed herself there.

Since she first began to go out to parties, Roberta had given her parents many sleepless nights. With the clear and accepted understanding that she must, like her friends, return home by 10:30 or 11 P.M., she often did not turn up until 1 or 2 A.M., and once or twice not until far later. Sometimes she would while away these postmidnight hours playing pinball and slot machines with several boys in small resorts about the edge of town. Once she rode on a motorcycle with a young man to another town fifty miles away and returned just before dawn. Disturbed by the usual talk about sexual irregularities in young people, her parents had serious discussions with their daughter. Privileges were taken from her, and, sometimes for a month or more after an especially gross act of disobedience, she was not allowed to go out with her crowd.

Having long feared that Roberta would in such circumstances lose her virginity, the parents, after her episode of staying several days away from school at the hotel, prepared themselves for the worst. She, of course, denied any sexual relations, but she also regularly denied stealing, truancy, surreptitiously charging things to her father, and all her other faulty conduct. When she missed a menstrual period shortly after running away from school, her parents were so perturbed that a medical examination was made. Not only was there no evidence of pregnancy, but a definitely intact hymen was obvious.

Roberta was sent to two other boarding schools from which she had to be expelled. She entered a hospital for training to be a registered nurse but did not last a month. Employed in her father's business as a bookkeeper, she used her skill at figures and a good deal of ingenuity to make off with considerable sums.

Although she had a number of boyfriends and spoke of having often been in love, Roberta was not the typical flirt. Apparently she had only mild experiences in kissing and necking, these activities seeming vaguely pleasant but not arousing any vivid passion. The war having been for some time in progress, Roberta met scores of young soldiers from a nearby camp. She kept up a lively correspondence with many of them after they were sent overseas or to other posts. She spoke of her satisfaction in sending letters to these men who were serving their country and expressed herself from time to time as being in love with one or another of them. One of those with whom she corresponded most regularly was killed in an accident on the West Coast and another during combat in Italy. She seemed little affected by these incidents, though her expressions of regret were verbally appropriate. Apparently she was unaware that under such circumstances another girl might have felt more.

In telling of her initial sexual experience, which had occurred about a year before I first saw her, she seemed frank and by no means embarrassed.

After her discharge from the WAC, which she had entered with apparent enthusiasm and wonderfully expressed intentions, she remained at home and, for a few months, despite relatively small irregularities, appeared at last to be making a better adjustment. She often seemed mildly bored but never pathologically restless or distinctly unhappy. She wrote many sentimental letters to a couple of dozen soldiers, read *True Story* magazine, *Little Women, The Story of Philosophy,* and comic books and attended movies and parties at the Red Cross.

With no explanation to her parents she suddenly disappeared. To me she explained that she had left with the intention of visiting a boyfriend stationed at a camp in another state. She admitted that she had in mind the possibility of marrying this man but that no definite decision had been made by her, much less by him. She had, it seems, given the matter little serious thought, and from her attitude one would judge she was moved by little more than what might make a person stroll off into the yard to see if the magnolia tree had bloomed. She left with a little over $4.00 in her purse. Getting off the bus in a town three hours' ride from home, she tried to reach the boyfriend by telephone and ask him to telegraph funds to her. She could not at the time reach him. She had realized her family might trace her if she continued by bus to the city for which she had bought a ticket. This was the chief factor in her getting off where she did.

Balked in her efforts to reach the soldier, she remembered another boy, now overseas, who lived in this town in which she found herself almost without funds. She decided to go to his family and spend the night with them. With the most artless manner and with no sign of uneasiness or tension, she explained to these people that she was hurrying to the bedside of an aunt, that her father had been away on business when she left, and that there had been a mistake in her understanding of the bus schedule. She found, she said, that she would have to take the morning train from here to reach the bedside of her aunt. There was much pleasant conversation and these people insisted on her staying for the night. While alone she attempted to place another long-distance call to the soldier. She still had in mind ideas about marrying him but had come no closer to a decision. The call not being completed, she began to fear the operator might ring back. She also was not quite sure her hostess had not overheard her at the telephone. After thinking of this and realizing that her family might trace her in such a nearby place, she slipped off after pretending to go to bed early, leaving no message for these people who had taken her in.

Catching a bus bound in another direction, she rode for a few hours and got off at a strange town where she knew no one. Not having concluded plans for her next step, she sat for a while in a hotel lobby. Soon she was approached by a middle-aged man. He was far from prepossessing, smelt of cheap liquor, and his manners were distinctly distasteful. He soon offered to pay for her overnight accommodations at the hotel. She realized that he meant to share the bed with her but made no objection. As well as one can tell by discussing this experience with Roberta, she was neither excited, frightened, repulsed, nor attracted by a prospect that most carefully brought-up virgins would certainly have regarded with anything but indifference.

The man, during their several hours together, handled her in a rough, peremptory fashion, took no trouble to conceal his contempt for her and her role, and made no pretense of friendliness, much less of affection. She experienced moderate pain but no sexual response under his ministrations. After giving her $5.00 with unnecessarily contemptuous accentuations of its significance, he left her in the room about midnight.

Next morning she reached her soldier friend by telephone and suggested that he send her sufficient funds to join him. She had not discarded the idea of marrying him, nor had she progressed any further toward a final decision to do so. He discouraged her vigorously against coming, refused to send money, and urged her to return home. She was not, it seems, greatly upset by this turn of events and, with little serious consideration of the matter, decided to go to Charlotte, which was approximately 150 miles distant. She seemed frank in admitting that she had no distinct purpose in mind, was prompted by no overmastering thrill of adventure or fear that her parents might consider her "ruined" or disgraced. She was, in fact, not conscious of any strong reason for not going home or for having left in the first place.

Reaching Charlotte, she had little trouble finding small jobs in restaurants and stores. She supported herself for several days by working but found that her funds barely provided for room and food. She thereupon began to spend the nights with various tipsy soldiers, travelling salesmen, and other men who showed inclination to pick her up. With all these she had sexual intercourse. From this she eventually began to experience a moderate, half-warmed pleasure, but nothing like intense passion. Despite extensive promiscuity since that time, she has never experienced a sharp and distinguishable orgasm or found sexual relations in any way a major pleasure or temptation. Nor has she felt any of the frustrations and unrelieved tension so familiar in some women who are aroused but left unsatisfied. Her family, meanwhile, not knowing whether she was dead or alive, was making every effort, through the police and otherwise, to find her. These efforts met with success after about three weeks.

On meeting her parents she expressed affection, running to them and throwing herself in their arms. At their prompting she found it easy to make use of the formalities indicative of penitence but seemed remarkably free from actual humiliation or distress. Neither the recent anxiety of her mother and father nor her own social jeopardy overwhelmed or even greatly daunted her. She seemed little vulnerable to the inevitable gossip that on her return beat like a tempest about town. As if armored by a sort of innocence, she went her way freely—affable, unembarrassed, the picture of an artless girl fond of others and expecting kindliness from all.

In this episode, as in most of her other behavior, it is not easy to see what such a girl as this is driving at. If she had, through hallucinations, heard God's voice telling her to leave home, or if she believed with the conviction of delusion she had been invited by a princely suitor to spend the night in love, her conduct would be easier to understand and would, in a very important sense, be more rational and appropriate. It would also be easier to understand if she had been driven by sexual craving to sacrifice social approval for an enticing hedonistic goal.

During her hospitalization she spoke convincingly of the benefit she was obtaining and discussed her mistakes with every appearance of insight. She spoke like a person who had been lost and bewildered but now had found her way. She did not seem to be making any voluntary effort to deceive her physicians.

Soon after she returned home, reports came, all indicating that she was continuing in her old patterns of behavior. A secretarial position was obtained for her in Spartanburg, S. C., with a large corporation. She was quick and effective in her work and was liked by all for her simple, friendly ways. Soon her landlady began to worry about her moral status as evidence accumulated that she let various men who were casual acquaintances come up to her room. She showed a good deal of skill in avoiding detection, and her manner made it hard for such suspicions to be taken seriously. She was so calm, so free of anything that would suggest a passionate nature, so polite, and so proper that irregularities of this sort were all but inconceivable to those she met. At last it was evident that this apparently candid and well-brought-up girl was turning the place into the modest approximation of a brothel. Before the kindly landlady could steel herself to have a showdown, Roberta disappeared owing a month's rent.

She had, with her convincing manner, succeeded in drawing a sum of money from a loan fund the employees of the company had built up for their convenience. Having obtained this, Roberta did not show up for work and was not heard from for a couple of weeks. Shortly thereafter she returned home. She told little of the real story to her parents but convinced them she had left her job under honorable circumstances. This was believed until the facts at last caught up with her.

Other positions were obtained for her in various towns and at home. Each time her failures were similar and always without adequate motive or extraneous cause. She returned for psychiatric treatment on several occasions, always saying she had been helped and expressing simple but complete confidence that it was impossible for her to have further trouble.

Despite her prompt failures she would, in her letters to us at the hospital, write as if she had been miraculously cured:

> You and Doctor _____ have given me a new outlook and a new life. This time we have got to the very root of my trouble and I see the whole story in a different light. I don't mean to use such words lightly and, of all things, I want to avoid even the appearance of flattery, but I must tell you how grateful I am, how deeply I admire the wonderful work you are doing. . . . If, in your whole life you had never succeeded with one other patient, what you have done for me should make your practice worthwhile. . . . I wish I could tell you how different I feel. How different I am! But, as I so well realize now, it isn't saying things that counts but what one actually *does*. I am confident that my life from now on will express better than anything I can say what you have done for me—and my admiration. . . . It is good to feel that as time passes, you can be proud of me and as sure of me as I am sure of myself . . . whether I go on to college or follow up my old impulse and become a nurse; if I become a business girl or settle for being just a normal, happy wife, my life will be fulfilling and useful. . . . If it had not been for you, I shudder to think what I might have become, [etc.]

Her letters, which she continued to send from time to time, were filled with similar statements. Occasionally she mentioned difficulties but never a serious discouragement. She continued in behavior such as that mentioned previously, and the actuality of her conduct and of her situation seemed not to weigh in her estimate of her present or future.

Though she realized I had been informed of recent episodes quite as bad as those in the past, on several occasions she wrote requesting letters of recommendation for various positions she had applied for or was considering. More than once blank forms appeared in my mail with notices that Roberta had given my name as a reference. It was interesting and not without an element of sad irony to note that these forms made specific queries about "good character," "high moral standards," "reliability," "would you employ the applicant yourself, realizing the position is one of considerable responsibility," etc. Roberta seemed sweetly free of any doubt that such recommendations would be given without qualification and in the highest terms of assurance.

With this young lady, as with many other similar patients, the psychiatrist is confronted with the family's serious questions: What are we to do now? What would you do if you were in our place? These are questions for which I have found no satisfactory answer. Such a girl causes more harm to herself and to others than the average patient with schizophrenia and a more tragic sorrow to those who love her. It can scarcely be said that she is safer outside an institution than the average patient who hears imaginary voices or that she can more satisfactorily be cared for at home.

When a physician is asked such questions week after week by honest people who for years have struggled futilely with such problems, he becomes at length rather firm in the conviction that any agency capable of taking an initial step to change this situation should be aroused from its scrupulous inattention.

7

Arnold

This patient had recently left the hospital (A.W.O.L.) while out on a pass. The following letters arrived from him after a few days:

Baltimore,
April 4th, 19___, Saturday,
2 P.M.

Dear Friend:

Physically I am a very sick man. Have had fever since last Friday. Cold all the time. Very dirty. No bath since I left. Clothes wet all the time. Four meals since I left. Chest hurts severely. *Can't give up.* Have tried to contact my people by phone and telegram several times but am ostracized. —Hurts—Really hurts. —but they do not understand—Have never understood. No use for details regarding what is past. Will you give me just one chance please. You must. If you receive this by Monday noon will you wire me some funds at the Western Union. Use my father's first name, Stephen, for reference. If I were not sick I would not ask this. Can't beg, can't steal; so am in the devil of a shape.

Please do not try to have me detained. If you would have sent Jack [a parole patient] to the hotel last Sunday I would not have tried what I have undertaken, as I have too much respect for you and a few others to break my word.

Have I registered? Will your response be O.K.? A chance! One chance!

As ever your friend,
Arnold

New York

April 10th, 19___, Friday A.M.

Dear Friend:

Man's limitations are many. I must say that it is hard, very hard, for me not to give up, but I am still trying to carry on. Frankly I was afraid and still am. It has rained ever since I left the Hospital and I believe every drop touched Arnold. Have enjoyed a fever since Tuesday morning. I will not give up. If you could see me at present you would wonder how it was possible for this condition to become mine. I am the worst looking tramp on the road

My regret about my departure concerns you, Miss Green [nurse] and Mr. Drayton [a physically ill patient]. Doctor, you and McDaniel [a physician on the hospital staff] must make him a well man.

Respects to all my boys [fellow patients] and to any of Ward A men [elopers] who want to leave, tell them to be sure and think

Would you stake me to a start of a few dollars? If so, write me at Hollywood Cafe, New York City. Place money order in envelope. Whatever amount is O.K. I don't think you want to be bothered with me any more so I won't suspect a trap.

Closing with my utmost respects to one of the finest characters I ever met:

I am, the young brigand from the South,

Arnold.

These letters were addressed to a physician at the hospital who had taken a special interest in the patient's case, trying over a period of many months to help him achieve some sort of adjustment.

For a while a measure of faint hope was entertained that he might be able to get along with freedom to walk about the grounds. He had been in and out of the hospital for seven years, spending most of his time on a closed ward with delusional and dilapidated schizophrenic patients. Struck by the man's friendliness and his frankness to admit himself in the wrong, his physician, despite the usual rules of dealing with such behavior, made an exception of his case, restoring his ground parole time after time when it was lost by failure to adjust. The experiment had been more or less innocent, since the patient did little harm to himself or others beyond cashing a few bad checks for small amounts, cheating unsuccessfully in dice games, stealing a bicycle for which he had no use, and behaving uproariously after a few drinks and getting into jail, whence he was brought back each time safe and apparently repentant.

An effort was made to see if this rational and intelligent man, even though he failed seven times, seventy times, and seven times seventy times, might at last achieve a positive reaction to indefatigable forgiveness and succeed in finding some way to exist without supervision as incessant as that required by a traditional *madman*. Little or no hope was held that he might leave the hospital and live as a normal man; but something would have been gained if, still sheltered in a psychiatric hospital, he could enjoy the freedom of the grounds and an occasional pass into town.

Be it noted that during seven years of psychiatric study and observation he had never shown any sign technically regarded as indicating a psychosis. That is to say, he was always entirely rational in conversation, alert, above average in intelligence by psychometric tests, free from delusions and hallucinations, and completely lacking in the slightest evidence of "deterioration." Nor had he ever shown retardation, a true depression of the cyclothymic type, increased psychomotor activity, flight of ideas, or any other condition which it is permissible to class as psychosis. He had been free also from any symptom characteristic of a psychoneurosis.

During his long and frequent periods within closed wards, he was superficially agreeable to his physicians most of the time but extremely fretful about his confinement. He spoke eloquently of having learned his lesson and always pressed his request for parole or discharge with good logic. Once after making an especially convincing plea for freedom and with the possibility of parole within the next few days, he succeeded during the night in obtaining whiskey by lowering on a cord an empty Coca-Cola bottle which he had obtained and which some confederate filled for him. He at once proceeded to get rather high in the dead of night to the great astonishment of the attendants, who had regarded him as a "sane" man but who were now at a loss to understand his senseless guffaws, sudden maudlin outcries, and impulsive lurches about the ward. Not realizing that he could possibly have obtained liquor, they feared for a moment that he must have developed an ordinary psychosis. On being approached he cursed, sobbed feebly, and was brought back to bed, passing intestinal gas with frequent loud and unpleasant effects, grinning almost triumphantly at the nurse who had hurried to him at each detonation.

The next morning he admitted the drinking after being confronted with the Coca-Cola bottle to which the string was still attached. He was at first superficially penitent but soon could be seen to show pleasure at his cleverness, which he seemed to feel afforded just cause for a bit of gloating. He seemed to have no deep sense of regret and could not understand why the episode delayed his parole. Indeed, he became definitely vexed and talked incessantly for a day or two about his failure to get a square deal.

This patient, entirely sane by orthodox psychiatric standards, having spent the better part of seven years closely confined among other men who, to him as to any layman, were unmistakable *lunatics* and nowise agreeable company, was given another series of chances to win his freedom.

The opinion has often been expressed that the psychopath, who in some ways seems to behave like a badly spoiled child, might be helped if he could be put in a controlled situation and allowed to feel the unpleasant consequences of his mistakes or misdeeds regularly, as he commits them.

With this patient such a policy was pursued and the effort was protracted to remarkable lengths. Such a plan of treatment or reeducation perhaps may accomplish a good deal with some patients of this type. With Arnold it yielded no discernible fruits.

His parole was restored time after time. He expressed a clear understanding that he was obligated not to leave the hospital grounds. Each time, in accordance with his past behavior, he would promptly disappear. After a few hours, several days, or perhaps a week, the police would call to say they had him in custody. Back on his ward he seemed properly regretful and immediately expressed confidence in himself, explaining that the last misadventure had served as the lesson he needed. He was soon allowed to go out on the grounds again. Two or three small acts of defrauding, the temporary misappropriation of an automobile (which he would usually abandon after his whim for a ride had been fulfilled), or some other succession of deeds incompatible with parole status always brought him back under strict supervision. After a short time he was given still another trial.

He spoke fulsomely of the handsome treatment he was receiving, protested an earnest affection for his physician, and swore staunchly that he would justify this faith shown in him. Always he seemed entirely sure that his difficulties were a thing of the past. Unlike the patient whose behavior is distorted by compulsion in the ordinary sense, he showed no evidence of a struggle, no awareness of anything that gave him doubt about his future success in achieving what he planned.

This alert, intelligent man remained always free from confusion, from any indication of powerful impulses or yearnings, from all conscious influences that might account for his spectacular failure to gain freedom. He expressed eloquently very natural desires to live an unrestricted life outside his familiar wards where he was locked in with very psychotic men. He mentioned no force or conflict, in many long interviews, that might make it difficult for him to conduct himself in a way that would bring him release from hospitalization. He denied experiencing the slightest pleasure from alcoholic beverages. And, indeed, he always seemed miserable, melancholy, and quite unlike his usual buoyant self when he had partaken of drink.

He did sometimes, as a matter of fact, continue ten days or two weeks without mishap. At his own request he was detailed to help the attendants on the infirmary ward, which he did ably, faithfully, and apparently with interest. A merry, rather witty person, he freely admitted that he had made a fool of himself and a mess of his life, but he always maintained that he would never again break his word, which he had given not to drink, not to stay out beyond the limits of a pass, and not to violate any other hospital regulations. He was usually friendly and courteous to his physician and to other personnel and went out of his way to be attentive to physically ill patients, apparently taking mild pleasure in any kindness he could do them.

He continued to request a pass to go downtown, but seldom insistently, often smiling or laughing with apparent relish as he admitted that his past performances did not justify the further confidence he begged. It was an academic point, apparently, this admitting of fault or guilt. It seemed more an expression of being polite and proper than anything indicative of comprehension about cause and effect. But he made these gestures attractively. His characteristic approach was tentative and with what looked like a dash of humor at his own expense.

One Sunday morning he was given a pass after he had made a special point that he wanted to attend church. Arnold did not return. Some of the hospital attendants on their way home that night found him several miles out in the country staggering about in the rain on a lonely road, his trousers hanging down about his heels, seriously impeding his progress and tripping him from time to time into the ditch, where he rolled and thrashed, hallooing wildly or cursing in aimless violence. Soaking wet, covered with mud and vomitus, he was brought back to the hospital.

The next morning he faced his physician with a hangdog expression through which a merry glance soon darted. Smiling, he lightly damned himself for the worst sort of fellow imaginable and swore good-humoredly that he had learned his lesson. Within a week parole was restored and shortly thereafter he celebrated his freedom by somehow obtaining whiskey without leaving the grounds and hobbling into the recreation building, where a dance was in progress, a picture of agitated dejection. He stumbled about in purposeless lunges, eyes rolling, mouth open, and drooling saliva, then collapsed sensationally on the floor before attendants could seize him.

These episodes are entirely typical of his last few months in the hospital. During this time a limited degree of freedom was restored to him within a few days after each episode and each time he failed as promptly and as spectacularly as in the incidents described previously. Altogether he was arrested some dozen or more times during this short period, nearly always within a few hours after leaving the hospital grounds.

He had frequent superficially serious talks with his physician in which he expressed despair over his situation, remorse for his all but incredible record as a failure, and a quick, cheerful confidence in his future. What might be called a thin and bright surface of sincerity which is hard to indicate without paradox seemed to distinguish him from his fellows who are also described in this book. This quality, not in the simplest sense false, seemed not only consistent but almost complete. It was, however, too bodiless to hold any true resolution or remorse or to be useful to him in gaining worthwhile insight. It seems likely that his sincerity, though not a literal fraud, was so thin as to be, for practical purposes, merely an academic abstraction. He was often in high spirits, communicative, boyish, and rather winning. Though fretting and complaining continually about his confinement and apparently unable to understand adequately why this was advisable, he seemed to find mild interest and trivial pleasure in small matters. He could give no explanation of why he committed acts that demanded his remaining in a psychiatric hospital. He always fell back on the plea that he would never do so again. When drinking, he was often noisy, always unhappy and distraught, silly, and tearful.

His physician's enthusiasm to rehabilitate him by a siege of patience slowly waned as failures accumulated. Finally on Easter Sunday he engagingly made another plea for a bit of freedom. If he could only have a pass for a few hours, to go to church for Easter services! His request was granted. Marvelously, he returned on time without indication of having sought disaster and exultant at his success. On the strength of this performance he was allowed to remain out in the sunshine on the grounds during the afternoon. At nightfall he could not be found. The two letters at the beginning of his story tell the rest.

All this, however, is but the merest glimpse of the man. The account as related to this point is a word, and no more, in the man's history. Seven years ago, when admitted for the first time, he had already spent some ten or twelve years in and out of jails and mental hospitals, scarcely ever passing a week of his life without attention from the police.

Small swindles, with property owned by another given as collateral for a loan, bad checks, wrecking an automobile which he had bought on credit and for which he made no effort to pay, surreptitiously selling a half dozen of his uncle's cows and blowing the cash—in these and scores of other but similar activities he kept the local law enforcement agencies extended. He seemed always so frank and honest, so thoroughly without malice, that often those damaged by him withdrew their charges to give him another chance.

Sometimes by pleading grave illness or other disaster and emergency in the family, he would, in his father's name, borrow $50.00 or $100.00, which he squandered before the misrepresentation was detected. Once, feeling himself in need of funds to make a trip, he rented to a stranger rooms in the house of a neighbor, cleverly timing his transactions so he could show the accommodations, close the deal, and obtain payment in advance during a period when the lady owning the property was downtown shopping.

The money he obtained and promptly wasted was seldom, if ever, sought for any appreciable need or to satisfy impulses that seemed more than mild and transient caprice. The frequent trips he made were all but purposeless. Whether he went to a nearby town or a large, distant city, he sought no job or other opportunity, found no adventure in the ordinary meaning of the word.

He often hung about street corners, went to a movie, loitered in a park, or spent hours in a poolroom or cheap hotel lobby chatting about trivialities, and then, finding his environment tedious, he would return home. Meanwhile, his parents, whom he never informed of plans for travel, suffered no little anxiety and grief wondering whether he was dead or alive and if they might see him again.

He did not write to his family while on these expeditions. If jailed for pawning a tire he had stolen from someone's car, pressed too unpleasantly for bills he had run up, faced with trial for fraud (after selling nonexistent commodities for which he successfully misrepresented himself as salesman), etc., he usually telephoned his parents and spoke convincingly of the ill fortune which had overtaken him and of his innocence of willful wrongdoing. They regularly sped to his aid and, usually with appreciable expense to themselves and with humiliation, succeeded in obtaining his release. Otherwise he simply turned up one fine day, nonchalant, gracious in his apologies, but apparently unaware of having caused any valid distress to those he always maintained he dearly and deeply loved.

On turning to drink he sought low company and often ended by wandering off. Sometimes days passed before he was discovered lying in forlorn swamps or wallowing drunkenly about remote cornfields. Not dozens of times but scores of times his friends and relatives had to search him out and bring him, inert or struggling farcically to no end, back home, where he was washed, reclothed, and nursed to sobriety. He had done no work at all since a brief gesture of helping his father in the store for a few months after he quit junior college in the town of his nativity at 17 years of age. He had no real friends and seemed to want none, though he was superficially sociable and mingled easily with both sexes. He had frequently sought the favors of prostitutes but had never showed a lasting or a wholehearted interest in any woman.

So he was presented to the hospital seven years previously: 28 years of age, a short, overnourished, quick-witted man, admitting many faults, acknowledging his human frailty, debonair but not pretentious, a close-cropped black moustache on his lip, a rather engaging, shy, swift light of merriment slipping at times into his glance. During the seven years that he was under observation, no delusion was ever noted nor any other sign even remotely suggestive of a mental disease that is accepted as such. He has never even experienced temporary hallucinations while under the influence of alcohol. He has undergone no disintegration of personality (as this is ordinarily understood), none at least that is discernible on prolonged observation, by psychiatric examination, or by any other means available. He is today plainly the same man that we first knew and who, according to all accounts, has been a problem to his community for years.

After his first admission he was carefully examined; social service reports were secured and he was observed day after day. No evidence of any condition officially known as "psychosis" could be found. He was granted parole privileges, with results that need not be described again. Time after time he was sequestered on closed wards, naturally among patients whose psychoses showed typical manifestations, and among them he stood out in arresting incongruity. Restored to parole, he regularly showed himself incompetent and was returned to constant supervision. On the request of his relatives, he was allowed to go home with them on trial-visit status, where, knowing that a failure to behave himself would mean returning to the confinement he naturally detested, he at once engaged in not one but several activities, each of which made his return to the restrictions of a hospital not only necessary but urgent.

Weary of his life behind locked doors among classically demented men, on several occasions he demanded his discharge. On being brought before the medical staff he was found obviously "sane" and released. Soon, however, his relatives were back with him, bearing tales of such mad folly as few, if any, people deranged in other ways could produce. Readmitted to confinement inappropriate to his plain sanity by the accepted criteria of mental disease, he soon became restless and, pointing out his legal status, left against medical advice.

Worn out by incessant traffic with police in his behalf, diverted from the customary uses of life by night-long searches for him in lonely hinterlands or in distant jails, his relatives finally succeeded in having him legally committed to the custody of the hospital as an "insane" person. There is little doubt that the personal influences and well-known political mechanisms of a rustic Southern community had weight with the courts, not to speak of common sense unversed in technical psychiatry but painfully aware of irrational conduct so long flagrantly demonstrated.

After a month or more of confinement under these circumstances, the patient demanded an interview with the staff. With admirable logic he maintained that he suffered from no mental derangement whatsoever. He lucidly described and recognized signs of mental disorder, made light and clever jokes about the impropriety of applying such criteria to him, and pointed out the absurdity of identifying him with the usual patient kept in such a hospital. Admitting his maladjustment and his inveterate but minor deeds of depravity, he insisted that he be left to ordinary legal measures in any future misconduct, which he did not deny was possible. The staff, as conscientious psychiatrists, could not do otherwise than agree that he was "sane and competent" and release him.

Three weeks later he was brought back to the hospital at midnight by a brother and a cousin. He had a fractured clavicle (memoir of his frequent brawls with local police) and was lachrymose, penitent, and all but homesick for his ward in the hospital. The physician on duty hesitated about readmitting him. His story was well known. His relatives thereupon threatened to telegraph high officers in the government. They were by no means assuaged at being told that the hospital was not maintained for the treatment of persons judged sane by the canons of psychiatry and considered responsible for their misconduct and misfortunes. After consultations with the physician in charge of the hospital, Arnold was readmitted. Some weeks later he called in local lawyers who, invoking the writ of habeas corpus, arranged a lunacy trial by jury. Of course there could be but one verdict. The man was plainly "in his right mind." No acceptable evidence of mental disease (as officially defined) could be brought out. He was taken from the custody of the hospital.

A month afterward, chastened and eager for his familiar ward which, compared to the alternative of jail, aroused nostalgia, he willingly returned, accompanied by relatives who furnished a tale of woe too long for telling here.

This brings us to his last hospital admission, which preceded the incident with which we began Arnold's story.

8

Tom

This young man, 21 years of age, does not look at all like a criminal type or a shifty delinquent. In fact, he stands out in remarkable contrast to the kind of patient suggested by such a term as *constitutional inferiority*. He does not fit satisfactorily into the sort of picture that emerges from early descriptions of people generally inadequate and often showing physical "stigmata of degeneracy" or ordinary defectiveness.[124,257]

Tom looks and is in robust physical health. His manner and appearance are pleasing. In his face a prospective employer would be likely to see strong indications of character as well as high incentive and ability. He is well informed, alert, and entirely at ease, exhibiting a confidence in himself that the observer is likely to consider amply justified. This does not look like the sort of man who will fail or flounder about in the tasks of life but like someone incompatible with all such thoughts.

There is nothing to suggest that he is putting on a bold front or trying to adopt any attitude or manner that will be misleading. Though he knows the examiner has evidence of his almost incredible career, he gives such an impression that it seems for the moment likely he will be able to explain it all away. In his own mind he has evidently brushed aside so satisfactorily such matters as those to be mentioned that others, also, caught up in the magic of his equanimity, almost share his invulnerable disregard.

Tom has so plainly escaped the ordinary and, one would think, the inevitable consequences of his experience that, in a sort of contagion, his interviewer is also affected. The effect is to make it seem more plausible to accept the whole detailed reality of a life as dream or illusion than believe that this man could so regard it were it otherwise. With indisputable evidence that a human being has been run over and dismembered by a series of freight trains and that the bodily remnants have subsequently been put through a sausage grinder, any investigator will have definite and vivid preconceptions of what he will behold. The evidence itself bleaches, suddenly and automatically, at the sight of the intact victim, whole, smiling, immaculate, unscarred, without a scratch. What happened to the anatomic unit in this allusion scarcely seems more drastic than what, as a social unit, the patient before me had experienced.

This poised young man's immediate problem was serious but not monumental. His family and legal authorities were in hope that if some psychiatric disorder could be discovered in him, he might escape a jail sentence for stealing. Despite many years of disappointment, the family still sought some remedy, some treatment or handling, that might bring about favorable changes in the patient's behavior. Those concerned with the legal aspects of the immediate problem had dealt with this man often in the past and saw in his conduct indications of something more than, and something different from, an ordinary or sane antisocial scheme of existence. His high intelligence made it difficult for them to account for what he did on that basis.

Evidence of his maladjustment became distinct in childhood. He appeared to be a reliable and manly fellow but could never be counted upon to keep at any task or to give a straight account of any situation. He was frequently truant from school. No advice or persuasion influenced him in his acts, despite his excellent response in all discussions. Though he was generously provided for, he stole some of his father's chickens from time to time, selling them at stores downtown. Pieces of table silver would be missed. These were sometimes recovered from those to whom he had sold them for a pittance or swapped them for odds and ends which seemed to hold no particular interest or value for him. He resented and seemed eager to avoid punishment, but no modification in his behavior resulted from it. He did not seem wild or particularly impulsive, a victim of high temper or uncontrollable drives. There was nothing to indicate he was subject to unusually strong temptations, lured by definite plans for high adventure and exciting revolt.

Often when truant from high school classes, Tom wandered more or less aimlessly, sometimes shooting at a Negro's chickens, setting fire to a rural privy around the outskirts of town, or perhaps loitering about a cigar store or a poolroom, reading the comics, throwing rocks at squirrels in a park, perpetrating small thefts or swindles. He often charged things in stores to his father, stole cigarettes, candy, cigars, etc., which he sometimes gave away freely to slight acquaintances or other idlers he encountered. Though many wasteful, inopportune, and punishable deeds were correctly attributed to him, these apparently were only a small fraction of his actual achievement along this line.

He lied so plausibly and with such utter equanimity, devised such ingenious alibis or simply denied all responsibility with such convincing appearances of candor that for many years his real career was poorly estimated. Among typical exploits with which he is credited stand these: prankish defecation into the stringed intricacies of the school piano, the removal from his uncle's automobile of a carburetor for which he got 75 cents, and the selling of his father's overcoat to a passing buyer of scrap materials.

Though he often fell in with groups or small gangs, he never for long identified himself with others in a common cause. In the more outlandish and serious outcroppings of group mischief, he sometimes played a prominent role. With several others he broke into a summer cottage on a nearby lake, stole a few articles, overturned all the furniture, and threw rugs, dishes, etc., out of the window. He and a few more teenage boys on another expedition smashed headlights and windshields on several automobiles, punctured a number of tires, and rolled one car down a slope, leaving it slightly battered and bogged in a ditch.

At 14 or 15 years of age, having learned to drive, Tom began to steal automobiles with some regularity. Often his intention seemed less that of theft than of heedless misappropriation. A neighbor or friend of the family, going to the garage or to where the car was parked outside an office building, would find it missing. Sometimes the patient would leave the stolen vehicle within a few blocks or miles of the owner, sometimes out on the road where the gasoline had given out. After he had tried to sell a stolen car, his father consulted advisers and, on the theory that he might have some specific craving for automobiles, bought one for him as a therapeutic measure. On one occasion while out driving, he deliberately parked his own car and, leaving it, stole an inferior model which he left slightly damaged on the outskirts of a village some miles away.

Meanwhile, Tom continued to forge his father's name to small checks and steal change, pocketknives, textbooks, etc., at school. Occasionally, on the pretext of ownership he would sell a dog or a calf belonging to some member of the community. His youth made long terms of imprisonment seem inappropriate, it being felt that this might confirm him in a criminal career or teach him additional and more malignant antisocial techniques. He was ineligible for the state hospital.

Private physicians, scoutmasters, and social workers were consulted. They talked and worked with him, but to no avail. Listing the deeds for which he became ever more notable does not give an adequate picture of the situation. He did not every day or every week bring attention to himself by major acts of mischief or destructiveness. He was usually polite, often considerate in small, appealing ways, and always seemed to have learned his lesson after detection and punishment. He was clever and learned easily. During intervals in which his attendance was regular, he impressed his teachers as outstanding in ability. Some charm and apparent modesty, as well as his very convincing way of seeming sincere and to have taken resolutions that would count, kept not only the parents but all who encountered him clinging to hope. Teachers, scoutmasters, the school principal, etc., recognizing that in some very important respects he differed from the ordinary bad or wayward youth, made special efforts to help him and to give him new opportunities to reform or readjust.

When he drove a stolen automobile across a state line, he came in contact with federal authorities. In view of his youth and the wonderful impression he made, he was put on probation. Soon afterward he took another automobile and again left it in the adjoining state. It was a very obvious situation. The consequences could not have been entirely overlooked by a person of his excellent shrewdness. He admitted that the considerable risks of getting caught had occurred to him but felt he had a chance to avoid detection and would take it. No unusual and powerful motive or any special aim could be brought out as an explanation.

Tom was sent to a federal institution in a distant state where a well-organized program of rehabilitation and guidance was available. He soon impressed authorities at this place with his attitude and in the way he discussed his past mistakes and plans for a different future. He seemed to merit parole status precociously and this was awarded him. It was not long before he began stealing again and thereby lost his freedom.

The impression he made during confinement was so promising that he was pardoned before the expiration of the regular term and he came home confident, buoyant, apparently matured, and thoroughly rehabilitated. Considerable work had been done with him at the institution, and he seemed to respond well to psychiatric measures. He found employment in a drydock at a nearby port and talked modestly but convincingly of the course he would now follow, expressing aims and plans few could greatly improve.

His employers found him at first energetic, bright, and apparently enthusiastic about the work. Soon evidence of inexplicable irresponsibility emerged and accumulated. Sometimes he missed several days and brought simple but convincing excuses of illness. As the occasions multiplied, explanations so detailed and elaborate were made that it seemed only facts could have produced them. Later he sometimes left the job, stayed away for hours, and gave no account of his behavior except to say that he did not feel like working at the time.

There seemed to be no cause for dissatisfaction, no discernible change of attitude toward the work. When he chose to apply himself, he did better than most. It was plain to the employers that this promising young man was not merely lazy or, in an ordinary way, fretfully restless.

The theft of an automobile brought Tom to jail again. He expressed remorse over his mistake, talked so well, and seemed so genuinely and appropriately motivated and determined that his father, by making heavy financial settlements, secured his release. After a number of relatively petty but annoying activities, another theft made it necessary for his family to intervene.

Reliable information indicates that he has been arrested and imprisoned approximately fifty or sixty times. It is estimated that he would have been put in jails or police barracks for short or long periods of detention on approximately 150 other occasions if his family had not made good his small thefts, damages, etc., and paid fines for him.

Sometimes he was arrested for fomenting brawls in low resorts, for provoking fights, or for such high-handed and disturbing behavior as to constitute public nuisance. Though not a very regular drinker or one who characteristically drank to sodden confusion or stupefaction, he exhibited unsociable and unprepossessing manners and conduct after taking even a few beers or highballs. In one juke joint imbroglio he is credited with having struck a fellow reveler on the head with a piece of iron. No serious injuries resulted, although great uproar and spectacular commotion prevailed. Under similar circumstances he was once in, or on the fringes of, an altercation in which gunplay occurred and another man received a minor flesh wound. Meanwhile, he continued to forge his father's name to checks, often insisted on sleeping through breakfast, obtained loans through ingenious misrepresentations, and ran up debts which he simply ignored.

Tom's mother had for some years suffered special anxiety and distress because of his unannounced absences. After kissing her good-bye, saying he was going downtown for a Coca-Cola or to a movie, he might not appear for several days or even for a couple of weeks. Instead of his returning, a long-distance telephone call might in the middle of the night arouse the father, who would be entreated to come at once to nearby or distant places where the son had encountered unpleasant complications or, perhaps, restraint by the police.

He expressed particularly heavy penitence for all the worry and sleepless nights he had caused his mother, admitting that he loved her dearly and that nothing about his life so displeased him as having given her even a moment's distress. He spoke as if with feeling about the patience, generosity, and understanding of his father and seemed to believe the filial bond was unusually fine and satisfactory.

Recently, an elderly friend of the family who was in town on business learned something of the situation. This man, whose experience in dealing with other people and their problems was considerable (and very successful), undertook the task of helping the patient. Though he had heard a good deal about past exploits, he could not but feel hopeful after his first talk. A little later he took the patient with him on an automobile ride, feeling that in this way he could bring the problem to full discussion by a more natural, informal approach.

The conversation, once begun, developed amazingly. The younger man not only promised to behave from now on in an exemplary fashion but analyzed and discussed his past in such a way that the older found there was little that could be added. Despite his interest and his experience in such matters, he had seldom, if ever, encountered a more plausible interpretation of human mistakes and social confusion, of how distortion of aims and maladjustment develop out of the complicated influences and situations of modern living. Even more than the pertinent presentation of cause and effect and the cogent steps proposed for solution, the young man's appearance of sincerity in all these realizations impressed the older counselor. He spoke as the wisest and most contrite of men would speak and seemed to have a more detailed and deeper understanding of his entire situation than even the most sagacious observer could reach.

The patient talked not only of what he would avoid but discussed plans for work and recreation, for development and progressive maturation. Tom emphasized how his irregular hours, his unforeseen absences, etc., had kept his parents much of the time not sure whether he was dead or alive. Before the ride was over, the judicious counselor was encouraged and deeply optimistic. In addition, he was so impressed by points this young man had brought out and by his apparent earnestness and resolution that he felt himself wiser from the experience. Moved and stimulated, he admitted that he had obtained new and valuable viewpoints on life and deeper seriousness. He had been stimulated to review his own patterns of behavior and to seek a better and more progressive plan of self-expression. In this frame of mind he bade the patient good-night, letting him out of the car at the front gate of the parents' home.

The patient did not even enter the house. After going in the gate, he walked through the grounds, went out by a back entrance, and was not heard from that night. He was not, in fact, heard from for a week. News then came of his being in jail again at a nearby town where he had forged, stolen trifles, run up debts, and carried out other behavior familiar to all who knew him.

This young man apparently has never formed any substantial attachment for another person. Sexually he has been desultorily promiscuous under a wide variety of circumstances. A year or two earlier he married a girl who had achieved considerable local recognition as a prostitute and as one whose fee was moderate. He had previously shared her offerings during an evening (on a commercial basis) with friends or with brief acquaintances among whom he found himself. He soon left the bride and never showed signs of shame or chagrin about the character of the woman he had espoused or of any responsibility toward her.

During the war Tom maintained over some months an offhand relationship with the wife of a man in combat overseas. When in town he ate at her house, sometimes slept there with her, but was as heedless of her and her feelings as of his parents. She apparently suffered some anxiety when, after making plans and promises to do something special with her, he disappeared and she heard nothing from him until he called her from another city (reversing the charges) to chat casually and sometimes to speak eloquent words of endearment. Sometimes he took precautions to deceive her about his sporadic sex relations with other women; sometimes he forgot or did not bother.

On returning from his trips during the war, he sometimes told interesting stories of having been for a time in the Navy, narrating with vivid and lifelike plausibility action in which he had participated and which led to the destruction of a German submarine off Jamaica or the pursuit of a raiding warship off the coast of Greenland. Again he would talk at length about his experiences transporting airplanes from Miami to Havana or accidents leading to hospitalization and operation and diverse adventures with nurses, other patients, interns, etc. Once, during a stag-party discussion of venereal disease, he even fabricated an account of having caught one or more of these unenviable maladies and enlightened his listeners about treatments he had received, drugs, dosage, and complications.

None of these fraudulent stories had a real element of delusion. When really caught in the lie about any of them and confronted with definite proof, he often laughed and passed it off as a sort of joke.

After these events and many others similar in general but differing in detail, Tom seemed modestly pleased with himself, effortlessly confident of the future. He gave the impression of a young man fresh and unhardened,

90

in no respect brutalized or worn by his past experiences. He also seemed a poised fellow, one who would make his decisions not in hotheaded haste but calmly, whether these were prompted by immediate whim or by intentions he had much time to entertain.

9

George

This man was 33 years of age at the time I first saw him and admitted him to a psychiatric hospital. He stated that his trouble was "nervousness" but could give no definite idea of what he meant by this word. He was remarkably self-composed, showed no indication of restlessness or anxiety, and could not mention anything that he worried about. He went on to state that his alleged nervousness was caused by "shell shock" during the war. He then proceeded to elaborate on this in an outlandish story describing himself as being cast twenty feet into the air by a shell, landing in his descent astride some iron pipes, and lying totally unconscious for sixty days, during all of which he hovered between life and death.

A physical examination showed George without any evidence of injury or illness. In fact, he was a remarkably strong and active man, 6 feet tall and 170 pounds in weight. Later, in an athletic meet held on the hospital grounds, he showed himself an exceptional sprinter and broadjumper, surpassing many able competitors ten years younger than himself in these events. Prolonged observation and psychiatric study brought out no sign or suggestion of a psychosis or a psychoneurosis. Despite his original complaint of "nervousness," he was at all times calm and without the slightest evidence of abnormal anxiety. He ate and slept well, did not complain of any worries, and was free of phobias, compulsions, conversion reactions, tics, and all other ordinary neurotic manifestations.

Records of this man's career show that he has been confined in various mental hospitals approximately half the time since he became of age. In addition to periods ranging from a few weeks to six months at federal institutions in Texas, Tennessee, Mississippi, Georgia, and Florida, he was also frequently sent by the government to private psychiatric hospitals and invalids' homes. Between these experiences he spent a good part of his time in the local county jail or in other jails at Birmingham, Montgomery, Mobile, or other towns which he visited. He was taken in sometimes for drunkenness and disorderly conduct, at other times for writing bad checks, petty theft, reckless driving of automobiles, obtaining money under false pretenses, snatching the purse from a prostitute, taking possession of a house whose owners were off on vacation, etc. Extravagant but insincere threats to harm his wife and four children made after taking a few drinks and lunacy charges also accounted for a dozen or so arrests.

During all the observation at various hospitals mentioned previously, as well as at a state mental hospital where George also spent a short time, no technical evidence of a psychosis or a psychoneurosis is mentioned. His wife and friends have repeatedly persuaded local authorities to consider him as mentally deranged and to have him sent to hospitals rather than let him face the various charges brought against him from time to time.

On other occasions, when he was refused admission by hospitals where physicians had already studied him more than once and declared him sane, competent, and not in need of psychiatric treatment, friends and relatives have had him arrested, have prevailed upon local doctors to sign statements that he is deranged and dangerous, and have brought pressure to bear so that hospitals, in the light in which the case was presented, had no choice but to readmit him.

The doctors involved in such procedures, country practitioners for the most part, never mention technical evidence that would indicate a psychosis or a psychoneurosis as they are described in the textbooks. Such statements as these are typical:

> Something is decidedly wrong mentally. I don't think I have ever come in contact with a man as unreliable as he is. He worries everybody that has fooled with him until they hate him. The County authorities are tired of boarding him as he is not a criminal. *(Family physician)*
>
> Everybody who comes in contact with him agrees that he should be confined permanently . . . very unreliable as to his word of honor. *(County physician)*

A physician who owns a private hospital located at a town nearby, in explaining his refusal to accept the patient again, ends by saying "we do not cater to his class."

He is described as frequently drinking whiskey to excess and as sometimes taking Veronal, Luminal, Amytal, and bromides to ease himself in the after-math of a spree. Although there is no record of alcoholic hallucinations, many bizarre and notable actions are described when the patient has had something to drink.

On a cold February day he rushed, fully clothed, down to the creek and sprang in. After thrashing about, yelling and cursing to no purpose and creating a senseless commotion, he swam back to land without difficulty. One fine spring evening he is said to have run entirely naked through the streets of the town. He once sat up all night under the house striking matches aimlessly.

Generally believed reports indicate that late one night he, with several drinking companions, succeeded in releasing a half-tamed bear from the cage in which it was kept at a filling station to attract trade. A good deal of fright, some civic uproar, and hasty precautionary measures ensued. Assiduous and painstaking effort by a number of local volunteers led to the bear's relatively uneventful return to his cage. According to available information, the bear was not terribly dangerous but sufficiently so to make a man of anything like ordinary responsibility sharply restrain all impulses to loose him on the outskirts of an unprepared community. The patient denied having been a party to this exploit but the evidence against him is strong.

In view of this man's failure to make any effort to conduct himself sensibly through so many years, there is no wonder that many are found to say that he is of unsound mind. He has done no work except for occasional periods when for a week or ten days he would show considerable promise as an automobile salesman, clerk in a grocery store, soda jerk, bootlegger's assistant, etc. It was not long before he proceeded, in the language of an elderly uncle often called on to deal with these problems, to "launch himself on another pot-valiant and fatuous rigadoon."

After studies of his case were completed, and on the basis of his cooperative and technically sane behavior, he was given parole privileges. He promised, of course, not to drink or to break any other rule of good conduct and expressed many fine intentions positively and reassuringly. Six days later he staggered into his ward and attempted to go to bed without being noticed by the attendant. On being found so plainly "in his cups," he raged petulantly, first denied any contact with stimulants, and finally, with indignation, admitted having taken one-half glass of beer. His eyes were bloodshot, he could scarcely stand, and he spoke in wild, boastful, almost unintelligible accents. A bottle of cheap whiskey was discovered hidden under his mattress.

According to the custom of the hospital, George was now confined to a closed ward where his superficial sanity stood out arrestingly from the delusional babbling and the blank-faced, staring inertia of his psychotic fellows. He was always intelligent and agreeable, frequently pointing out the obvious inconsistency of his being confined among "insane" people. Pleading important business downtown, he was, after three weeks, given a pass to go out in the care of a hospital attendant for a few hours. He returned in good condition, but when night came on, he refused to go to bed, cursed, and spat at the nurse who tried to advise him. His breath reeked of raw liquor, and a search disclosed a half-empty pint bottle in his pocket. The attendant who took him to town denied having allowed him to purchase whiskey and could only surmise in astonishment that the patient must have slipped off for a moment and obtained the bottle while pretending to go to the toilet.

A few weeks after this incident, the patient's wife came to town and asked to take him out on a pass, agreeing to assume full responsibility. When she returned him to the hospital, it was evident that he had drunk liberally, and the wife confessed herself as having been unable to deal with him.

The next day a man living near the hospital advised that he had fired a revolver at the patient on being alarmed by his behavior. George, after loitering about the premises boisterous and vaguely threatening, began to fumble at a window as if trying to force his way in. The shot had not been aimed at George but only in his general direction in order to frighten him. This end was satisfactorily achieved, for at the report he made off in a clatter of undignified haste.

About a month later, on strong promises of good behavior, George was again given parole. Within a few days he climbed over the fence and hired an automobile. After racing in this for a while about the road to no special purpose, he wrecked it in the city streets and was taken to jail.

This cycle of events was repeated several more times. The man was obviously not where he belonged when confined on a closed ward with extremely psychotic patients of the ordinary type. Just as plainly he showed himself unable to remain on an open ward with mildly psychotic patients who succeeded in adapting themselves to a life of limited freedom. Finally, on being kept under close supervision for several weeks following a senseless and troublesome spree, he demanded his discharge in a well-written letter emphasizing his sanity and the inappropriateness of his hospitalization. He was released accordingly.

Six months later he was sent back to the hospital from the local jail, where he had been confined after striking a Negro man with a shovel. He had, as was his wont, been drinking but showed little evidence of being affected by alcohol. The other man was walking peacefully by when our patient engaged him in a dispute about possession of the pavement. "Flown with insolence and [perhaps] with wine," he found the other's conciliatory attitude not to his taste, waxed more overbearing, and ended by felling his presumed adversary with a deft blow. He did not on this occasion seem to lose control of himself like a man in a genuine rage who might have struck blow after blow. His deed seemed prompted more by fractiousness and impulses to show off than by violent passion.

His application for admission was at first refused by the hospital, since only patients suffering from mental disorder in the commonly accepted sense are eligible. His wife and influential friends thereupon invoked higher authorities, who arranged for him to be taken. This time he was again found to be free from all symptoms of recognized mental disorder, and his condition was classified in the following terms: (1) *no nervous or mental disease* and (2) *psychopathic personality*. He did not complain of nervousness as he had at the time of his first admission but instead insisted that he was a sane and well man and demanded full privileges to come and go as he pleased, saying that the authorities who arranged for him to come to the hospital had promised him this.

It was plain that George regarded the hospital simply as an expedient by which he might escape the legal consequences of his behavior. After being kept for a few weeks on a closed ward, he was allowed to go out on the grounds alone with the understanding that after a few days he would be discharged as sane and competent. He could not, however, keep out of trouble. On the third day of his freedom he was seen by the guard driving at high speed through the gate in a car belonging to one of the physicians. Chase was offered, and after a lively race he was overtaken about fifteen miles from the hospital, having battered in a fender and knocked off a headlight of the car on the way.

It is hardly necessary to point out that this man had repeatedly been instructed in the rules to be observed while on parole, that he knew the driving of an automobile by a patient in this hospital to be a serious violation of his trust, not to speak of the theft, or the unauthorized borrowing he proclaimed it to be. When finally caught, he appeared as sane as before, showing no evidence of any episodic loss of his usual reasoning power. He had not been drinking when he took the automobile and, of course, the pursuit was too hot for him to obtain liquor while in flight, though in view of his previously demonstrated ingenuity and dispatch in fulfilling this want, it would scarcely have been surprising to find him properly raddled.

On his return to the hospital, he did not show the slightest sign of remorse over having taken possession of and having succeeded in damaging the car belonging to a physician who had always been particularly kind to him.

96

The owner's willingness to free him from responsibility for his deed he took as a matter of course, expressing neither gratitude nor satisfaction. In fact, he dismissed the whole matter as insignificant, and his prevailing attitude was that of a man generally ill used. Some weeks later he was sent home.

About six months afterward his wife telegraphed the hospital that she could no longer cope with her husband, whom she described as being still in such folly as that already recounted. He did not, however, arrive by the train he boarded. It was subsequently learned that he got off along the way, obtained a few drinks, and made a clamorous nuisance of himself in the station until the police came to cut short his activities.

A little later he was readmitted following a series of misadventures in no way different from those already mentioned but including a period in the state mental hospital. He was alert and rational and just as he had always been before, except for the presence of a urethral discharge of gonococcic origin. He gave a false account of his activities, saying that he had been working on a farm and had been in no trouble at all. The records showed that he had not turned his hand to make an honest dollar since he left and that a week had seldom passed without his buffoonish or antisocial activities arousing consternation in the neighborhood and bringing him to the attention of the police.

He was freely communicative and scarcely waited for encouragement to give an explanation of how he came by his gonorrhea. The records show that after causing some commotion in town by maudlin or threatening outbursts on the streets and silly, pompous threats about harming his wife, he had been brought in, bedraggled and disconsolate, from a ditch where he lay and confined to jail.

The jail, George said, was crowded, and the jailor, who knew him to be a good fellow, placed him in a cell on the women's section of the building. The bars of his cell were about six inches apart and so, according to his story, he was separated from and yet provocatively close to the women prisoners. These, his neighbors, were seven girls ranging from 14 to 20 years of age and awaiting transportation to the women's reformatory.

He said that at night, when the lights were out, these girls would disrobe and, coming to the bars, would entice him, calling him "pretty boy" and "country boy" and otherwise teasing and challenging him until he began to indulge in sexual intercourse with them between the bars in order to make them leave him alone. He says that he continued this practice with each of them every night during the rest of his sojourn there, the transactions taking place always in the dark and through the separating barrier. From one or all of these women he says he caught the gonorrhea which now troubled him.

He appeared to be no little proud of this story, which, however, is probably no more accurate than his stories of exemplary behavior and hard work or his frequently expressed intentions to conduct himself like a sensible person. Prolonged observation of the patient in the hospital showed him to be more prone to drift about street corners and bars, to indulge in petty gambling or theft, to cadge and impose on chance acquaintances, or to raise some puerile and futile clamor than to seek intercourse with one woman, much less with many.

Since this last admission, his story has been the same as before. On recovering from gonorrhea, he was, after being found sane and competent, given freedom of the grounds. He soon left without permission and was found in the hands of the police. Back again on a closed ward he was dissatisfied and with irrefutable arguments pointed out the incongruity of his being assigned to a place among men content to sit all day in silence staring blankly at nothing or who murmured incessantly that their heads were full of gold, radium, and diamonds, that they had no stomachs or intestines, that the Masons were playing on their sexual organs by radio, that they were sickened by the odor of the bells.

It was here, however, that George had to be kept, a perfectly clear-minded person, neat, polite, and quick witted, in striking contrast to his fellows, whose lips moved inarticulately as they responded to hallucinatory voices and some of whom urinated and defecated on themselves, sought to eat dead roaches, etc.

This was not, of course, an ideal environment for him. He was therefore replaced on the parole ward time after time, only to prove himself unadaptable after periods ranging from a few days to a few weeks. When put on the closed ward among better adjusted patients with schizophrenia or dementia paralytica, men who worked on a farm detail or at woodwork, he took advantage of his situation and escaped. During much of his time in the hospital it has therefore been necessary to keep him among the actively disturbed, badly deteriorated patients where supervision is complete and possibilities of escape are limited.

When last heard from, he was again hospitalized. Opportunities are continually offered him to improve his situation. From time to time parole is restored, and occasionally his wife takes him home on furlough. Always, however, he causes trouble for himself and others and always for no discernible purpose.

The last news of him was that he violated his parole by leaving the hospital. After sustaining himself by his customary activities for a week or ten days and staying clear of the police, he again came to grief. With the aim evidently of stealing a hen or a few fryers or perhaps to evade pursuit, he slipped into a Negro farmer's chicken house. Having brought along a bottle and perhaps being delayed by needs to avoid detection, he drank injudiciously. Next morning he was found in the coop, where he had apparently wallowed and groped through the night. Called by the farmer, attendants brought him to the hospital. Here on a closed ward we find him, among helpless, irrational people and subject to the strict control and attention required for those who cannot direct themselves.

Though he left school after completing the eighth grade, he writes letters which would do credit to a college graduate. In these he insists on having his freedom, stating that his difficulties in the past have been minor and that he is ready and thoroughly able to settle down to an exemplary life. He often stresses the fact that his wife and children need his protection and support. His family history is entirely negative. Parents and grandparents were hard-working, sober folk, liked and respected in the little rural community in which the present generation lives. One sister and three brothers are leading normal lives there today.

10

Pierre

Some of the patients who have been presented give concrete and abundant evidence in their behavior of a serious maladjustment and one of long duration. The diagnosis of sociopathic personality can seldom, if ever, be made with confidence except on such a record. Many persons at some time in their lives steal, cheat, lie, forge checks, indulge in foolish or destructive conduct, behave regrettably while drinking, and engage in unfortunate or paradoxical sexual activity. It can hardly be denied that some of the most stable and admirable of people have, during the course of achieving maturity, done all these things and worse. One important point that distinguishes the psychopath is his failure to learn and adopt a better and more fulfilling pattern of life. Another and perhaps a more fundamental point, which will be elaborated subsequently, is that psychopaths give a strong impression of lacking the fundamental responses and emotional susceptibility which probably play a dominant part in helping other people avoid this type of maladjustment.

It is perhaps worth while for us to consider now a patient whose record so far may not establish him beyond question with our group of those clinically disabled but whose inmost reactions, in so far as one can judge them, strongly indicate that his disorder is the same and that his subsequent career will unmistakably place him.

Not long ago his parents made an appointment for him by mail. They accompanied him from a thriving community in northern Florida where for the last sixty years the members of this family had been sober and respected citizens. There was a good deal of pride in these people, not a vain or pretentious self-esteem but a modest dignity that seemed to be cherished more as a responsibility than as an ornament.

These parents were truly concerned about their son. A dozen or more letters and reports from schoolteachers, from the family physician, the rector of the church, the scoutmaster, a high school coach, etc., arrived before the patient. From this material came many facts and opinions. The patient's remote antecedents had lived in or about Charleston, S. C., in colonial times. They had never been famous for wealth or political influence, but in the Revolutionary War, as well as in the War Between the States, they had played a part which rooted them deeply in sectional traditions of distinction. In Florida, where this branch of the family had moved almost twenty years before the present century, they had established a good name and a sound, unsnobbish sort of prominence. Unlike the fictional Southerners preoccupied with (frequently exaggerated) glories of the past, the _____'s had continued to live primarily in the present and to live rather effectively.

One schoolteacher who had done graduate work in psychology gave a good deal of consideration to this boy's name, which, as a fair equivalent, we shall give as Pierre. As she pointed out, an Englishman can be called Percival, Jasper, Evelyn, or Vivian without much risk, but in the ordinary American community such a name might endanger a boy's soul. This young man had been christened Pierre _____ _____ _____, probably not as an extravagant gesture toward the exotic or to past glories but almost as a matter of course. Such given names had been customary among these descendants of early Charleston Huguenots, and the present generation felt nothing conspicuous in what to them was so familiar and commonplace. In these parents speculation probably never arose about how a French name might sound to the fellows who played football in the vacant lot by the gashouse and "rabbitted" sissies with brickbats. In agreement with his thoughtful teacher's final conclusion, I am inclined to believe that his name, despite its potential dangers, caused the patient little difficulty. Even before he began school he was always called Pete. And his family conformed to this custom.

After his parents had been interviewed separately and together, Pete came into the office. He stood about 6 feet tall, held himself well, and appeared more mature than would be expected of an 18-year-old boy. He at once impressed me as being enviably at his ease. Though not extraordinary in its features, his face was pleasant, candid, and alert. As our conversation progressed, indications of excellent intelligence soon appeared, along with suggestions of a character forceful but not undesirably self-assertive or aggressive.

Pete expressed disappointment about having had to withdraw from college and seemed remarkably frank in discussing the causes of his predicament. His story was the same incomprehensible story already heard from his parents and corroborated by the several detailed reports.

A forged check had brought Pete before the dean. He did not deny his guilt but, in a straightforward way, seemed ready to meet the consequences like a gentleman. The dean was puzzled not that a young man might forge a check but that it should be this particular man with his fine record, his appearance of sincerity, and his brave way of handling a situation presumably painful and embarrassing.

Several points made the incident difficult to explain. The check had been cashed at a little tavern by the gates of the college, a place virtually integral with the campus where students were intimately known to the cashier and the waitresses. The owner of this place, a college-life character for generations, prided himself on calling the freshmen by name and on his closeness to the boys. It would have been easy for Pete to cash such a check at dozens of places where his chances of escaping detection would have been vastly better. He had, it would seem, picked the place where his misdeed could most easily be traced to him. Furthermore, he had not chosen as victim someone unlikely to find him out but the father of a girl he had been dating regularly during the seven months he had been at college. In forging the name, he had taken no great care to disguise his handwriting or to make a good imitation of the real signature.

There was difficulty in conceiving of a possible motive. With the dean Pete seemed thoroughly at ease. In a manly, well-controlled manner he expressed his profound regret and his willingness to make restitution or to submit to any penalty. The check amounted to only $35.00 and could scarcely represent an urgent need or something deeply longed for. Pete's allowance, although not injudiciously large, was a little more than the average among his fellows. Despite his apparent frankness he could give the dean no substantial reason for the self-damaging act by which he had neither gained nor hoped to gain anything of consequence. During a prolonged consideration of the affair, Pete remained so calm, so free from ordinary signs of guile and excuse-making, that those in authority could not dismiss the possibility of some point that this boy might, through honor or chivalry, be concealing. No definite hypothesis of this sort could be devised, but the dean, despite such plain indications for drastic action, decided to temporize. Meanwhile, another forged check, this time for $15.00, showed up. This was drawn on the account of a lady in his hometown, an intimate friend of his mother's. While judgment was pending, two or more forged checks were discovered—one for $15.00, another for $23.00.

Even now the authorities found it difficult to regard this boy as an ordinary forger. He showed nothing in common with people who are placed in the category of the delinquent. Instead of being expelled, he was allowed to withdraw from college.

He made a good record during his seven months as a freshman and was popular with the students. Letters were contributed in his behalf by the high school principal at home, by his minister, a former Sunday school teacher, a scoutmaster, and even by the mayor of his hometown. All of these expressed confidence in Pete as "a splendid young man of high moral standards," "a regular fellow," "a fine Christian character," "a well-behaved and clean-minded boy who deserves every consideration."

During our numerous interviews, Pete seemed to express himself freely. "I just don't know why I did it," he said at first. At other times he said he must have been impelled by desire for money. As the subject was returned to from day to day, his explanation varied. "It seems there was some sort of an impulse I can't account for," he once suggested. A few days later it was, "I just didn't think what I was doing."

No one familiar with the whole material of these interviews would have difficulty in seeing plainly that none of these reasons were very pertinent. Pete admitted he had not even spent the money. He had no particular need and no special plans that might call for extra cash. His statement about some impulse is, of course, interesting; but the more Pete discussed this the more evident it became that he was not referring to anything like compulsive behavior in the ordinary psychiatric sense. Apparently he fell upon this remark as upon his other ever-varying explanations in a vague effort to fill out verbally a framework of cause and effect which as human beings we all tend to manufacture when we cannot find it in actuality. There was no specific breathtaking and unbearable drive to do this irrational act and no vivid fulfillment in its accomplishment. He had done it as a lazy man might swat a fly. Pete was not discovering real motives in himself but reaching at random for plausible or possible reasons that might have influenced some hypothetical person to do what he had done. It was rationalization in the purest sense but not adequate enough to convince the patient himself.

Among dozens of other possible explanations he mentioned that shortly before one of his forgeries he had received a letter from one of his friends in Florida mentioning the friend's plan for a weekend trip to Miami. Pete recalled a feeling of envy and suggested that he might childishly have felt that he, too, would like to have a sort of treat or adventure or break in the routine. By getting this extra money he would, in a vague way, be keeping up with his friend, having a little lark, or indulging himself in a sort of reward or bonus. Or he might think up some way to spend the money that would constitute an equivalent to his friend's weekend of pleasure. Under discussion this, too, broke down as a factor of much pertinence. The envious thought of his friend's trip had been brief and trivial. It had not preoccupied him or exerted strong or persistent emotional pressure as sometimes such apparently illogical and inadequate factors do exert in human behavior. And he had neither executed nor continued to plan any adventure in which the money might be used or wasted.

The patient realized that all the impulses he mentioned were without strength to drive him into a dangerous or even a mildly unpleasant act. The more one talked with him, the more plain it became that he had realized how readily such forgeries could be detected and laid at his feet and that he had, before and during the acts, been far from unaware (intellectually) that serious and undesirable consequences were likely to follow. There was no question of Pete's having been merely thoughtless or impulsive in the ordinary sense. He was not negligent in reason and foresight, but somehow the obvious, and one would think inevitable, emotional response that would inhibit such an act did not play its part in his functioning. There had been no anxious brooding over consequences, no conscious struggle against temptation or overmastering impulse. The consequences occurred to him, but rather casually, and he did not worry about them even to the point of carefully estimating his chances of getting away with the forgeries undetected or just what penalties he might face if he failed. He drifted along, responding to rather feeble impulses but without adequate consideration of consequences.

This boy, as he clearly pointed out, had no inclination to leave college. He had been remarkably free of homesickness and, in fact, happier, he said, than ever before in his life. He had chosen the college himself, largely on the basis of renown and social prestige. Though very much smaller, it was regarded by many as more or less equivalent to Harvard or Yale. He had won a scholarship awarded by a hometown civic group on the basis of character and all-around qualities rather than on mere superiority in grades. He had no difficulty in passing examinations and obtaining admission at the college of his choice.

In this discussion several points of interest emerged. Until his last year in high school he had planned to go to West Point. There had never been, he admitted, any real interest in military life, and he frankly stated he had never intended to remain in the army after graduation. The idea of wearing an impressive uniform and the most superficial aspects of being a West

Pointer seem to have been almost his sole motive. In explaining his change of mind, he frankly spoke of his desire to be among wealthy and socially prominent people and pointed out the particular advantages of the place he had chosen. Such motives of course influence in a way most, if not all, people. But this young man seemed influenced to a degree truly remarkable. As the discussion progressed, it began to appear as if such values alone affected him. In the ordinary climber or snob it is usual to find this sort of dominant attitude only under concealment that fools the subject if not the observer. With Pete there seemed to be no awareness that such aims should not be given primacy and, indeed, exclusive sway or that there was reason to pretend otherwise.

In further talk along this line his fundamental attitude began to shape up into something much less simple than that of the ordinary opportunist or the vulgar schemer. Something distinctly and almost terrifyingly naive emerged behind a readily volunteered and not very appealing life aim. It became clear that this was far from a truly dominant and persistent aim. It has been donned like momentary apparel, somewhat as revellers may try on for a moment paper masks or fancy costumes at a party, only after a moment to discard them. Pete apparently was not an ordinary example of the shrewd opportunist intently set on pursuing a policy of material success with little regard to ethics or esthetics. Gladly, and in a deep sense innocently and sincerely, he accepted such a scheme and such evaluations. And these motivations probably influenced his conduct more often than any other conscious motivation. But even here there was no persistence of aim, no goal regularly beckoning, no substantial emotional force driving, even in a poor or perverse channel, toward fulfillment. Such values prompted Pete, but their influence was more that of transient recurrent whims than of adequate human striving.

This bright and pleasant young man volunteered information about numerous acts in the past which had not been detected. He had occasionally stolen, usually taking articles of little value, from friends and from stores. No evidence of any distinct motive or any strong thrill of adventure could be brought out in connection with the petty thefts. He had also, with gracious and "between us as gentlemen" approaches, put pressure on a number of his father's friends to "lend" him small sums which he never thought of repaying. During the previous summer he had, by complicated and ingenious schemes, secured sugar for a Negro man who made whiskey illegally. In this way he obtained several hundred dollars, nearly all of which he squandered aimlessly and unexcitingly while on houseparties with a group he liked to impress. Though he worried little about getting caught, he had proceeded with some caution and cunning. Even his closest acquaintances had not suspected him. Earlier, when rationing was in effect, he devised a method of stealing gasoline from an uncle who managed a business considered important in the war effort. Through this connection he gained access to relatively large quanties of gasoline and, by careful planning and clever execution, made off with a few gallons at a time until he accumulated enough to bring substantial sums on the black market. Though a member of the honor council in high school, he had never hesitated to cheat on examinations. He did this not only when he felt he might otherwise make a bad mark but also routinely somewhat in the manner of a gentleman paying respect to the conventions. This practice had not been officially detected or become widely known among his classmates.

Pete did not bring out these facts painfully and with reluctance. It was not as though he were taking advantage at last of an opportunity to unburden himself by confession. Apparently he had never been burdened. Nor did he show that boastful relish sometimes seen in people who seem proud and defiant about the delinquent acts they confess. In a gentlemanly way he seemed to be discussing ordinary matters of a conventional life.

He had repeatedly spoken of his remorse about the forgeries at college and spoken convincingly of his resolution never to make such mistakes in the future. In telling of his earlier delinquencies, which had never been discovered, he did not spontaneously bring out an opinion that this sort of behavior also should be avoided. When reasons for this were suggested, he readily agreed. There seemed, however, to be little shame or real regret and no effective intention that would last much beyond the moment of its utterance.

Though a considerable number of delinquencies and examples of very badly adapted conduct emerged as this patient was seen over a period of time,* it is not these in themselves that so strongly suggest he shows the disorder called psychopathic personality. What is most suggestive of this disorder is very difficult to convey, for it came out in attitudes disclosed as he talked about his emotional relations, his principles, his ambitions, and his ideals. It is easier to demonstrate such things by citing concrete acts or failures to act than by commenting on what has been merely spoken and what from this and the accompanying expressions, tones, etc., has been sensed or surmised. It may be worth while, however, to attempt a few points.

PETE'S LOVE LIFE

This attractive and fine-looking young man had been going out with girls for several years. Apparently they found his attentions welcome. Though

---

*Not all of these need be brought out here.

he sometimes spent the evening alone with a girl, he still preferred double-dating or getting together with several couples. He had almost entirely escaped the shyness and unpleasant self-consciousness that trouble so many boys in their teens. He had never attempted sexual relations and seemed to have less than ordinary conscious inclination in this direction. No overt homosexual inclinations could be brought out in ordinary interviews or with the patient under Amytal or hypnosis.

For over a year Pete had been going regularly with the daughter of a millionaire who had recently moved to Florida from the Midwest. Jane was only 16 years of age. Though not an only child, she had been born very late in her parents' lives and after her sister and two brothers were almost adults. The siblings had long ago married, leaving her to grow up as the center of her aging parents' concern and attention. This situation may account for the early overprotection and domination Jane experienced and for her tendency toward social withdrawal and her deep and painful insecurity.

Her parents, by now quite old, set in their ways, and out of touch with Jane's world, sensed something wrong and set out on the disastrous course of pushing her, managing her, and trying by an irresistible tour de force to make her precipitately into a reigning belle.

A few years earlier her mother had nagged her day and night about overexerting herself and had insisted that she have breakfast in bed and not arise until 10:30 A.M. She had also insisted that she take tomato juice between meals (for vitamins) and milk (for calories). There had also been arguments about taking a nap every afternoon, swallowing numerous vitamin pills or unneeded laxatives, and carrying out all sorts of quackish health rituals which had attracted the mother. Now this frustrated, frightened, and unprepared girl was pushed suddenly into equitation instructions, tennis every other afternoon, private lessons in Italian, and elaborate parties with imported champagne. The mother took her to New York and arranged some rather artificial frolics at the Stork Club and El Morocco. There were also yachting parties during which this sensitive girl tried valiantly to make conversation and carry out the motions of gaiety from Daytona to Miami. Jane seemed like a gun-shy yearling pointer and promptly developed nocturnal enuresis.*

The more difficulty she showed in handling herself, the more vigorously her mother pushed her, and the more she suffered and showed her terror. Most of the young men herded by the mother's almost ferocious efforts and by all sorts of indirect bribery to these overdone parties made almost open

*I have reliable, firsthand information on Jane's situation in addition to what came through the present case.

fun of Jane. Her uneasiness and dutiful but brittle efforts to carry out a false role led them to speak of her as a "drip."

This good and essentially normal girl, in the midst of constant mockery which she, unlike her mother, often detected, found herself attended by Pete. He was without mockery. Nor did he, like some of the condescending youths drawn by parental largess, attempt lovelessly to feel her breasts and to initiate her into the intimacies of a *soul kiss*. Pete behaved "like a gentleman." He was cordial and polite, and he treated her mother and father with a respect that seemed properly deferential in contrast with many in that brash, immature gang who came for the handout and the opportunity for mockery.

He was more acceptable also than the snide older men who were inclined to show her attention. Among these she encountered a few partial and cynical homosexuals who apparently enjoyed any travesty on what ought to be a normal coming together of girl and boy. Jane did not know which ones were the homosexuals or scarcely even that there was such a thing as homosexuality, but she sensed under their superficial politeness what seemed like subtle attitudes of defeatism, condescension, and only formality where it is natural to seek warmth. They gently mocked her taste in reading and in music and were politely supercilious about her clothes and about how she rode a horse.

After them it was almost a joy to be with Pete. Her parents, too, found him respectful and a lad of fine, manly qualities. He was obviously intelligent, and he lightly and unpretentiously expressed principles of the highest, truest order.

Too much a child still and too backward to seek a mature heterosexual role, too inexperienced to recognize or even to imagine what a genuine lover might offer to seek, Jane found Pete the most acceptable companion available. Unacquainted with the feelings and attitudes of young men in normal love, or even with milder but real interests of this sort, she had no frame of reference in which to evaluate her chief suitor's monumental inadequacy. She had, in fact, little means even of perceiving it.

Pete himself discussed his girl without the slightest awareness that he lacked any requisite of a romantic lover or of a satisfactory husband. Both of Jane's parents encouraged his attentions. An impressive mahogany speedboat and a new Cadillac convertible were virtually put at his disposal. He found himself not quite the possessor of these and of many other luxuries but conspicuously in the center of them. It would not be difficult to imagine such a situation turning an ordinary boy's head, confusing him with grandiose fancies, and, perhaps, initiating a career of delinquency.

Perhaps such an explanation is correct, but I am not convinced. Pete was not dazzled and swept off his feet. He was not, it would seem, particularly excited. He expressed a liking for Jane and her family and showed evidence of being attracted by the outer appearance of things in this rather glittering world. There was no indication that wild passions for wealth had been aroused and a steady young man lured off toward false goals. Nothing seemed capable of arousing any real drive or passion in Pete, much less a wild one. The pseudoideals about wealth and prestige and the halfhearted impulses of which he spoke had existed long before he knew Jane. They were, however, at best tepid and unsteady aspirations, not strong or really purposeful drives, not constantly beckoning temptations deflecting natural aims. Pete might let himself drift toward a fortune and, when caprice stimulated him, even paddle a bit toward this goal or effigy of a goal, but he was not the sort of man to swim with frantic vigor toward either positive or negative shores. Fortune hunting might come nearer to arousing him than another aim, but even this did not challenge him to life and human purpose or bring to birth a long-range plan of action. Even in this direction he found nothing to which he could commit himself in actual emotion.

Though his plans were not definite, Pete admitted he felt he would like eventually to marry Jane. He had not weighed his chances to do so very carefully but he felt they were good. "Oh, yes indeed!" he replied, when asked if he were in love with her. As his feelings about her were discussed, it remained impossible to detect any sort of affective content to which those words might refer. The more one investigated Pete's attitude, the more strictly verbal his statement appeared. His reply was a reflex response, the carrying out of a superficially polite routine, a purely formal nod doing justice to vague conventions more or less to the effect that of course one loved a girl if he were seriously considering her for a wife. Pete approved of such conventions. Rather proudly, he denied any outstanding physical passion for her or any specific attraction of this sort. He had sometimes held her hand and he kissed her good-night. These contacts, one would judge, were little more stimulating to him than such doings between brother and sister. The ideas of kissing her as a lover would have seemed to him vaguely repellent, perhaps "common." He was more neutral, however, than negative toward this as a possibility and seemed pleased that he could say he had never given such things much thought. He was consecrated to higher and more practical aims.

As the discussion of his attitudes toward his girl developed, it became increasingly apparent that he neither liked nor disliked her. He had not questioned his heart particularly along these lines or so formulated it to himself, but it was plain that she was little more than something incidental in the eventualities toward which he felt himself drifting and was willing to drift. When this was suggested to him, he agreed that it was correct, with no shame or sense of having been detected in anything to regret or explain.

"Many people put too much emphasis on love, it seems to me," Pete said, not argumentatively or even with strong conviction but somewhat gropingly, as if he were feeling his way toward some position on which he could base his comments. It was not hard to believe he might just as readily have drifted into the opposite position.

"I don't feel the way so many other people do about love," he continued. "Other things, it seems to me, are a lot more serious and important." On being urged to make this point more concrete, he added, "Well, for instance, if a boy and a girl decide to marry and unite two families so they can own a good insurance business or a big pulpwood mill."

There was nothing that suggested active cynicism in this young man. He was shaping up something that might pass in his awareness as a sort of goal. In a sense his attitude was idealistic. It was at least the shadow or verbal form of what might be called an idealistic or "higher" type of impulse, but the shadow was, I believe, without substance. Even here one felt an affective hollowness, a lack of the energy that goes into purposive human functioning, and to such a degree as to convince one that this verbal evaluation could never muster sufficient strength, could never matter enough to him, to become a real goal or to make him work toward it consistently or with enthusiasm.

●　　●　　●

His other activities, convictions, and relations gave indications of a similar deficit in his functioning. In response to leading questions he mentioned numerous "ambitions." He was not at all evasive, and he seemed entirely unaware that his inmost self might contain anything incomplete, pathologic, or deviate. In fact, one felt that nothing could really embarrass this bright, agreeable, and poised young man.

"Another thing I'd like when I get older is to be a vestryman in the church," he said, with what looked a bit like enthusiasm. I believe, however, that enthusiasm is a misleading word. His tone of voice, his facial expression, and the myriad other subthreshold details not clearly perceived, in which we feel out our evaluation of a person's reactions, all suggested affect. But this affect did not, it seems, extend deeply enough into him to constitute enthusiasm or anything else that could move a person very much. Nor do I believe that what affect might have been present will be capable of directing him toward any consistent aim. A well-made cardboard box carefully gilded could scarcely be distinguished by visual perception from a cubic yard of gold.

I do not think his expressed wish to become a vestryman can be accounted for by a desire on his part to impress people that he was penitent about the forgeries and meant to compensate for them in the future. I think this wish was as real as anything could be real for this person. It had been a feature in his plans over some years.

In discussing his motives he said, "I don't exactly know why it seems such a good idea to be a vestryman. It just seems to me sort of pleasant and I think I'd like it. It might strike you as a little odd, too," he continued thoughtfully, "because I'm really not very much interested in religion. Now Jack _____ and Frank _____ are terribly interested in religion. They're all the time talking about it and bothering themselves. I'm not like that a bit. I can't see any point in making such a commotion about something of that sort."

To the next question he replied: "Oh I don't mean that I don't absolutely and completely believe every word of the Bible. And I believe everything the church teaches. Of course I believe things like that." I hardly think he was trying to deceive me or, as this is ordinarily understood, trying to deceive himself. A person to whom rigid theological beliefs give comfort might deceive himself in order to overlook implausibility in what he would like to assume is true and might, I am sure all will agree, do so without being quite aware of it. This boy did not seem to have any such need. It seemed, with due respect to the difficulties of putting such matters into words, rather a case of there being nowhere within him any valid contrast between *believing* and *not believing* or even between a thing of this sort being *so* or *not so*.

"Probably why I want to be a vestryman," he went on, "is because people seem to think a lot of them, consider them important, and sort of look up to them." There was no sign of irony, playful or otherwise, toward the social group or toward himself. Sincerity is a word which for most people implies positive emotional reactions. Not merely in this boy's superficial attitude, but in an important sense, one could say there was a striking lack of ordinary insincerity.

In discussing his relations with others he admitted a decline in his affection for his father. He expressed no negative feelings and said he felt, perhaps, he loved his father about as much as, and probably more than, one might expect of the average boy of his age. "But, being prefectly frank, I can't say I love him the way I do my mother. I am crazy about mother. She and I are very close to each other." By leading questions it was brought out that he estimated his love for his mother as deep and genuine. He rated it as a feeling not less strong than the maximum that an ordinary person can experience, though he was not boastful or extravagant in phrasing his replies. A few minutes later he mentioned, among other people, the mother of a male friend.

"Oh, Mrs. Blank is a wonderful person. She and I get on perfectly. She understands me. I love Mrs. Blank better than anyone."

"Do you love her better than your mother?"

"Yes," he replied without hesitation, "I love Mrs. Blank a great deal more than I do Mother. I couldn't love anybody as much as I do Mrs. Blank!"

He had been frequently thrown with this lady, but apparently his relations with her were superficial and there was no evidence of particular or uncommon affection on her part toward him. She had no idea that he would express himself about her in such a fashion.

A little later he said that his ideal of what a woman should be and of the sort of wife he would like was embodied in the fictional Scarlett O'Hara. It was pointed out that this character was thought by some to be portrayed as amazingly selfish, frigid, dishonorable, ruthless, faithless, and petty and that, furthermore, she was scarcely the sort of woman to make a husband happy. He did not deny any of this. Mrs. Blank, who in his own appraisal and in reality was honest, faithful, gentle, and, in nearly all important respects, the opposite of Scarlett O'Hara, was now recalled to him and he was asked how he could choose both these incompatible figures as a single ideal. He then said that maybe he was mistaken about Scarlett. He had read the novel and remembered it in detail.

There was no indication in him of a reaction such as awakening to an error, or even of surprise accompanying his verbal withdrawal from his fictional heroine. He did not seem to feel any need to revise his attitude as the ordinary man does on finding himself in error. The fact that he had been, as admitted by himself, on the wrong track seemed in no way to stimulate him toward getting on another track. He impressed me as being this way about the most serious and practical matters and no less so than in this small theoretical question. It was not hard to get the feeling that he had never been on any track at all, that he had not really been committed to his first proposition and so he had nothing to withdraw.

This young man's parents, in his absence, spoke of his having been an unusually loving and demonstrative child until he was about 14 years of age. "We worried," his mother said, "because he was too considerate and affectionate. He never did anything wrong. He would do so many sweet, attentive little things to show us how he felt. He used to stay at home and seem to want to be with us so much that I thought it might not be good for him."

After 14 a difference became discernible and finally striking. He gradually changed from being overattentive until, in recent years, he seemed cool and showed little convincing evidence of affection to his parents. He seemed to want to be out all the time. Though the parents felt uneasy about these changes, they reassured themselves. He did not drink and had the reputation of being very moral, "pure-minded," and proper. He was liked by his friends, did well but not brilliantly in school, and usually took the lead in superficial activities at clubs and social gatherings.

Occasionally incidents arose that briefly alarmed the parents. The boy, when he wanted to have his way about small matters, sometimes seemed utterly unable to see the other side of a question. Once when his mother was physically indisposed and needed to get a number of articles downtown, he refused to help her, saying that he was going to the movies with another boy. His indifference struck her as extreme, and she suffered not only considerable inconvenience and discomfort but also sharp hurt. That night when, as usual, he wanted the family automobile, his father refused him, pointing out that he had not behaved toward his mother in a way to deserve this favor. According to his parents, he reacted as if an arbitrary and vicious injustice had been done him, showing what looked like a quiet indignation, politely controlled in its grosser aspects but consistent with what one might feel who is for no fault provoked and deeply wronged. Both parents felt that they had often given in to him too much.

On another occasion when he had shown unwillingness to put himself out in even the smallest degree for the comfort of his mother, who was then recovering from a serious attack of illness, his father had pointed out to him that his mother might have died and still was in danger. "Well," he said, "suppose she did. Everybody has to die sometime. I don't see why you make so much of it." He seemed honestly surprised at his father's reaction. In discussing this with me, he still seemed to feel that the most important point in the matter was the factual correctness of his statement about mortality.

Unlike most psychopaths, this patient as yet shows relatively little obvious disturbance in his social situation. There is no trail behind him now of a hundred thefts and forgeries, repeated time after time in clear knowledge of the consequences. He has, in general, avoided outraging his friends and acquaintances by vividly antisocial acts or distasteful and spectacular folly. Many of his contemporaries smoke, swap bawdy jokes with gusto, sometimes get a little drunk, and not a few indulge in illicit sexual intercourse.

Not doing these things, by which "goodness" or "badness" in people of his age is often judged by the community, he has acquired a considerable reputation for virtue. He goes to church regularly. All this tends to offset what negative qualities he has shown and makes it hard for his friends to realize things about him they might otherwise grasp. Though far from being truthful, his frank manner and his ability to look one in the eye without shame have so far concealed most of his serious shortcomings, not only from his parents but also from a fair percentage of his acquaintances.

Many of Pete's contemporaries do not, as a matter of fact, regard him as the excellent character and promising young man he appears in the eyes of his elders. He has no really close friends. Bound by no substantial attachments, he has, one might say, the whole of his time and energy for superficial relations and is able to cultivate many acquaintances with whom he is in a sense popular. He does not get close enough to anyone in true personal relationships to be recognized well in his limitations or to be well understood. What little warmth he possesses is all on the surface and available to one and all. What he offers to the most casual acquaintance is all he could offer to friend, parent, or wife. In general he is accepted as a person representing virtue and manifesting affability. Having no serious interests or aims, he is free to devote more attention than others to social clubs and to young people's organizations sponsored by school or church for moral purposes. It is easy for him to say the right things and go through the proper motions, for he has no earnest convictions or strong conflicting drives to cause confusion.

Behind an excellent facade of superficial reactions that mimic a normal and socially approved way of living, one can feel in this young man an inner deviation, an emotional emptiness, comparable in degree with what seems to lie at the core of schizophrenia. He lacks, however, all the characteristics by which a diagnosis of schizophrenia is made. Not only are the gross and demonstrable symptoms such as delusions and hallucinations absent, but there is no oddness, no peculiar inwardness and constraint, no abtruse stiffness of manner, or any of the other subtle, sometimes inexpressible, qualities and shadings that can be felt in the patient with simple schizophrenia or in those with schizoid personality. On the contrary, he is glibly sociable, utterly at ease. He mixes readily and tends to lead in his group. There is nothing guarded and shy on the surface of his personality and probably nowhere within the range of his consciousness.

Whether or not the formal diagnosis of sociopath (or psychopath) is established in this case is a question I am willing to leave open. There is much in his conduct that would indicate such a disorder. It is not what he has done that points so strongly in this direction but how he feels and inwardly responds. When one deals with him directly, he offers more of an opportunity than the previous patients to sense at close range some of the attitudes that can often be surmised only at a greater depth beneath the unaccountable conduct and the verbally and logically perfect front of the psychopath.

11

Frank

The following letter was received by an influential senator in Washington and referred by him to the hospital.

Dear Sir:

It is with regret that I find it necessary to seek consideration from higher authority but I have been confined in the Veterans Administration Hospital at _____, _____ for two years.

During my period of incarceration here I have tried in every available way to cooperate with the officials, but it seems an impossibility to get any consideration from them toward gaining my freedom.

I was placed here on the recommendation of my sister because she thought I was a drug addict, and she has written some pretty nasty things against me to the officials here.

I can prove to the satisfaction of all concerned that I am not a confirmed drug addict or habitual user of any form of drug sufficiently to warrant continuous confinement. I am not a criminal, nor had I the slightest minor charge of any description against me at the time I came here. The Staff here has rated me less than 10 per cent disabled and discontinued all government compensation; therefore, I believe you will agree with me that any man with a less than 10 per cent disability could not possess a physical or mental disorder sufficient to prevent his having his freedom and making his own livelihood.

I am not even allowed parole privileges of the grounds as a great many of the patients here are. Some are continually violating institutional rules and still retain their parole privileges undisciplined.

I have two children, who need my support and as long as I am kept incarcerated I can't assist them in any way for I have no means other than my labor to support them.

I hereby humbly request you to intercede in my behalf and demand these officials here to grant my release in order that I may be able to support my children to the best of my ability as is every man's duty.

There are quite a few men in these institutions that are nothing short of impositions on the government and taxpayers of the United States. They, the same as myself, are perfectly capable mentally and physically to support themselves and should be forced to do so.

I have begged for parole, trial visit, or any other means to prove myself self-sustaining, but the authorities here seem to take my plea as a joke and make a lot of promises that they have no intention of putting into action.

I will gladly submit to any physical or mental examination you may deem necessary to assist you in obtaining my release from this place.

I pray that you will give my earnest request your immediate consideration.

Please be assured that I hold no malice toward any of the officials here or elsewhere but my only objective in writing you is to gain my freedom and support my children.

Please let me hear from you personally,

Yours very respectfully,

Frank _____.

The writer of this letter has behind him a formidable record of misadventure.

Detailed knowledge of Frank's early life is not available beyond the following facts. The son of a rustic blacksmith, he was raised in a small hamlet near the mountains of north Georgia. So far as can be learned, no members of his family suffered from nervous or mental disease or made themselves objectionable in the community. He completed the fifth grade in school, where he was considered by no means a dull boy, though often truant. Many of the hours he was supposed to have spent in school or working at some necessary chore for his family he is reported to have idled away in loitering about a local millpond drowning goats and doing other senseless or uninviting deeds of mischief.

Before the United States entered World War I, Frank had forged his father's name to a false statement about his age and enlisted in the National Guard. He was given vocational training by the government after his discharge from the army. He was tried at several courses but made no serious effort to complete any of them. In his community he soon made himself a problem, sometimes drinking to excess, often behaving in a rowdy and threatening manner, contracting to buy filling stations, farms, etc., but never living up to his agreements.

Local ex-service men, believing that he took morphine and that treatment might help his maladjustment (commonly referred to as "nervousness"), had him sent to a psychiatric hospital. He remained for a month, then returned to continue in his old ways.

Now began a series of hospitalizations which extends to the present time. He would be sent first to one place, then to another. He has been treated in state hospitals, in federal hospitals, and in private institutions at the expense of the government. All told, he has been admitted no less than nineteen times to strictly mental hospitals maintained for the purpose of treating psychotic people. Sometimes he remained only three or four weeks and sometimes six or even eighteen months. Over the years his periods of hospitalization have grown slightly longer and his intervals outside shorter. He has never, during the past fifteen years, been free longer than a few months. While not under the care of psychiatrists he has received considerable attention from the police. His jail sentences number seven at the present reading, including a term of nine months in the Leavenworth Penitentiary (where he was sent for forging a prescription for morphine) but not counting a score or more of overnight or weekend stops in police barracks.

Despite these preoccupations Frank has found time to marry and have four children and to become ordained as a minister in a small religious sect noted for vigorous evangelical fervor. His marital relations have been most unsatisfactory during the interludes when he was free to be with the family. His wife reports that he curses her and fights with her, and it is well established that he seizes any money that is available, hires automobiles, and drives aimlessly about the countryside, often drinking to excess and, according to some reports, occasionally taking morphine.

At times he has seemed proud of his ecclesiastical title, referring to himself as a pastor and assuming unctuous and haughty airs. He has not, however, occupied himself with whatever ministerial duties he was supposed to fulfill any more consistently than with other work.

His friends, especially those interested in the American Legion and other service organizations, have obtained many positions for him. He is shrewd, neat in appearance, and an excellent talker. He makes a good impression at first but always shirks his responsibility to such an extent that it is impossible to retain him.

A few years ago he was given a place at a filling station and seemed, surprisingly, to show considerable interest in his work for several days. It was then discovered that he had been drawing off all the gasoline he could and taking it to a nearby town where he sold it and bought morphine from dope peddlers, most of which he, in turn, sold at a tremendous profit to local addicts.

He has been consistently arrogant and aggressive toward his neighbors and acquaintances over trifles. After taking a few drinks, he has often threatened others, claimed things that were not his own, and made such a nuisance of himself that local police would be called to deal with him.

He is boastful and histrionic, more eloquently and aggressively so with a few highballs, and much given to temper tantrums. He frequently threatens to kill himself over some petty vexation and once offered a pistol to his wife, urging her grandiloquently to shoot him. He has never made an attempt, however, to harm himself, though his opportunities have been unlimited.

He has been reported as having convulsive seizures. These developed when he was refused special attentions by physicians and seemed, according to descriptions of them, plainly and consciously designed toward obtaining various ends. This manifestation has also been noted when he was confined to jail and wanted to be sent to a mental hospital in order to escape charges that had been brought against him. These so-called seizures have been observed several times in this hospital by competent psychiatrists. They did not in any way suggest epilepsy nor were they convincing as possible reactions of true hysteria. The patient is unquestionably conscious and shows that he is behaving intentionally in this way to gain a recognized end. Unlike a conversion phenomenon, the purpose is not concealed from his conscious awareness.[63,85]

Though occasionally confused after heavy drinking (perhaps with the addition of drugs), he has at all other times been entirely rational, alert, shrewd, and free from delusions and hallucinations.

Early in Frank's career his disturbance was diagnosed on several occasions as hysteria, sometimes as both psychopathic personality and hysteria. Once he was given a diagnosis of psychopathic personality with psychotic episodes. There was not, however, any evidence of behavior or symptoms different from what he has shown on other occasions. There is reason to suspect that the real and pressing need to keep this patient hospitalized may have played an important part in his being so classified. The genuinely irrational and incompetent behavior, no doubt, supports the use of such a term as psychosis, despite the lack of any additional symptoms.

The irrational behavior which has characterized him is not based on a delusional system or on any loss of the good reasoning ability he shows on examination. Some of his most turbulent misconduct has, of course, been exhibited while he was intoxicated. At such times he naturally lacked his customary shrewdness and alertness. However, this cannot conscientiously be called a psychotic episode beyond and above his well-known inadequacy but rather the manifestation of inebriety. I do not mean to say that this man is normal but only that he has none of the recognized types of mental disorder, episodic or constant. If his drunken and wayward episodes are to be termed psychotic, then his state at other times must be termed psychotic, since it is in his shrewd, technically sane condition that he decides to add the picturesque touches of intoxication which he well knows will bring him to the attention of the police.

At this hospital, at the state hospitals, and at the other institutions to which Frank was sent in recent years, he has been considered a sane man without psychotic episodes. The symptomatic diagnosis of drug addiction and chronic alcoholism have been added. During all these years he has shown no evidence of deterioration or regression, and today at 38 years of age he is the same clever, alert person he was described as being twenty years ago. Unlike nearly all real morphine addicts, he does not show ordinary withdrawal symptoms or other signs of physical illness and acute distress when, after being admitted to the hospital, he is deprived of opportunities to obtain the drug.

If the reports that he takes morphine have any factual basis, such use must be sporadic. There is little or no evidence that effects of the drug have regularly played any major role in his behavior. It appears that his chief connection with drugs has been through his part in peddling them illicitly.

His career in the hospital has been marked by frequent paroles which are always terminated by his failing to return, returning drunk, or being taken up by the police for petty theft, swindling, and futile and unprovoked disorder. Though ingratiating and outwardly cooperative when he is trying to obtain parole or discharge, he constantly schemes to escape or, surreptitiously, to call upon high authorities to have him released. Once, while helping attendants on the disturbed ward, he succeeded in turning hot water into a tub in which a psychotic patient lay in a continuous bath. He did not try to injure the man seriously, but merely to hurt him a little as a joke. This is a fair example of the inane, humorless mischief that underlies the pretentious front assumed by this former pastor.

Despite his medicolegal status, which, of course, is technically regarded as constituting sanity, those interested in finding some practical way to protect him and his family and to cope with the ever-accumulating problems succeeded on one occasion in having him committed by the court. Those close to the situation evidently found in his behavior reasons for action more compelling than the abstract criteria which stood in the way of such a step. After being held in the hospital for several months, despite his reiterated demands for discharge against medical advice, he called in an attorney.

Frank had in the past always found no difficulty in leaving when it suited his purpose or his whim. In view of his well-demonstrated inability to live in freedom, he was now, by means of the legal commitment, kept against his wishes in order to spare his family, the community, and himself the hardships he had brought about before and was sure to bring about again. The attorney for the government, in attempting to resist habeas corpus proceedings, found himself in a familiar dilemma, as the following quotations from his letter will show:

It is evident that the medical staff at the hospital are using the term insane to convey the meaning of the medical definition of the word rather than the legal definition. In other words, the thought back of the use of the word appears to me to be that it is the opinion of neuropsychiatrists that this man is not suffering from a mental disease as physicians understand the term, that he does not have a psychosis. It does appear, however, that it is their opinion that the state of his mind due to drug addiction and also manifested by his past antisocial behavior is such as to warrant the conclusions that he is incompetent and that he should receive treatment in a hospital for the cure of nervous and mental diseases. To say, however, that he is incompetent but not insane presents a rather inconsistent picture with which to go into court. We may be confronted with such a question as why he needs to be in a hospital for the care of nervous and mental diseases if he has no nervous or mental disease.

I am inclined to think that the terms *insanity* and *incompetency* so far as their legal significance is concerned are used interchangeably and that the important point to be considered, whether you call a man insane or merely admit that he is incompetent, is whether the person is incapable of administering his personal estate in the normal manner of a prudent man and whether there is definite evidence of a more or less prolonged departure from normal behavior as compared with the standards of the community, such as dissipation of funds, unwise purchases, and utter lack of appreciation of values.

Because of the fact that I anticipate some difficulty in trying to show that the man is incompetent but not insane, I would appreciate an expression of your views on the matter. It occurs to me also that a man ought to be confined who is a menace to others and likely to do harm to others, even though his mental condition may be due in part to inadequate mental development and in part to the use of drugs. He may be just as dangerous to himself or to others as a person suffering from a mental disease and who, according to the purely medical definition of insanity, would be pronounced insane.

Of course, it might be asked why these people are not let out of the mental hospitals and left to the police. If they are considered responsible for their misdeeds, let them be punished. This, as a matter of fact, is what the average psychiatric hospital is nearly always forced to do, whatever its physicians may think of the wisdom and practicality of such a procedure. These men are studied, found free of recognized mental disorder which might make

121

them unaware of what they are doing, and are sent back out into the world. They are arrested not once but many times. Most of them seldom commit very serious crimes. Only rarely can they be kept for more than a few days. They do not follow any purposive criminal life. They make a nuisance of themselves to the community as a whole and often tragically wreck the lives of those close to them, and all to no discernible end. The police and the courts tire of them. Through various influences they are forced back on the mental hospitals where they take legal action to regain their freedom, only to begin the process again.

If, as stated in the quotations previously cited, it would be difficult to prove this man incompetent but not insane, it would be far more difficult, by existing definitions of psychiatry, to prove him "insane." His perfectly rational (superficial) behavior under scrutiny, his freedom from delusions, his shrewdness, his alertness, and his convincing plan for a normal, useful life, in short, his plain sanity as this is ordinarily understood, make it all but impossible for a judge or a jury to call him insane. Psychiatrists, familiar with his long record of senseless behavior, are able to see more reason to do so than could be brought out before a court in terms of abstract criteria by which the decision is determined. But according to the accepted standards of psychiatry, his diagnosis carries with it an official and automatic endorsement of the patient as sane and competent. No matter how strongly impressed by real and practical evidence to the contrary, all physicians testifying in such a case must admit that the official technicalities approve this paradox.

Having won his case in court, the patient was released against medical advice. Frank did not go home but remained in the city where he at once claimed the attention of the police. On being released after a few days in jail, he took a room at the best hotel and annoyed other guests by trying to borrow money, sponge on them for a meal, sell them something useless or nonexistent, etc. He became at times loudly boastful or rowdy and eventually fell on the floor drunk. He refused to pay for his room and resisted the management's attempts to remove him.

He sought loans under bold-faced pretenses, ran up debts without regard to the possibilities of payment, and telephoned and wrote to his family, threatening suicide unless his demands for money were promptly met. There are indications that he was not inactive during this period in old devices of petty thievery, shortchanging, and various types of fraud, sharp practice, and connivance that exist on the fringe more or less of organized but illegal racketeering found in any city.

Nothing, however, could be pinned on him by the law that led to his being effectively controlled. In all issues of this sort that arose, he had his record as a patient once legally committed and often confined to psychiatric institutions. This record was, in his ingenious hands, of considerable value as insurance against penal restraint.

After several arrests, the police began to call on the hospital to relieve them of their problems with this man. They were told that nothing could be done since he had been legally removed and the hospital was enjoined by the court not to hold him. Soon afterward the police and various local people began to seek advice on how to deal with him from the attorney who had liberated this man.

The patient himself soon joined in, coming repeatedly to the attorney's office or his house, sometimes drunk and always unreasonable, to shout about the injustices of the world, borrow money, evade threatening penalties, and to demand divers preposterous services. The veteran had promised to pay the attorney's bill with bonus money, but now it appeared that this money had already been squandered. Hoping to collect his fee and, no doubt, from humanitarian impulses, the attorney sought to keep in touch with his client. Those with whom he had run up bills, floated little loans, etc., joined others swindled or defrauded in small matters and took up their problems with the patient's legal representative. Soon the incessant complaints from annoyed people, the client's own nagging or uproarious invasions upon him at all hours, and the constant queries of the police drove him to seek relief. The patient being again in jail, the attorney persuaded him to agree to return to the hospital voluntarily and pled with the physician in charge to take him back, confessing himself at fault ever to have released such a scourge on the community and on himself.

Arrangements were made for readmission. The patient arrived in custody of a policeman. He was still somewhat stimulated from a recent intoxication but, though overbearing and pompous, showed no signs of real drunkenness nor of an officially recognized psychosis.

Frank took a high-handed manner, swaggered about, and finally refused to come back into the hospital, saying that he had no mental disease and that he preferred to return to jail where he would soon be released to carry out important business plans and social activities. He enjoyed the incident, played up his role dramatically, and took a peremptory and haughty tone with everyone.

He soon obtained his freedom, but some weeks later after running up big debts, giving several more bad checks, and participating in a series of senseless, bawdy escapades, he was finally returned to the hospital. Three months later he again obtained his discharge on a writ of habeas corpus but not through the same attorney. The story in its broad essentials was repeated.

Since his last admission, following the exploits just mentioned, he has been true to form. After varying periods on a closed ward, parole has been given; he has lost it repeatedly and gone back among "demented" and helpless groups with whom he is, to say the least, not at home. He has continued at all times free from the technical stigmata of psychosis, remaining crafty, intelligent, and superficially cooperative while trying to gain his ends.

Frank takes advantage of every opportunity to make trouble in the hospital and is rather restless and extremely dissatisfied. He sends frequent letters to women in town to whom he regards himself as paying court. These are written in a neat hand, well spelled, and well expressed and are much better letters than would be expected from a man of his education. They are marked with self-righteousness, extreme egotism, trite sentimentality, and monumental falsehood. His tone is that of a lover who regards his own passion as very high and rare.

"Only God knows," he writes, "why I wasn't left over there among the poppies with my heroic buddies," falsely describing himself as a captain in charge of 272 men. "My wife never understood me!" he complains in the same letter. What does he expect of her? The question invites meditation.

12

Anna

There was nothing spectacular about her, but when she came into the office you felt that she merited the attention she at once obtained. She was, you could say without straining a point, rather good-looking, but she was not nearly so good-looking as most women would have to be to make a comparable impression. She spoke in the crisp, fluttery cadence of the British, consistently sounding her "r's" and "ing's" and regularly saying "been" as they do in London. For a girl born and raised in Georgia, such speaking could suggest affectation. Yet it was the very opposite of this quality that contributed a great deal to the pleasing effect she invariably produced on those who met her. Naive has so many inapplicable connotations it is hardly the word to use in reference to this urbane and gracious presence, yet it is difficult to think of our first meeting without that very word coming to mind, with its overtones of freshness, artlessness, and candor.

She had passed her fortieth birthday some months before. Neither her face nor her figure had lost anything worth mentioning. Despite her composure, she gave a distinct impression of energy and playful spontaneity, an impression of vivid youth. In response to ordinary questions about her activities and interests she spoke of tennis, riding, and reading. More specific inquiry brought out opinions on Hamlet's essential conflict, comparison between the music of Brahms and the music of Shostakovitch, an impressive criticism of Schopenhauer's views on women, and several pertinent references to *The Brothers Karamazov*. She expressed opinions on current affairs that seemed to make excellent sense and talked with wit about the cyclic changes in feminine clothes and the implications of atomic physics for the future. What she had to say was particularly interesting and she said it in just the opposite of all those many ways of talking that people call "making conversation."

As discussion progressed, the picture of a rather remarkable woman became more and more distinct. Here was evidence of high intelligence and of considerable learning without discernible bookishness or consciousness of being "an intellectual." Her manner suggested wide interest, fresh and contagious enthusiasms, and a taste for living that reached out toward all healthy experience. Having a cup of coffee with her or weeding a garden would somehow take on a special quality of fun and delightfulness. Something about her over and beyond her looks prompted the estimate that she would be very likely to elicit romantic impulses, strong sensual inclinations, from most men who encountered her. Here, it seemed, was natural taste without a shadow of posed estheticism, urbanity without blunting of response to the simplest of joys, integrity and good ethical sense with the very opposite of everything that could be called priggish or smug. She showed nothing to suggest she meant to give such an impression or that she had any thought as to how she seemed.

Even with a detailed record of Anna's career clearly in mind, it was difficult indeed not to come to a conclusion that all the well-authenticated facts of that record should be ignored since they were so thoroughly contradicted by the obvious character of this appealing woman. The banal but nevertheless insistent thought that such a psychiatric history must apply to some other person was hard to dismiss. Prior to this interview a great deal of trustworthy information had been made available to me. Anna's mother and father had given her story at length. A reliable psychiatrist in whose small private hospital she had been treated on numerous occasions furnished not only an ordinary history but many details from his firsthand experience with her over the last twenty years. Her family physician had grown up in the same community with the patient and, through his personal acquaintance with her and her associates since childhood, had access to a remarkable amount of unusual information. He, as well as another medical practitioner who was also a relative, gave further details. Other sources of fact and opinion lay in several patients treated in the past whose relations with Anna at various periods of her life were significant. In the course of treatment, material had emerged in these other cases that rounded out her history and afforded additional means to evaluate her own reactions in interpersonal relations.

It is too much of a story to tell in a chapter or in a single book. And,

126

no matter how told, it could not be believed except by those who have already had experience over years with such patterns of behavior. Familiarity with a temporary cross section of such a life (as, for instance, during a single period of hospitalization), plus a generalized account of what preceded, would almost surely convince any psychiatrist of the diagnosis, but this would probably fail to give him the challenging sense of wonder, the awe that arises from a contemplation of the accumulated detail in its specific essence.

Her family first became aware that Anna had serious problems through the discovery of a boys' club in the local high school which, if not exactly founded in her honor, had at least been organized about her as the central figure. Comprised of ten or a dozen members in their early teens, a secret society in a sense, the group, like many Greek letter fraternities, had special phrases, symbolic signs, and countersigns. Encountering each other at the soda fountain or passing in the school corridor, two boys might slowly flex the fingers of their hands (so as to suggest a rounded aperture, possibly), leaving their arms dangling as if to veil slightly from alien observers a mystic communication.

Amid the chattering of groups over their chocolate sodas or hamburgers, certain phrases were thrown out stamped with idiom by the tone of voice and a special knowing quality in the accompanying glance. Small talk proceeded along lines common to pubertal groups. Baseball scores were predicted and estimates were voiced as to whether or not a certain girl would neck or pet or perhaps do a French kiss on the third date. The occasional gestures and the allusive words provoked curiosity among the uninitiated without actually revealing the secret content. Numerous small groups of boys, sometimes only three or four, sometimes more, banded by a common interest in postage stamps, firearms, a secret shack in the woods where they met to gamble, or in some other affair, often reserved for themselves a peculiar connotation in bits of familiar language or devised codes of slang, verbal, digital, and postural, to transmit among the elect understandings of special recognitions best reserved from the surrounding masses.

First and fundamentally, the comprehension of the entire adult world was glibly evaded by this communication system. In mixed gatherings, such as at dancing school, allusions could be made, say, to a half bottle of cheap liquor stored weeks ago in a hollow tree near the riverbank. This often evoked an arcane deviltry through which the girls could be teased but in which they could not fully mingle. Groping among confused and paradoxical concepts of virility, some boys could find stimulus (or protectiveness) in neologisms and fresh innuendos pertaining to the act of excretion and its subtle relationships to insult, sexuality, and infinite defilement.

Like dozens of other small, spontaneously forming and dissolving fraternities centered around interests that ranged from bird study to techniques of mutual masturbation, the group whose special interest lay in Anna did not for a while attract undue or sustained scrutiny from the adult world. The club had come into being after a discussion among several boys heretofore not particularly well acquainted with one another. Chat had veered desultorily from literal accounts of what they had done to certain girls to playful variations on the theme of personal insult by the versatile (and at times fantastic) use of strongly obscene words.

As every junior high school boy knows, this argot of double-talk can bring a stimulus of exaggeration into the simplest statement and at the same time literally indicate matters so grotesquely perverse that they probably lie beyond biologic experience. Though at times seized upon to express actual rage or contempt, even the most objectionable formulations are oftener used in amiable or even affectionate badinage and horseplay. The actual nouns and verbs, chiefly those of four letters (occasionally those of three or five), denote parts of the body involved in excretion and the genital organs of man and woman, and eliminative and sexual activities. Mingled in a sort of cloacal chaos, seasoned with qualifiers of coprophilic and more broadly scatologic significance, weirdly sadistic, rounded out with participial references to olfactory and other sensory outrages, this unprintable language is worn so smooth by continuous repetition among pubertal boys that even its more literal meaning often bypasses their awareness.

In calling this language unprintable I am not uncognizant of the fact that there is not one of the forbidden words which has not occasionally appeared in books and that all of them can be seen scrawled on the walls of latrines. These words, however, in isolation or in different contexts, cannot even hint at the terrible significance so obvious in the context of speech into which they are woven. Though some attention has, of course, been given by psychiatry to what is now being mentioned, it is an area that deserves further study.[82,100,235,256] The material is so highly charged that even in medical or in any other technical writing it cannot be handled freely. The actual discussion that led to the beginning of the club to which we are giving attention cannot be presented to the reader.

It is, of course, for one thing not directly accessible to me in full detail, although there is sufficient information to reconstruct a reliable approximation in concrete terms. The nature of Anna's behavior and experience in her relationship to the club can scarcely be conveyed by a generalization. From what material is available about this specific incident and with the aid of confirmatory detail gathered from the review of many similar situations, let us, as best we can (tentatively, but with sufficient evidence to give confidence that the approximation is in substance valid) attempt to reconstruct a little of the scene. Even a few bowdlerized and typical fragments may be helpful.

The boys had been hanging around together at a spot near the riverbank where they sometimes fished, talking in the sort of bull session that often arose.

"Butch, you sure ----ed me up on that algebra assignment last night."

"Aw ---- Jack, you ----ed yourself, you damn old horse's ---. Just because the prof wouldn't suck up all that bull ---- you tried to hand him, don't give me that kind of ----. The prof just up and ----ed on you. That's all there is to it. He ----ed on you good. Right in your eye."

"---- ----- to Prof. Blank! Why that ---- half ---sted ----sucker almost ------ed me out of a pass on the last test."

Another boy diverted this trend of conversation by claiming he got a piece of ---- from the colored woman who washed dishes at the Greek's hot dog stand, boasting that it was plenty good ----, and cost only fifty cents.

"---- on that old black ----." Butch commented disparagingly, "If you put a croker sack over her head I might give two bits for it." Thoughtfully he added, "Nigger ---- -----s too bad for me. You can have my share of that -----y stuff!"

Butch had been raising his .22 rifle to his shoulder from time to time as he talked, idly glancing down the sights as he aimed it at distant objects.

"Lemme see your gun a minute," Jack asked, impatiently stretching out his hand. When Butch signified refusal by silently shifting the rifle out of reach. Jack expressed mild vexation: "Well, stick the goddamned thing up your ---."

Bill, another one of the group, caught up the momentarily abandoned subject. "Some fellows say nigger women got the best damn ----- in the world." Bill referred to an ingenious method learned from his older cousin, now a grown man at college. The boy had overheard him and another man discussing their exploits of miscegenation. Bill had not yet had an opportunity to try the technique personally, but this he did not disclose. It involved the use of an old towel (a hole having been cut near the middle) and offered advantages worth knowing about. He went on to explain how you could, in this way, "--- it to 'em" with no bodily contact except that imperatively necessary and with minimal suggestions of intimacy. Jack laughed and expressed approval of the approach described by Bill, then tilted his head toward the boy with the rifle, shouting, "Reason old Butch talks so finicky is because he can't even get up a ----! Betcha a hundred dollars if all the ---- in the world was sprawled right there in front of him that ---- ------- couldn't even raise a ----!"

129

"You dirty ------ --- you," Butch answered, slightly irritated, "You're talking about your-----self. Everything you say goes back on yourself." Apparently feeling this was a little lame, he added quickly, "Bet old Jack ain't ever even ----off in his pants!"

"Maybe all he's done is just to ---- in 'em," Bill commented merrily. "Bet that's what old Butch would do if a girl had no better sense than to let him think she'd let him ---- her."

Turning now from this exchange of compliments, the boys offered bits of information and speculation about several girls with whom all had some acquaintance through classes, dancing school, or Sunday school.

"I understand Sue White's begun to put out a little ----," Bill said. "---- no!" Butch disagreed. "Sure would like to get myself a little of that ----. But Sue's a nice girl."

"Pete Green says he finger ---ed old fat ---ed Rita . . . ." Pausing a moment he continued listlessly, "Can't think of her last name. You know who I mean. Lives in the big house next to Sam Beech's uncle."

"Wouldn't be surprised," Butch agreed. "I dry ----ed her myself the second time I ever got her alone. On the other hand, you can't believe anything that damn mother ----ing --- ---- Green says," Butch added.

Feeling his enmity to Pete Green, who, a month or two ago, had made him back down with the threat of "slapping the living ----" out of him, Butch continued in unspoken thought. *Damn that Pete Green! If that ---- ---- ever tries to cross me up again I'll tell him I'll ---- his ---- mother up the --- ---- with a two by four and then ---- in his ---- face! That would shut him up, maybe!* Pete had intimidated Butch several times in the past. He knew he wouldn't dare to provoke a fight by talking to Pete in any such way, but it eased his feelings a little to think about it.

"Tell you what I'd like to try," Bill admitted, after a moment of silence, "is some of that ---- Anna Blank packs. Every day in Latin class I keep thinking I'll take a shot at it . . . but somehow with a girl like that . . . . . I just don't know . . . . ." Bill could not quite express what made him cautious. It was not only that her father and mother were rich and prominent and powerful in the community and her older brother strong enough to beat him half to death if anything, even about a try, was found out. It was more than that. Most of the girls you did these things to were sort of *from the other side of the tracks*. But by no means all of them were. You could get away with it lots of times with ones supposed to be real nice. Lots of goofy fellows still thought some of them *were* nice, Bill realized in an inexpressible wave of superiority and vague elation. Some poor damn ---- ----s would even marry them some day.

The sort of thin, ruthless exuberance that glowed in the boy screened an underlying stratum of personal insecurity probably common to all mankind and sometimes particularly disturbing at this age. He did not try to account for the triumphant feeling or to ask if it sprang chiefly from ideas of debasing the female or, perhaps even more, from the scornfully superior position he thus attained in fantasy to the other male. Thoughts of this sort did not enter Bill's consciousness, but factors influenced his feeling which, if he had understood them, might have produced such thoughts. By no means given to violence in action, this boy would not have inflicted physical injury on another. In imagination, as in the comic strips, all sorts of fatalities occur without anyone really getting hurt.

Still musing on Anna, Bill continued. "She sure is built, that girl! She's built just like a brick ---- house."

Butch and Jack, who had been looking slyly at each other, gave a low whistle almost simultaneously. Then they began to interchange a sort of chuckling that was half laughter and half teasing, designed to provoke curiosity in their companion. After a while Bill was told how easy it was to get ---- from Anna. Each of the other boys gave a detailed account of his own experiences, including one success by Jack in the storage room at school. These experiences were quite recent and until now had not been widely discussed by either Bill or Jack.

Each had, in fact, been surprised and, though this was not admitted, also shocked to discover that Anna was not a "nice girl." A confused disillusionment no doubt played some part in their present emphasis on the opposite evaluation of this girl who had, rather typically, represented the "sacred" (sexless) female in their thoughts. The fear of so honoring a female who turned out to be this other sort of thing loomed as a threat to one's own manhood. The untouchable priestess, once disclosed as an impostor, must be thoroughly defiled. Thus man sometimes seeks protection from confusion through which he himself risks the defilement of personally enshrining one who will make his virility (honor) the laughingstock of the group.

Fortified by this enlightenment, Butch partook of Anna's favors soon afterward. All of the boys found a special pleasure in talking together about their achievements. Soon a friend of these three was told about their source of pleasure, then another friend, and still another. At first each boy had gone alone, but as time passed it became more practical for several to visit Anna together. An appointment would be made by one of those interested. Anna, under the pretext of taking a walk or going to visit a friend would, without detection, make her way to a building situated on the other side of the large garden behind her house. Now used as a storehouse and garage, the building was originally a stable, and its former hayloft afforded reasonable privacy. The boys, by coming from another street through a hedge back of the garage, could make their way unnoticed to the rendezvous. Safe opportunities, though fairly frequent, were limited because the chauffeur was

131

sometimes in the garage. There were also days when the yard man worked nearby, or, rarely, Anna's brother might be there exercising with barbells and other gymnastic equipment he kept in another part of the building. This, no doubt, was a factor in the group's choice of coming together, particularly as its membership expanded. Of even more importance, perhaps, was a specific satisfaction found by some in entering upon the venture together. The closely shared experience seemed to enhance the pleasures of club conversation when they gathered later to talk over what happened.

After chapel in the morning it was customary for the captain of the baseball team, the chairman of the debating club, and others interested in extracurricular activities occasionally to announce plans for meetings of their various groups. One morning, in response to a dare by other club members, Jack came forward and in a bold voice called out: "At the beginning of lunch hour there'll be a meeting of the *Animal Crackers* in Room 49." There was a scatter of giggling and some random speculation on the part of a few teachers, but no official inquiry about the club was made and no adult thought of any play on Anna's name or caught improper innuendos.

The existence of the club and their daughter's undesirable situation was finally brought to the attention of Anna's parents through its effect on another person.

Among the older boys who had been attracted by Anna was one who had apparently turned to her in the utmost seriousness. All accessible information indicates that this boy fell in love with Anna not by a trival attraction but with all the vividness and lifeshaking stir that the first complete and genuine experience of this sort can bring to an earnest young man almost ready for college. The younger girl, suddenly having become mature in body, loomed like something never seen before upon his awareness. There is reason to believe that he was determined to marry her and resolved to be scrupulously faithful through all the years he must wait for this. There is nothing to suggest he did not seek her with strongly passionate physical desire, but apparently his idealization of her and fear of arousing even further impulses, which it would have been for him a desecration to fulfill under these conditions, caused him to treat her, if not like an untouchable goddess, at least with extraordinary restraint. Anna, it seems, behaved in such a way that he was sure she reciprocated his feelings not only in kind but also in degree.

Reports as to how he discovered the relations of Anna with the club are somewhat conflicting. It is almost impossible to believe that fortune was so unkind as to have him blunder upon an actual meeting of this group with the customary activities in progress. So it is said to have happened. At any rate, he received enlightenment in such a convincing way that the impact was sudden and trenchant.

In his immediately subsequent state, rumored to be a "nervous break-down" at the time, his family physician, after considerable difficulty, seems to have obtained some idea of what he had experienced. Being a relative of Anna's mother and a boldly conscientious man, he felt that the situation demanded attention and disclosed something of it to her parents.

Insofar as the complicated and seldom obvious attitudes that enter into the administration of parental authority and guidance on such an occasion can be evaluated, it seems that this girl's father and mother avoided the typical mistakes that might have been made. Neither attempted to conceal the humiliation and distress brought upon them by such conduct. After adequate frankness about their reaction to the conduct itself, they tried to avoid rubbing it in by moralizing reiteration. A decision was made for Anna to be sent at once to a fine boarding school in a distant state. Apparently feeling that the daughter could not fail to be critically traumatized by realizations that withered them with pain and shame, Anna's mother and father tried, as some people are able to do after losing eye-sight or a first child, to accept what has happened without evasion but nevertheless to turn with all resolution available to what is ahead and not to stir what is tragic or hideous, but now past and unmodifiable. There does not seem to have been gross error in glossing over what had taken place or minimizing the possible consequences. Both parents tried to support Anna by emphasizing opportunities in the future and by their knowledge that in the process of growing up it is not uncommon for people to make mistakes that in the adult world would be fatal.

Anna's apparent reactions were such as to enable all the family to be entirely sincere in showing her their continued confidence, their respect, and their love. In choosing a fine private school with high academic standards, she seemed to be showing her serious intentions about the future. Her keen interest in choosing clothes, her care in getting exactly the right sort of cur-tains for the dormitory room might have suggested to some almost too easy and quick a recovery from the fell blow she was thought to have suffered, but at the time this seemed instead a fit and appealing veil of insouciance that she bravely, if not almost heroically, pulled about her to conceal with stoic and patrician grace the terrible trauma her spirit had sustained. Even in the short period of time before she left for the East, Anna's outwardly blithe air that she displayed when she joked and laughed with friends who came by (her ability to seem blandly preoccupied in getting the new jazz records and those popular dancing slippers that the shop was expecting any day now) provoked fleeting but ominous thoughts in the family that such poise, considering the full circumstances, might be a little excessive.

Excellent reports on Anna came for several months from the distant school. She was doing well in her studies and already she had won a place on the swimming team. She seemed also to have found herself almost at once in the warm affection of teachers and students. One teacher, in a letter to her mother, spoke of Anna's "unusual promise in English" and of her "surprising maturity of outlook." Anna's own letters, though few, were warm with expressions of devotion that seemed to follow the inimitable idiom of sincerity.

In these letters she sometimes mentioned her conviction that she knew of no way to express her gratitude except to show by her own conduct that she did deserve the trust her mother and father had shown in her and the support of their love and understanding. No happiness could mean more than that she would find in making them feel they could be proud of her again.

Such letters were building up in these parents an encouragement they sorely needed and offering (as an anodyne for their anguish and humiliation) increasing hope that as parents they had not, perhaps, failed their daughter utterly. Meanwhile, reports began to come from the school which seriously disquieted them.

Anna had apparently broken a number of rules, most of them involving minor issues, it is true. She had twice been caught smoking with several other girls; she had four times stayed out considerably beyond hours; she had cut several classes; she had spoken disrespectfully to a teacher. But, after all, such misdemeanors often indicate a healthy sort of growing up and her parents were anxious to avoid forcing Anna into a rigid pharasiacal propriety as compensation for her terrible error.

When a final decision was reached that Anna could not be kept at school, a good many more serious symptoms had come to light. Several petty thieveries (at first assumed to be absentminded borrowings), flagrant but ingenious cheating in laboratory work, calm lies about matters that were accepted as points of honor—all of this added up to make her expulsion imperative.

At the half dozen or more subsequent schools attended by Anna, she often seemed to have changed, and for varying periods her family's hope was high. Her behavior at each place fell into similar but not identical patterns. Like the persisting theme in a complicated work of music, her actions took diverse courses but came always to an identical point, which for her was failure. A Brahms concerto may spread and range, with woodwinds at one phase carrying the movement and, a little later, the violins manifesting something of another sort or the piano (as if in reply to the orchestra) weaving a fresh subject into the manifold skein; so through her history appeared episodes of variety and genuine novelty, all contributing to a design of impressive versatility but leading to an inevitable conclusion.

Once or twice Anna completed the entire year, but nearly always each new institution found itself unable to handle her after a few months. Sometimes she worked steadily during the summer and easily completed courses she had missed in her numerous shiftings about. Perhaps on the basis of an excellent performance on the entrance examination, she gained admission to a distinguished college for women and, after being expelled, briefly attended a smaller college and two state universities. On other occasions she undertook training in business school, in hospitals (nursing, x-ray technician, etc.), and welfare work. She often expressed spontaneously a lively interest in this or that career and worked out her plans with good judgment, but, after widely varying periods during which she applied herself, she regularly ended by quitting voluntarily or being dismissed.

When Anna sought some new job with which to occupy herself or to enter some course of training, she seemed to have no hesitation in giving as references those who had no choice except to describe her as entirely unreliable and unfit for what she planned. Sometimes the reason for her failures seemed not to lie so much in antisocial or spectacularly improper acts as in other maladaptations. A few excerpts from a letter follow:

Mrs. Anna _____ has requested that we write you in regard to her work as a student in our School for Roentgenological Technicians . . . . Because of her irregularity in attendance she lacked fourteen weeks of the period required in our course . . . . It was necessary to admonish this student on several occasions because of her poor work . . . She repeatedly made mistakes, the seriousness of which seemed not to concern her in the least . . . . Similar complaints were handed in against her by several instructors. The mistakes were never made through lack of intelligence . . . but apparently from disregard of consequences or some type of distraction . . . . She was put on probation, twice for avoidable and grave mistakes, and once for her attendance record . . . . On being threatened with dismissal because of her apparent disinterest, she, for a while, regularly demonstrated her fine ability, [etc.] . . . . This student, we are compelled to say, was a definitely dangerous worker to have around roentgenological apparatus. It became necessary to watch her carefully. She could not be trusted to carry out things on her own responsibility . . . . When told of her failings, she always showed amazement and disbelief that she could possibly be doing anything wrong. She appeared to be sincere in such reactions . . . . I find it impossible to recommend this person for work along these lines . . . . I am convinced that her performance would be detrimental to the profession or to any group for which she might work . . . . We

135

regret that it is necessary to submit so unfavorable a report . . . . This letter is written in response to her request. . . . .

Among the almost limitless accumulation of incidents that loom in a retrospective glance at her career, only a few can be given here, and these in the utmost brevity.

From one prep school she was dismissed though standing high in her classes after it was proved she had placed a half dozen or more rubber condoms so that these useful items would become unmistakably evident when several couples seated themselves on the two sofas that flanked the fireplace. Here, almost directly under chaperoning eyes, the younger pupils not yet given permission to go out with their boyfriends had circumspect dates on certain evenings. No sudden scurrying of mice could have evoked more hearty squeals or such quick explosive male laughter than the magiclike appearance of these unmistakable objects, some neatly rolled, others generously stuffed. Had only one or perhaps even two of the condoms emerged inconspicuously into view as the soft cushions shifted with the seating of couples, it might have been possible for an alert girl, or perhaps even for one of the self-conscious and preoccupied boys, to cover it and hide it away before general attention was aroused.

Anna, it seems, had given some thought to this. Perhaps with time and retelling, some exaggeration has colored the event. It is said that an elastic band was set to snap one condom boldly forth and that others were placed so they would slip down from under the knitted antimacassars. At any rate, Anna made certain of a conspicuous display. Struck almost witless by the magic appearance of such an object in her lap (whence it had dropped from the top of the sofa), one girl released the initial squeal. Such uproar ensued automatically that hastening chaperones missed little of the scene.

On numerous occasions Anna made difficulties for herself by driving off in cars that belonged to teachers or other school employees. Only once, or possibly twice, during her teens does it appear she had serious intentions of stealing the car for permanent possession. On the other hand, there were periods when she frequently stole underwear, stockings, and ornaments (usually inexpensive costume pieces or club pins) from other students and even from those in authority.

While at the university, for a time she fell into the sporadic practice of relieving her dates of small amounts of cash she discovered in their pockets during heavy petting. Under such circumstances she also, but more rarely, took a pocketknife or a bunch of keys. At one finishing school where personal dignity among the faculty was emphasized, she is said to have lost her place as a student by neatly lettering on the door of the office of the sedate Latin instructress a concise advertisement.

Hot p_____ available here—cheap!

After making good grades in a well-known college and having been in no serious trouble for several months, she began lying in bed too late to attend her early classes. Interviews with the college physician, and eventually with a psychiatrist, followed. After several warnings and probationary measures, and just in time to avoid expulsion, she began to attend all classes again.

During an interval in which she had no further trouble with the faculty, Anna alienated and outraged several girls in the dormitory with whom she had been very friendly. After a few bottles of beer which the group had shared, she entered the rooms occupied by two of these friends and, in their absence, urinated on several evening dresses which they highly valued. (After the act she refolded the dresses neatly and put them back, sodden and malodorous, in the drawers.) It was a number of days before evidence emerged that unmistakably connected Anna with this deed.

Observations which in themselves were highly suggestive but not final proof were for a while withheld by those who could not bring themselves to believe Anna capable of such behavior. She easily denied such a possibility to several who spoke with her separately in the hope of finding facts that would exonerate her. She also fabricated evidence to establish her innocence so calmly and so freely that it carried almost axiomatic conviction. On being confronted with plain proof from several sources, she was able to smile off the affair and dismiss it as a whimsical prank. Some felt it was their responsibility as a group to report this incident, but so much was brought out in Anna's behalf that all finally agreed to let the affair go no further.

Merely tabulating these and many other details of Anna's behavior tends to suggest rather easily formulated motivations. With a more complete story these appear less likely. If a good many of the stealing incidents are isolated, some would no doubt be inclined to interpret them as ordinary compulsive reactions. On the other hand, personal contact with her does not give the impression of an underlying anxiety or of any strong drive against which she struggles or which she would like to reject. In addition to taking things for which she has little or no need (and which might symbolize some ordinary unconscious aim), she also steals in response to a real though mild desire to possess or for convenience.* With a more inclusive view of her activi-

---

*See p. 272 for further discussion of these points, particularly of the contrast between "compulsive" and "impulsive" symptoms.

ties the thefts become more difficult to account for satisfactorily by the specific and familiar theories of compulsion. They, like so many of her other symptoms, seem part of a different and far less circumscribed psychopathology.

Concentrating on the long record of her outlandish sexual promiscuity (some of which will soon be given), the most naive observer would perhaps think of "nymphomania" or at least of very powerful erotic drives. Others might surmise that she is and has always been a genitally frigid (or partially frigid) woman who finds stimulation but never orgasm (or only a clitoral response) and who is driven more or less consciously to all sorts of indiscretions in a never-ending quest. Neither of these hypotheses seems to account for Anna's behavior when one becomes familiar with more evidence pertaining to her inner experiences.

Anyone's real inner experience is, of course, difficult to arrive at even by conjecture and perhaps impossible to establish by proof. In a person so accomplished in devising falsehoods on any subject and in making them so convincing, Anna's own statements can hardly be taken as necessarily true. There seems, indeed, but one way (and this one obviously not permissible) to discover directly a lady's physical reactions to intercourse; and even then she can, it is said by some, often be misleading if she so wishes. Despite these difficulties, a rather convincing impression emerges that Anna's sexual problem is very different and far more complicated than anything that has been mentioned.

It seems likely that she has frequently experienced the physiologic reactions of orgasm but that these reactions have been a minor factor in her behavior pattern. Sometimes, while having technically satisfactory relations with a husband, she would continue intercourse with other men who, it seems, failed entirely to arouse or to gratify her in the usual sense. As a matter of fact, while living with the husband who, more regularly than any other man she can recall, made her "respond," she initiated and continued relations with several other men. From some of these she neither particularly wanted nor ever received pleasure that could be called sensual or romantic.

Although such conclusions are necessarily speculative (as they are, indeed, about any patient) and not scientifically verifiable, it seems most probable that this woman has somewhat less than ordinary conscious sexual motivation and that the most significant feature of her sexual experience is that, despite frequent mechanical responses, it has meant so little to her. The localized sensory reaction has not been greatly valued nor has it seemed to play a dominant role in directing her conduct. Anatomic intimacy with man has never been associated with interpersonal relationships of any consequence or duration. Important as this fact may be (granting that our estimate is in some measure correct), it still does not offer a circumscribed area in which a final explanation for Anna's career can be readily drawn. In every other aspect of social experience also this woman has similarly failed to develop any sort of relationship with another human being that seemed to have much meaning for her or, to put it another way, that could influence her to any consistent, obviously purposive behavior.

It is true indeed that this casual or "cheap" use of physical sexuality often appears to be a confused sort of vengeful or self-destructive response to hurt and rejection or to misleading essential concepts of "male" and "female."[170] The pattern followed sometimes suggests that such behavior may represent (with varying degrees of awareness in the subject) a "throwing of oneself away." It may at the same time seem to return a hurt and symbolize a protest too profound and too complicated for words.*Anna's sexual behavior and her generalized self-destructiveness (at social and personal levels) might be interpreted on such a basis. Let us remember, however, that such an interpretation is speculative. Let us refrain from projecting items of psychiatric theory into Anna's unconscious and from assuming that they constitute evidence of emotional reactions in infancy that have shaped her subsequent course and by which we can confidently explain her career. Perhaps, some might say, serious and subtle traumatic events unknown to herself and others, even during the first year of her life or later, planted the seeds of a profound (unconscious) conflict which she has been forced to act out in this malignant pattern. No real evidence of this, however, has emerged in the study of her case.

We may also consider the possibility that such a person as Anna might be born with a subtle and specific biologic defect. Perhaps, despite a high capacity for intelligence and charm, something necessary for wisdom or for sincere and major human feelings was left out or incomplete in her development. Capacities very different and much simpler are incomplete in the person born with color blindness or with a spastic deficiency in the motor system. Such biologic deficiencies are not necessarily hereditary. Let us assume that a defect in development may leave such a person as Anna without the capacity to attain deep loyalty or genuine love or to adequately recognize and react to the major goals and values of human life. The lack of major satisfactions and aspirations and the freedom from serious scruples or remorse might leave such a person free to act out any whim of folly or rebellion and offer some explanation for such a career as Anna's.

At 40 years of age, during our first interview, Anna absentmindedly

---

*See pp. 288 to 302.

checked the preliminary information blank to indicate her status as divorced. She spontaneously changed the pencil mark to show that she was married. As a matter of fact, Anna's current marriage had lasted a good many years. It is true her husband was such in name only, but he served a practical purpose. The couple had not seen each other or otherwise communicated since shortly after the nuptials, but the legal existence of this union deterred Anna in one aspect of her behavior that had formerly given considerable trouble to her family and their attorneys.

Before her last wedding and over a long period, she had fallen into the habit of marrying on an impulse apparently as trivial as what might lead another woman to buy a new hat. With one man after another she casually completed the legal ceremonies and entered into this monumental contract, the groom being now an adventurous taxi driver, now an opportunistic bar companion, or, again, a delinquent idler she encountered in her welfare work.

The succession of divorces and the repeated financial settlements demanded by vagrants and petty rascals she had on several occasions espoused threatened the family resources. Gratifyingly (and in contrast with some other cases of similar illness), Anna's marriage series was halted by the prospect of legal bigamy.

The husbands of this series were not (or certainly not usually) men who took the bride very seriously. This cannot be said of her earlier husbands, two of whom were distinguished and wealthy men and, according to the evidence, genuinely and deeply in love with Anna. With one of these, an architect of international repute, she lived for a while in England. To him and almost simultaneously to his wayward brother Anna is said to have given gonorrhea which, as the first year of marriage drew to a close, she inadvertently picked up from a sychophantic interior decorator, a person, according to report, more active homosexually than otherwise.

I entertain some skepticism about the details of this episode. Such an extravagant and perfectly timed series of events scarcely seems possible. Though usually ready to deny anything inconsistent with chaste and honorable behavior, this patient has in other moods seemed to relish adding fanciful touches to the already spectacular reality. Her promiscuity has, however, been so lavish that coincidences almost impossible in a hundred other lives combined hardly seem unlikely in hers. There is little doubt that she was sufficiently unfaithful for this or something equally bizarre to have befallen the husband.

On being detected in activities that would produce fear, shame, or consternation in others, this patient often showed simple insouciance. Once at college she did so well for so long that hope returned to her family. Ap-

140

parently she had found herself at last. After a succession of excellent reports, one showing failures in four subjects appeared. Anna was called on long-distance telephone by her father, who wanted to lose no time in trying to find some remedy for the trouble.

Her easy, happy laughter relieved him deeply, even before she had time to go on and explain the mistake that had been made in the dean's office. She had just heard of it but had not realized the rather comical error had been transmitted to any report that reached him and her mother. Actually she had not realized it was quite time for these reports to be mailed out. She had been, you see, pretty busy—but "mighty happy," too. Warmed within and deeply reassured, he left the telephone completely at ease.

Within a few days, sure enough, there came official acknowledgment of the mistake. The grades of another girl had been confused with those of his daughter. The true report was even better than those excellent ones that had been coming regularly now for months. The dean's signed name and the official school paper and forms would have dispelled any suspicions of fraud had suspicions arisen. Anna's tone and manner when she spoke over the telephone were such, however, that no doubt at all seemed justified.

Soon truly disturbing information came from the school. Not only was Anna failing dismally in all studies, but serious misconduct had brought the question of her expulsion to a crucial point. Wiring his daughter that he was taking the first train, the father also instructed her to make appointments for him with the college authorities.

On arriving he found that no appointments had been made. He was entirely unexpected. He was surprised, furthermore, to find that Anna had left for the weekend, after convincing the house mother that she had parental permission to visit an imaginary aunt. Apparently she typed letters and forged signatures to bring off this deception with cleverness comparable to that employed in getting the school stationery and report forms and successfully utilizing these to send back the false reports to her family.

On her return after the weekend she seemed surprised to find her father still there and at first expressed vexation with him. He never learned just what misadventures befell his daughter, who had apparently roamed about in a large city nearby. She took all the discussion of her recent acts with equanimity, apologized for her mistakes, and admitted that it was quite inexpedient to bring off such deceptions when it was apparent to her they would certainly and promptly be discovered. She said she did not know precisely why she had acted in such a plainly injudicious way, but she never seemed curious or really concerned about the possibility of discovering a reason for the behavior.

What would have happened to this patient had it not been for the extraordinarily ample estate of her family and for their persistent care? One can only speculate. We need not here estimate how many times she was released from jails in widely scattered cities by their efforts, how many times she was hospitalized, how many beginnings with psychotherapy were made by various experts. It is interesting to note that Anna, like so many whose conduct closely resembles hers in other respects, seems never to have committed a major felony or tried to do serious physical injury to another.

It is true that she was badly beaten up in some sort of night spot brawl in St. Louis. On this occasion several of her ribs were fractured, and a lung was punctured; her brother, who flew to her aid from Baltimore, thought at first her injuries would prove fatal. Though occasionally, when drinking, she has taken an active part in slapping or hair-pulling incidents, she has shown little inclination to attack. In similar episodes she rarely initiated gross vocal disputes or was vulgarly aggressive with words. Calmness seemed more characteristic of her than high temper, although it is recorded that in her teens she was expelled from one academy for publicly telling off a school authority in a speech vehemently and versatilely obscene and closing with references anything but flattering to the state of his "third leg."

Many of these incidents which in isolation appear spectacular occurred while Anna passed in the community as a reliable, conforming, and extraordinarily attractive woman. Much of the time she seemed poised, polite, and a paragon of happy behavior. For a while during her early twenties she taught a Sunday school class. Her teachings were ethically admirable and she gave a strong impression of sincerity. She often worked for a month or more at a time, efficiently and with what seemed pleasure, at the Red Cross and in other welfare activities. Most who knew her casually in these endeavors would have been genuinely astonished to learn that she had any serious personality problem.

Once while hospitalized for a week or ten days, she left the almost universal impression of being a delightful patient. Courteous, composed, undemanding, and cheerful, she took discomforts and minor pains in a way that elicited admiration. During this brief period, in which a benign nodule was surgically removed from her breast, she casually accepted cunnilingual attentions from a female attendant (apparently a true lesbian) and also sought to entice an intern. In these enticements she went so far as to get the fly of his trousers open before accepting his determination to refrain.

Occasionally during her early thirties, but also a few times since, Anna had engaged in a pastime known in some circles as *gangbanging*. There were minor variations of procedure. Usually drinks with five or six men, whom she might pick up in one of the less inviting honky-tonks or frolic spots about town, constituted the first phase. Later the group rode out into the country and all her companions had sexual relations with her, each taking his turn. On such an exploit, argument once arose about whether or not she had stolen a cigarette lighter belonging to an escort, and the group, uniting against her, threw Anna in a creek and then drove off, leaving her to walk home.

This patient spent a good deal of time reading. In contrast to many psychopaths who readily claim all sorts of entirely imaginary learning, she showed considerable familiarity with literature of many sorts. She seemed to read Shakespearean plays, the major Russian novels, pulp magazines, and comic books with about the same degree of interest. Her factual knowledge about what she had read seemed good, though it must be admitted she often falsified with assurance when questions led her into unknown areas.

She played complicated music on the piano with fine technical skill and spent a good deal of time doing so. She had an accurate acquaintance with current scales of intellectual and esthetic fashion and could probably have avoided offense even to the most snide of editors of the most avant-garde of little magazines. How she reacted to such matters in the innermost and final chamber of her being can only be surmised. My impression is that *King Lear* and *Amazing Confessions* elicited responses in no fundamental way different.

There is little I can offer in explanation for the biologic enigma I trust is apparent. Despite abundant time to approach the patient directly, unusually rich detail furnished by others, and even the rare chance of treating psychiatrically more than one other upon whose life her own had impinged traumatically (and, so it would almost seem, of seeing her through more than one set of eyes), despite all this, I cannot reveal the forces that patterned her. I have opinions, but opinions are not facts.

Without claiming there is anything demonstrable or profoundly explanatory in such an appraisal, I would give these impressions. It is unlikely that she experienced (in what can reasonably be called ordinary awareness) much of the emotion that we associate with the various deeds she has carried out. In both quantity and quality her emotions, I believe, have regularly fallen short of the affect we almost automatically assume must prompt, accompany, or follow such actions as hers. I will not say that Anna never loved or hated or suffered. I think there was a time when she probably did all of these precociously and beyond ordinary degree. All that, however, is beyond an iron curtain. On this side of the curtain, though she had vexations and minor satisfactions and though she could at times get mad and could be a little fond of people, Anna never really seems to have meant much harm to others or to herself.

One of the physicians who had often treated her expressed his bewilderment about how real seemed her disregard of what was obvious, how strangely she escaped the subjective consequences of her experiences. Taking a phrase from the Russian novel about prostitution, *Yama,* to embody his reaction, he said, "All the horror is in just this—that there is no horror."*

A thoughtful and now elderly member of her family whose advice her parents and one of her early husbands had often sought was particularly impressed with what he described as an unbelievable but somehow authentic innocence that Anna never seemed to lose. Experiences which would harden an ordinary person conspicuously or ensure a conscious cynicism, mordant and profound, seem to fall lightly on her spirit, to leave her surprisingly serene. The person just mentioned, after more than two decades of concern with her problems, finds even more surprising than all the unfortunate acts combined, Anna's thoughtless assumption that she is to be trusted in all matters, that her behavior has been essentially honorable and ladylike, and the fact that her self-respect is apparently bright and unblemished.

Seeking to give his impression of this strange equanimity, of these paradoxical attributes of innocence, he once quoted:

> She hath wasted with fire thine high places,
> She hath hidden and marred and made sad
> The fair limbs of the Loves, the fair faces
> Of gods that were goodly and glad.
> She slays, and her hands are not bloody;
> She moves as a moon in the wane,
> White-robed, and thy raiment is ruddy,
> Our Lady of Pain.†

---

*From Kuprin, Alexandre: Yama (translated by Bernard Guilbert Guerney), New York, 1929, The Modern Library.
†From Swinburne, A. C.: Dolores. In Selected poems of Algernon Charles Swinburne, New York, 1928, Dodd, Mead & Co., Inc.

13

Jack

My prolonged acquaintance with our next subject began on the occasion of his return for a fourth period of hospitalization. He was accompanied by the sheriff who had brought him from jail in Winston-Salem, N. C. He was affable and courteous, entirely rational in his conversation. Though rather carelessly dressed, he made an imposing figure of a man; he was 6 feet, 3 inches tall, weighed 210 pounds, had red hair, blue eyes, a quick, humorous glance, and a disarming smile. Though 45 years of age, he appeared to be in the early thirties. His body retained good athletic lines, and he sat or stood with an easy poise.

Jack gave no impression of evasiveness but, on the contrary, seemed rich in understanding and serious in his desire to be helped. He admitted that he had been a periodic drinker for many years, stating that he worried about his life and drank to forget; he described fleeting alcoholic hallucinations which he said he had occasionally experienced. "I once thought there was a 6-foot porpoise in bed with me all night. I have seen a little man no bigger than your finger standing at the window talking to me. One night cats came with heads like lions, also lions with heads like cats." He was perfectly aware that these manifestations were unreal and attributed them to the effects of alcohol, expressing amusement at their absurdity.

As a matter of fact, it is doubtful if these hallucinatory experiences were real. After knowing him better, it seemed likely to me that he had made up these stories, thinking they would help him gain admittance to the hospital. Any difficulties aside from that of merely drinking excessively he denied, emphatically but good-humoredly dismissing all such questions as obviously inapplicable to a man like himself.

He is a man from an urban community, of a family, though not particularly distinguished or wealthy, generally regarded as gentlefolk. The details of his childhood are not known except from his own account. He got along satisfactorily in his studies, completed high school, and decided not to go to college but began to work. He first obtained a minor position in a bookstore, changed to various other clerical employments, and then took up engineering. He had begun to drink a little when 17 years of age but, according to his own report, did not go on serious sprees until in his early twenties.

Although Jack changed about rapidly and lost many positions, he apparently found it rather easy to succeed, once earning a large income as assistant city engineer. Evidently he had at this stage already begun to cause trouble. His relatives, most of whom had much less income than the patient, were called upon frequently to pay him out of debt, to exert influence on his employers, and occasionally to get him out of jail. His work was sporadic and frequently interrupted by protracted bouts of drinking or by sudden trips to other towns during which he lost large sums gambling, ran up debts buying things for which he had little use, borrowed heavily from old friends, now and then forged or otherwise defrauded, and often fell into the hands of the police. His confident, reassuring manner and his easy way with people went far to make up for his lack of reliability or any serious, sustained interest in his work.

His relations with women have always been casual. He had frequent sexual experiences but failed to develop any lasting attachment. He contracted syphilis in the early twenties, received intensive treatment, and was apparently cured. During the war he was promoted to the rank of sergeant and had the misfortune to contract gonorrhea.

Though genial, talkative, and a splendid mixer when sober, he did not choose to do his drinking in convivial surroundings. Whether he started alone or with others, he would on occasions continue to drink day after day, keeping himself in a sodden, maudlin, or highly irritable state, more or less barricaded in some cheap hotel room or brothel until succored by his friends or relatives or arrested as a nuisance by the police. Sometimes, after being primed with a few drinks, he would hire a Negro boy to drive him out into the country where, having brought along a supply of raw corn whiskey, he would alternately drink in sullen fits or lie snoring and semistuporous among the weeds. His stock being at last exhausted, the boy would faithfully bring him into town and throw him on the mercy of hard-taxed friends or relatives.

One can but imagine the young Negro as he would sit hour after hour, sometimes day after day, in solemn attendance on his *white gentleman,* watching the latter crash stumbling about the bushes, lie semicomatose, breathing stertorously in the underbrush, or come lurching again up to the automobile, muttering a demand for more liquor. It is easy to imagine the naive face remotely amused but never entirely free from awe and wonder as he listens to his temporary employer blubbering and raving in meaningless syllables of despair or waking echoes from lonely pinelands with his inane curses. What can he make of his nonsensical melodrama in which he is called on to play his inconspicuous but necessary part? He has been taught that the white man is *boss* and that his ways are marked out by wisdom. The white man has money and influential friends and seems to be free from penalty for his folly. Yet this young and inexperienced Negro is humorous. Though mystified as we all are by these happenings, he cannot but smile as he contemplates the ways of this world.

As years went on, this man's conduct became worse. No matter how hard Jack's relatives worked to obtain positions for him, he lost them within a week or ten days, sometimes through drinking, sometimes through simple, gross neglect without the benefit of drink. Other jobs he lost by haughtily dressing down an employer, by overcharging customers and pocketing the gain, by engaging in petty rackets and illegal schemes to defraud, or by various additional misdemeanors and delinquencies.

He was sent several times to take whiskey cures at various private sanitoriums and was also hospitalized for short periods in psychiatric institutions and once at a state mental hospital. He was always found "sane and competent" and discharged after a short period.

In time he became an all but unbearable burden on the other members of his family. The oldest brother, vice-president of a local bank, another brother successful in business, a married sister in good circumstances, and another sister unmarried but financially independent and prominent in club work all strove to their utmost to help him. The task of supporting him was but a small part of their problem. If kept in the house by any of his family, he persisted in his overbearing, riotous ways, proved unmanageable, and disorganized the entire household. Sometimes he took silver or other valuable objects belonging to a sister or a brother and pawned or sold them. He seemed unable to feel that there was need to make restitution. If he boarded outside, he shortly fell into the hands of the police, usually after incurring debts and behaving in such a way as to involve all concerned with him in great embarrassment and difficulty.

During observation at the hospital he was always alert and polite, free from any suggestion of delusions or hallucinations. He impressed his exam-

147

iners as being very open and frank. He admitted that he had never realized the seriousness of his problems until recently. He took a lively interest in his surroundings, showed excellent reasoning power at all times, and seemed eager to take advantage of his treatment in the hospital in order to gain a fresh outlook with the earnest intention of leading a happier and more successful life in the future. His memory was excellent; he was nearly always in good spirits, energetic, affable, and fond of company. The Wassermann blood test was negative, as were spinal fluid Wassermann and colloidal gold tests. Neurologic and psychiatric examinations were entirely negative. The medical staff, after six weeks of study, considered him sane and competent, granted him parole of the grounds, and recommended discharge after a short time.

Jack remained on parole for about two months without getting into serious difficulty. His family, citing his long record of maladjustment, asked that he be kept in the hospital until the staff was "sure he had become normal." He began at this stage to grow impatient about leaving, insisting that he was now able to go out and live a satisfactory life and that there was no reason for him to be kept longer. Indeed, on the basis of his appearance then one would have been at a loss to find even the flimsiest excuse for holding him.

After considerable correspondence his relatives agreed to his returning home. In the meantime, they had been busy removing obstacles that might lie in the way of his readjustment. A good position had been found, one offering easy hours, congenial work, an excellent salary, and opportunity for advancement. Attractive quarters were being prepared where he could live under the supervision of his relatives until he got established. His brothers and sisters all showed themselves not only eager to help him but extraordinarily aware of subtle subjective difficulties that lay ahead and always tactful to spare him the humiliation that one might think inevitable in his situation. They were as anxious not to embarrass him and to avoid any appearance of meddling as to give encouragement and support. His future seemed certainly to offer a maximum of security against all the factors that lead men to fail.

These encouraging developments were explained to the patient. He admitted himself pleased but his manner did not imply feelings proportionate to his good fortune. In fact, he seemed to take things somewhat as a matter of course. His restless impatience to go out at once was not assuaged by preparations for him to leave within seventy-two hours. The money to pay for his transportation had already been received and he knew this. He pressed his demand to leave at once although he knew that the brief delay was requested by his relatives in order to prepare things to his own advantage. On being told that he could not leave immediately, he insisted on having a pass to go into town for a few hours, stating that he had to buy a hat, some shoes, and a few other things before going home.

A man considered sane and plainly of superior intelligence could scarcely seem to be in danger of doing anything at this stage of events to interfere with the plans devised for his rehabilitation. His physician, nevertheless, had a long talk with him, reviewing his history, trying to exert a helpful influence, to focus his attention on possible dangers, and to review with him his plans and resolutions.

Superficially Jack did not appear to need help. Laughing, he stated that he would scarcely be such a fool as to throw away the freedom that now awaited him after all these months of unhappy confinement. He knew perfectly well why it had been necessary for him to come to the hospital. He said he realized clearly that if he took a drink his family would not take him back, that it would be necessary for him to begin all over again the weary, distasteful life on closed wards among "insane" men. With quick reassurances he stated that he did not even feel an inclination to drink but admitted that he knew, from his former experiences, if he took even one he might take too much. He had learned his lesson, he said, smiling confidently. The impression of excellent insight, of a steadfast determination to avoid any setback in his new career, was perfect—a little too perfect perhaps. His own confidence in himself was too quick, too easy, and too sure. He gave all the right answers with a glibness that, had he not been so polite, might have suggested a slight impatience. He used all the words that a man would use who understood and appreciated the miserable folly that lay behind him and meant to have done with it.

He was given a pass and left the hospital smiling, well dressed, his head high with confidence, his firm promise to return after a few hours given in ringing tones of conviction. Nothing further was heard from him until the next morning when, behind bars at the police barracks, he regained his wits sufficiently to identify himself. A policeman on night rounds, attracted by his hoarse groans, had come upon him floundering among rubbish and weeds in the mire of a canal bank in a squalid neighborhood. Though blubbering and abusive, he offered no definite resistance and was led off in slovenly shame, his new clothes torn by brambles, tin cans, and broken glass and stained with mud and urine.

He was returned to the hospital and after sobering up could give no plausible explanation for his conduct. He did not appear to feel that one was needed. He showed no indication of blaming himself and far less disappointment than one would have expected. His tendency now was to hold others responsible for his failure. He insisted that he had only taken a little beer and explained that he took it because the doctor in charge of his case had promised to send him home but failed to do so.

This disheartening escapade naturally interrupted the plans for his going home and he was put back on a closed ward. His family, however, soon decided to try him again and within two weeks asked for his release, stating that the position for him was still available.

In order to prevent any further complications, the patient was put on the train by an attendant. He arrived at home with a pungent odor of cheap whiskey on his breath and strongly under the influence of alcohol but still able to walk. For several weeks his family busied themselves to keep him sober, at work, and away from crap games, from expeditions to sell mill workers nonexistent insurance, from glib attempts to float loans with his father's business associates, etc. He ignored their efforts.

Among many other unacceptable items of conduct are recorded these: driving off in his brother's car and not returning it for three days, becoming involved in a scheme to dispose of stolen goods, and participating in an illegal game of chance known as "the numbers," by which many Negroes were defrauded of small sums. From time to time Jack would drink himself into the familiar state of maudlin stupefaction and lie around disheveled, inert, and apparently quite miserable.

On being returned to the hospital he dismissed his failure with nonchalance, smiled cavalierly, and admitted, "I just fell off the wagon." This was his attitude long after all effects of intoxication had subsided.

He remained on a closed ward for a month, never showing the slightest indication of any recognized mental disorder. He was at this period somewhat fault-finding and wanted many small attentions. This was, however, entirely in keeping with his natural dissatisfaction with confinement. While going out with a group to the dining hall one evening, he escaped. Instead of making any serious or intelligent effort to get beyond reach of the hospital, he went to a disreputable roadhouse nearby and promptly became so obstreperously vocal and conspicuously offensive that he was located and brought back to the hospital by attendants.

After being successfully kept on a closed ward for six more weeks, he again escaped by opening a door with a key he had stolen from an attendant. Two days later he was taken up by the sheriff in a nearby village, dirty, disheveled, and miserable, after an inane spree.

He was now placed on a closely supervised ward to prevent him from escaping again and repeating these adventures. Here he was surrounded by extremely psychotic patients, many of whom were disturbed most of the time, babbling unintelligible nonsense and waving at the empty air, and all of whom he of course found vividly unsuitable as company. Obviously he did not belong in such surroundings, but it was difficult to find any other way to keep him in the hospital. After several weeks, in order to make his situation a little less unpleasant, he was allowed to go out on the lawn in front of the ward for short periods. His physician hoped that his recent unhappy experience might have taught him to handle himself a little more judiciously. This proved, however, to be false, for he again violated his parole by leaving the hospital and indulging in all sorts of nonsensical behavior typical of that already mentioned. This led him promptly into the hands of the police.

His subsequent history is the same. Each time he is confined on a closed ward among delusional, hallucinated patients, or those deteriorated to a "vegetative" level of existence, his physician, struck with the incongruity, hopes that he will be able to take more responsibility upon himself and, encouraged by his completely rational external aspect and conversation, not to speak of his reassuring promises to abide by the rules, gives him a little freedom. Sometimes he gets along well for a few weeks, perhaps for a month or more, but always he ends up throwing away what has been gained, violating his parole, and soon becoming involved in activities that demand the loss of his liberty.

Every possible effort is made to keep him in pleasant surroundings and on wards where patients are in relatively good mental condition, but he makes this difficult by his repeated violation of all agreements.

When last heard from he was, after a long period of confinement, out again on parole and for several weeks had conformed to rules. He is energetic, quick witted, alert, and jovial. No one talking with him would ever think that it had been necessary to keep him on closed wards among psychotic people.

How long Jack will last in this status no one can say. I have little hope that it will be long and no hope at all that he will be able to leave the hospital and lead a normal life outside.

14

Chester

On his first admission to the closed ward of a psychiatric hospital, Chester W., 24 years of age, was friendly and alert. His freedom from anything that would suggest an ordinary psychosis was immediately noticeable. He explained to the examiner that he did not suffer from any nervous or mental disorder and emphasized the statement that no question of such a condition had ever come up in his case. He said that he came to the hospital for further examination of a serious injury to his ankle which he sustained while in the army and for which he hoped to get a pension.

When told frankly that, according to accompanying reports, he had been admitted because of persistent antisocial and irresponsible behavior, spectacular alcoholic episodes, and extreme maladjustment, he affected considerable surprise and insisted that some mistake had been made. In fact, his surprise seemed real.

It was pointed out to him that unquestionable evidence from his parents, relatives, and friends, as well as from a social service report, established the fact that he had been stealing, defrauding others, making a boisterous nuisance of himself when drunk, etc., since he was 16 years of age.

It was brought to his attention that he had been expelled from a military school for gross and inveterate misconduct, had been confined in jail a dozen times recently for similar reasons, and had been supported and protected by his father, who spent a good part of his time getting this son out of the troubles which he made for himself and others almost daily. The patient appeared as if very much astonished at such reports, denied everything, and, in a convincing fashion, dismissed the question of all personal difficulties and maladjustment as little short of preposterous.

After careful observation in the hospital for a month, no evidence of delusions, hallucinations, or any other sign of what is regarded as a psychosis could be discovered. Chester was presented before a medical staff of ten psychiatrists who unanimously considered him sane and competent and made the diagnosis of psychopathic personality. He was kept in the hospital on pretexts and out of common sense because of his long history of extreme maladjustment.

He was at all times alert and usually cooperative, reacted with a very natural dislike to being on a closed ward, and continually asked for a discharge, insisting that he was entirely sane and improperly hospitalized.

On being granted parole of the grounds, he promptly left without permission and went home. At the insistence of his father he was granted a furlough status. Within a few days he had insolently suggested sexual intercourse to a respectable matron, committed several inconsequential thefts, and sold for $1.25 a good rug taken from his parents' home. After having a few drinks, he is reported to have spit on, or at, the foot of a great uncle who encountered him on the street and engaged him in conversation. Later that afternoon he talked eloquently to a half-dozen or so bystanders in the park about patriotism, honor, God, and the true meaning of morality.

Meanwhile, he had cashed several small checks on a nonexistent bank account and, posing as the emissary of a respected cousin (whose husband was cashier in a local bank), obtained $15.00 which he convinced an old friend of the family was needed to settle a small obligation that had arisen after banking hours.

When drinking, he usually became rowdy. He made no effort whatsoever to find employment and roamed about the town or countryside, often sleeping in the woods and fields. His father and brothers had no choice but to seek him out in the byways and hedges and bring him in, often laboring strenuously at this task far into the night. He was often found dirty, disheveled, and alone. Toward his family he was sullen and carping, his reactions those of petty irritation. He complained constantly that his father meddled with him and at times ascribed all his troubles to this interference. Finding it impossible to supervise such a person, even with the frequent assistance of local police, who obligingly locked him up in jail for a day or two during his worst episodes, the father soon sent him back to the hospital.

On arrival he was manifestly vexed and at a loss to understand his situation. "I can't see why they don't let me alone. I don't bother anybody. Why can't I go about my business like any other man?" These and similar remarks he repeated many times in tones showing well the dissatisfaction that any normal man would feel on being, without cause or reason, deprived of his liberty.

Before returning to the hospital, Chester had complained bitterly to his father, stating that he would kill himself rather than come. The father recognized this threat of suicide as insincere but typical of the somewhat dramatic airs often assumed by the patient. Except for past experience with such threats, it would have been natural to think desperation would be consistent with his intensely strong distaste for restraint of any sort.

He was kept now on a closed ward, from which he repeatedly schemed to escape, once stealing keys from an attendant and several times fomenting plots among other patients. After two weeks he succeeded in his efforts and soon appeared at home (fifty miles from the hospital) in a magnificent state of boisterous intoxication. He continued at home in complete idleness except for some enterprising petty thefts, long speeches about the need of increased virtue in women (delivered in local poolrooms), several brawls arising from his being caught cheating at dice games, some bold-faced begging, and numerous maneuvers to obtain money illegally, including forgery.

Despite peaceful intervals of a week or more, he continued to demonstrate an irresponsibility so utter that one is taxed to describe it. After several additional experiences in jail he was brought back to the hospital by his father, who confessed himself at his wit's end.

During psychiatric examinations the patient again denied that he had caused any trouble or done anything which would justify his being brought to the hospital. He admitted having taken a few drinks and tried to conclude some wise business deals but still insisted that he never drank much or ever behaved irresponsibly or in such a way as to cause trouble.

He glibly dismissed all the massive accumulation of detail concerning his lack of responsibility, his failure to show normal interests in life, his indifference to the serious trouble he gave relatives and friends, and the purposeless folly that had consumed all his efforts for years. The adroitness with which he denied everything and the brisk, facile manner in which he excused himself and glossed over his record made it clear that his mind was free of any seriousness whatsoever in regard to his past and of any real intention to behave more sensibly in the future. One thing only in this man impressed his examiners as having some emotional weight. This was his vivid chagrin at being confined and his persistent, restless longing to be free.

Many attempts were made to make him realize that he could stay out of the hospital only by avoiding inappropriate conduct and acts plainly damaging or embarrassing to others and by conducting himself so as not to be an unbearable burden on his family and on the community. He admitted that he did not really enjoy or have any particular reason for doing as he did, and reports substantiate this, representing him as a sullen, glum fellow in bars and poolrooms, a man without convivial gaiety or other signs of stimulation, apparently more unhappy in his efforts to celebrate than in his usual state.

I am convinced that this man obtains no delight at all from whiskey, that whatever may be his purpose in drinking, it does not result in the attainment of pleasure. Every effort was futile to make him see what was so obvious, that he had brought his troubles on himself, and that only by staying sober could he retain his freedom. He absolutely refused to face any fact and slipped nimbly from reality to the world of his evasions.

A few weeks later, because of a death in his family, he was allowed to go home in custody of his father. He immediately got out of the house and slipped off to a nearby town, where he drank himself into a state of maudlin intoxication, made a nuisance of himself in several public houses, engaged in minor street brawls, and wandered cursing and muttering aimlessly through the streets until found by his relatives.

At the funeral the next day, having skillfully obtained more whiskey, Chester appeared at first poised and sober. Signs of drunkenness, however, soon appeared, and the patient proceeded to make a shocking and memorable impression. Vomiting and defecating while in the aisle of the church contributed to this effect. As an elder brother was attempting to expedite his departure with minimum conspicuousness, these momentary and incomplete reactions took place.

The father sent him back to the hospital as soon as arrangements could be made. Although the patient could not have been unaware that his father had informed the hospital of his conduct and explained the circumstances under which he returned, he said with the greatest assurance on arriving that he had voluntarily come back before expiration of his furlough, merely for the day and in order to have the furlough extended. He insisted that his conduct at home had been above reproach and demanded parole privileges until arrangements were made for him to leave the hospital. At this time he was entirely free from all effects of alcohol.

This man is the son of a rather prosperous farmer and merchant. His home is in a Southern town of 4,000 inhabitants. His father, though not highly educated, is a successful, sensible man and genuinely respected in the community. Of his three siblings, a sister is married and in good circumstances, one brother is a physician, and the other is a lawyer. All are successful and seem well adapted to their environment.

The patient was raised in the same environment with his sister and brothers, but from early youth, unlike the other children, he showed some signs of his present inadaptability. He learned rather easily in school and successfully completed his studies each year until he reached the sixth grade. His truancy then became so pronounced that he could not be kept in school any longer. On being sent to a strict military school, he proved intractable and was expelled after a few weeks. Though remarkably lazy and unpersevering, he showed at this time what appeared to be a slight interest and an astonishing talent in tinkering with radios. His parents, who throughout his whole life have shown exceptional patience and gone to no little expense and trouble with him, sent him to New York to study radio work. He was very eager to go and urged this plan on the family. His older brother, the physician, was a house officer in a New York hospital at the time and agreed to keep in touch with him and try to exercise any necessary supervision.

From the very beginning it became apparent that the venture was useless. The patient could not be induced to attend classes. Chester showed no interest whatsoever in his work or in anything else, lying about his room much of the time and going out alone on adventures without much purpose or content—on missions to borrow a dollar through solemn-faced fraud or, by cheating or some sort of chicanery, to pick up a little extra change or to beat the game by getting a free ride on the bus or the subway and, perhaps, to climax the day by slipping out of a restaurant without paying for his meal. His brother, after earnest and persistent efforts to persuade him to take advantage of his opportunities, had to give up and send him home.

Many other efforts have been made to help this young man find some place in normal life. Various positions have been found for him, but he always refuses to maintain the slightest interest in any work.

The ordinary pleasures of mankind seem to have as little charm for him as work. Though he has had sexual relations with prostitutes and other available girls, he never formed a real attachment for any. Even casual physical encounters with women claim his interest far less than sporadic bouts of solitary drunken torpor in remote cotton fields or aimless hours spent idling about uninspiring hamburger stands, poolrooms, etc. When, he ran off to enlist in the army, at 22 years of age, his father did not try to interfere, hoping the discipline of that life would stabilize him.

Since the incidents just mentioned, he has on several other occasions obtained parole and violated it promptly by carrying out various antisocial acts which seemed to have no definite purpose, no conceivable explanation in terms of human impulse. He has also succeeded again in escaping from closed wards. On getting out, he always repeats his former conduct. Sometimes he has remained cooperative for a month or more, abiding by the rules of his ward, helping attendants with their work, assisting and directing frankly psychotic patients. During such periods he would talk frequently with his physician, discussing his plans for the future, maintaining that he fully realized drinking or stealing or not taking life seriously enough, etc., was his trouble, and declaring that he would never act so unwisely again.

He appeared to be a sane, quick-witted young man with good judgment and reasonably earnest intentions. So convincing was the impression he made that time after time the various physicians who had charge of his case would decide that parole was advisable despite his history. Within a few hours or sometimes a few days, he would appear at his home in a wretched state, land in jail because of unacceptable behavior, take an automobile and get caught, or, lacking opportunity for something more active to do, get himself too drunk to leave town and fall into the hands of the local police.

On one occasion, several days after being returned by his family from such an escapade, Chester came to me smiling and at ease. He spoke briefly of his plans for the future and insisted on having parole at once. In support of this request he sought to make the point that he had proved himself trustworthy and reliable under all circumstances. Looking me squarely in the face, he asserted with modest firmness, "You know that I'm *a man of my word.*" He repeated this statement several times and spoke most intelligently and convincingly in his own behalf. When asked how he pretended to be a man of his word after breaking it so many times, so flagrantly, and so recently, he showed no sign of being confounded.

His memory was of course clear, and he accurately recognized all the circumstances under which he had given his word not to leave the hospital, not to steal or to forge or to drink whiskey, as well as his invariably and prompt violations of every promise. He seemed to seek in the phrase *a man of his word,* which he uttered in tones of quiet pride and assurance, some magical charm which would irrationally persuade me to trust him. Indeed, he himself appeared to be well convinced by his statement. On seeing this man for the first time, one would have read into him a fair degree of sincerity and conviction. To me he seemed rather to be activated by a mimicry of these things, an insubstantial shadow of emotion which the patient, knowing nothing else, confused in his own mind with what he assumed other people felt when they used such a tone. Having never in his whole life, so far as I could find in examining him, looked a fact of this sort in the face, he was untroubled by even the hardest, sharpest contrast between fact and falsehood and stood free to indulge, with a kind of automatic imitation-sincerity, in any fantasy he chose.

During his repeated hospitalizations, his case was reviewed many times. No evidence of a psychosis in the commonly accepted sense of the word was found in his past record or in his current behavior or thought. At each presentation before the medical staff, every member has agreed that he is "sane and competent" and that he should be classified under the term *psychopathic personality*. He is bright rather than dull, and his reasoning powers on all general matters and on test questions are average or better than average.

Here, then, is a man whose measurable intelligence is not at fault, whose extrinsic situation is normal, and who is entirely free from the delusions and other mental disorders of the recognized psychoses. His environment is favorable and his opportunities, past and present, insofar as they can be estimated, appear better than the average. He is not visibly indifferent or emotionally isolated in the ordinary sense of those words, but, in sharp contrast to the schizophrenic or the deteriorated patient with organic brain disease, he reacts with a very natural antipathy to his situation. Several of the psychiatrists who observed him have expressed the belief that he detests being in the hospital more than any man they ever saw there.

Why, then, does he always take these active steps to get himself back in confinement just as soon as he gets away? It has been clearly demonstrated to him that he will have to spend his life in confinement as long as he persists in his present ways. The opinion held by some physicians is that such people as this patient are merely spoiled, that they would behave more sensibly if not pampered, and that if promptly confined to jail or left in whatever other difficulties they bring down on their own heads, they would finally control themselves. This opinion is sharply in contrast to the facts in the present case. No ordinary punishment could be much more severe than confinement on a closed ward is to this particular man. He has had it thoroughly explained to him that he will remain here until he can adapt himself to normal life outside. He not only gives up everything that other people seek but also, because of confinement, he sacrifices the chance to follow the inappropriate and bootless patterns of behavior into which he falls at once when left to his own devices.

Whatever strange goals or pseudogoals there may be to prompt and shape his reactions as a member of the community, these too, it seems, fail to motivate him sufficiently, fail to induce decisions and acts that would give him the freedom to pursue them. It has been demonstrated to Chester repeatedly, in the harshest aspects of the concrete, that his characteristic acts put him back in a situation he finds particularly disagreeable. This does not produce the slightest modification in his behavior.

If we attempt to interpret his antisocial conduct as a rebellious manifestation, a symbolic protest against customs, principles, people, institutions, etc., which he will not accept, we might presume he would take more pains to avoid the interruption of his efforts along this line. If there is unconscious need for him to make trouble in the community and to achieve heroic stature as a general nuisance, his steps to fulfill this need seem peculiarly illogical. They promptly result in the termination of his action. Arguments for such motivation in more effective criminal careers and in circumscribed patterns of delinquency seem more plausible than in such a case as this. If loitering, theft, swindling, "disgracing himself," running up debts, and social sabotage in general are his goals, the pursuit of these he must give up when he comes under close supervision on the closed ward.

Is he seeking, then, not to fulfill these goals but to frustrate the impulses to fulfill them? Or is he seeking punishment as something even more desirable than the perverse goals surmised above? The claim of such motivational schemes has been advanced.[8,213] Perhaps some patients who show more interest in their predicaments may reveal hidden attitudes, old wounds or grudges, forgotten but distorting influences, etc., that suggest such an interpretation.

From this patient, however, none of the many psychiatrists who dealt with him could obtain any underlying material to confirm such speculations. As hypotheses about his disorder, such interpretations impress me as having very little plausibility. It might be assumed that if deep penetration of his personality and adequate exploration of his innermost life could be achieved, substantial evidence of cause and effect would emerge in some convincing explanation. It seems likely, however, that a valid explanation would prove to be one far more complex than anything just suggested. An important clinical feature of his disorder seemed, nevertheless, to lie in the specific and obdurate difficulty in finding out anything at all about less superficial attitudes or real inner purposes and meanings.

In closing the summary of this case, let the point be emphasized again that this man does not seem driven by hot temptations to his injudicious deeds. What he does when free fails to give him much pleasure. Chester is in no way like a man who sacrifices all the ordinary satisfactions of life for some enthralling sin which will later bring him to ruin. The well-known human motives which sometimes lead a respected and successful businessman to lose fortune and family in his pursuit of an illicitly loved woman or of some other transitory but enticing joy are not discernible in this case.

My candle burns at both ends;
It will not last the night;
But ah, my foes, and, oh, my friends—
It gives a lovely light.*

Such a scheme of life, whatever might be said for its final wisdom, has no apparent place in this patient's maladjustment. The allegory of Faust selling his soul to the Devil in order to quench a thirst for rarer joys than this life holds is absurdly inappropriate.

It is most difficult to believe that he is reacting to powerful drives which *force* or *compel* him into obviously disastrous actions. On the contrary, everything about him suggests a drifting approach, a casual and weak impulse, a halfhearted whim rather than an explosive release of passion in the forbidden deed. Instead of a pathologic intensity of drive there seems instead to be a pathologic general devaluation of life, a complex deficiency, confusion, or malfunction in what chooses aims and directs impulse.

Nothing that he expresses or that can be observed about him suggests a great stress or inner conflict in which strong opposing forces clash and from which emerges deep instinctual gratification as he makes off with a stolen automobile, thoroughly cleans out an opponent by fraud in crap shooting, saddles his father with a heavy debt, or drains his bottle and brawlingly defies the police. Nor is there anything yet detected about him that suggests true relief of inner tension as he reacts to society's restraints and retaliations. If these are his fundamental mechanisms, they are so deeply concealed that they show no surface or subsurface repercussion of emotion that suggests in the least their nature or their existence.

---

*From Millay, Edna St. Vincent: A few figs from thistles, New York, 1932, Harper & Brothers.

15

Walter

Walter is an only child. In the old South Carolina city where he spent his early years, he is remembered by his first playmates as having been not only normal but also a particularly desirable friend. During his grammar school days he was a good but not an exceptionally bright pupil. He was happily at ease with boys his own age, being generally looked to as a leader, though never aloof or dictatorial. He was somewhat less inclined than usual to the more destructive forms of mischief so dear to the typical young male, yet no child could have been more secure from the taunts often evoked by primness or piety in the schoolboy. It is nothing short of incredible to imagine the term *sissy,* withering and still unhackneyed stigma of those times, ever having been applied to Walter by anyone. That term, in fact, could not have been defined better by those who used it than as his direct opposite.

Even to the present, several men who were slightly younger schoolboys on the fringe of the group in which he held his admired position testify to the graciousness and kindness with which he treated them. All agree that he was the only older boy they recall as being entirely free from the popular tendency to bully and persecute his worshipful juniors. If his subsequent course were not known, it is likely that a poll taken among his former associates would reveal an almost unanimous belief that Walter showed more promise of becoming a respected, happy member of his community than any of the group.

In the pleasant little city of some 50,000 people his general situation in life appeared fortunate. The father was particularly honored.

Starting life with a good name but little money and only a high school education, the father established himself as a cotton factor and soon attained complete financial security. During his son's infancy he had played an important part in freeing the city of a corrupt political machine, and he continued active in civic work, one of the genuine ornaments of his community. Never a politician in the unpleasant sense of the word, he has all his life exercised strong and altogether unmercenary constructive influence in municipal affairs, occasionally heading committees to treat with the state or federal government about public matters.

Notably upright and capable, the father is still, in his early seventies, a man of sincere geniality and unusual tolerance. Though free from professional camaraderie, he is gifted with an unself-conscious knack of friendliness, an easy, unforced humor. Younger people, feeling in him a lively, almost naive warmth of humanity, tend to forget that he is a very old man. His dignity is and has always been indisputable but entirely without stiffness.

The mother is known as a quiet woman of gentle breeding, chiefly interested in her home but generally liked and admired. Both parents are Episcopalians and attend a church which has come down from colonial times.

It would be hard to imagine an environment farther from moral laxity on the one hand or fanaticism and excessive efforts at piety on the other than that of Walter's youth. He apparently enjoyed all the pleasures and advantages available to boys of the leading families in his community. Not only social service reports but also the opinion of his contemporaries indicate that he was as free from pampering and undue license as from overzealous severity.

After entering high school he gradually drifted away from his earlier friends, began to lose interest in his studies, and began to show alarming irresponsibility. The change in him was at first imperceptible. No one could say definitely when he began to lose identity with the modest, frank character of his early youth and to become, instead, notable for juvenile arrogance, a petulant irritability, a quick and limitless facility at lying.

His parents soon began to find him a problem. Nothing seemed to suit him. Purposeless truancy from school, night wanderings, a disrespectful attitude toward his elders, and open, fretful defiance at any attempt, however gentle or however firm, to guide or control him became ever more prominent. He became dissatisfied and carping and always spoke as if the world were to blame for each difficulty that he made for himself and for others.

Some of the other boys with whom he had grown up began at this stage of their lives to indulge in what they regarded as dissipation. Cigarette smoking, occasional surreptitious experiences with strong drink, and indiscreet behavior with the opposite sex were adventurously essayed and almost incessantly talked about by the more wayward spirits. Many of these boys were regarded by their elders as sowing their wild oats, as perhaps preparing to go to the dogs. Their conduct was far more weightily regarded by themselves, many exulting in what they imagined to be precocious careers of worldly license. Walter did not concern himself particularly with these pursuits.

During his third year of high school Walter ran away from home, having no plan or discernible purpose. His money soon became exhausted, and his father brought him home. Shortly afterward he ran away again. He had been very disagreeable to his parents since his first misadventure and seemed bored and aimless. The father, thinking he might learn something to his profit, allowed him to stay away, supplying him with sums of money from time to time.

Before long he succeeded in getting work as an unskilled laborer at a factory in a large industrial city on the eastern seaboard. Losing this place, he soon found another. After working a few weeks or sometimes a few months, he always fell into difficulty with his employers, often losing positions because of his high-handed and dictatorial ways, drifting about from one place to another. He dressed rather flashily and squandered money that his father sent him on making a cheap display. Much of his leisure was spent standing around on street corners or strutting about in front of cigar stores. Meanwhile, he lived among uneducated and depressing people in a dreary section of town and seemed to have no interest in finding suitable associates or surroundings. Though he indulged in casual relations with prostitutes, there is no record of his ever having regarded any woman as a love object. What relations he has had of this sort, though not infrequent, seem very insignificant in the story of his life, involving little emotion, implying no sexual contact of two personalities beyond the more or less mechanical friction of the parts technically involved.

He was considered an intelligent workman during his brief periods of activity and several times advanced in various companies, occasionally attaining promising positions as salesman only to throw them away by neglect or by petulant bickering with his superiors.

When his country entered World War I, he promptly enlisted. After going to France, he was promoted to the rank of sergeant in the air corps. According to reports, he showed considerable skill as a mechanic. He was, however, reduced to private for going A.W.O.L. before his discharge from the army at the end of the war.

On returning home he referred to himself as an aviator, implying that he had been an officer and a pilot, and assumed the airs of one who imagines himself a distinguished hero or who means, at any rate, for others to hold this opinion of him. He made no attempt to associate with people his contemporaries found interesting, worked for short periods as a mechanic in local garages, and caused his parents deep mortification and distress by going on periodic sprees either alone or with the most vulgar and uninspiring companions. He continually spoke of his dissatisfaction with the town in which his parents lived, complaining that it offered no opportunities for a man such as himself, and, taking a superior manner, harped exasperatingly on his travels and adventures and his alleged successes afar.

He soon left home again for Chicago, where he obtained and lost several positions as mechanic or as salesman. He drifted on to Cincinnati and Detroit, following the same career. His father was frequently called on to furnish money when he got into difficulties or was without work. Occasionally he came home for short periods during which he remained arrogant, idle, and full of absurd stories about his own importance, the superior positions he had held, the high and mighty people he associated with, the fashionable gatherings he graced. He sometimes drank until he was in a deplorable condition, staggering home disheveled and rowdy, creating a great uproar in the simple, dignified household of his parents, or from time to time ending up at the police barracks where his father had to come at inconvenient hours of the night to remove him from the filthy and disreputable group of prostitutes, vagrants, and petty criminals among whom he had been confined. When not drinking he showed, in less dramatic form, the same attitudes and qualities.

During all this time his father supported and protected him with unvarying tact and persistence. Though the public at large knew how disheartening and harrassing a burden the son had become and what a particularly bitter change he had brought into his parent's serene and honored life, they both continued to treat him with dignity and consideration. The whole town regarded Walter as a heartbreaking disappointment, but little of this was learned from complaints by the parents.

Time after time the father obtained positions for his son; time after time he paid the son out of debt, effected his release from jail, and submitted to abuse for his pains. Although he reasoned with his son and sought in every possible way to influence him, the father did not allow an attitude of hopeless contempt to possess him.

In some subtle way that is difficult to describe, he seemed to accept his son before the world and, while denying none of the son's faults, to put his whole attention on offering new opportunities, none of it on lamenting what he had been made to suffer or on throwing this up to the person who caused his suffering. He tried, it seemed, not only to wipe the slate clean of material hindrances to a fresh start but also to wipe it clean subjectively, to let

the son start over without the burden of shame that one in such circum-
sances might be imagined to feel.

There seemed, however, to be no attempt on the father's part to deceive
this son into thinking his behavior was condoned or minimized. In dealing
with such a problem one can err in either one way or the other, and usually
one errs in both. He seemed, however, hardly to err at all in the long and
trying years of struggle to rehabilitate his son. Numerous psychiatrists who
worked with the case over a decade were impressed and considered it a remarkable performance.

Finally, after several other short sojourns in psychiatric institutions, Walter
was sent to a Veterans Administration hospital. He did not want to come.
His running up of bills and his small but very spectacular offenses against
legal statutes and public taste had become so extreme and so frequent, his
trips to jail and his bawdy, argumentative tantrums at home so trying, and
his sporadic sprees with drink so extraordinary it was plain that desperate
measures should be taken. The parents did not hesitate to make it clear to
Walter why he had to come to the hospital. The son knew that the father,
by relaxing his protection, could in a few days leave him only the alternative
of jail. So he came.

On arriving, he confessed that he was astonished at his family for sending him to a mental institution. He simply could not understand such an
attitude. He said that he had, perhaps, taken a quart of whiskey during the
two previous years, behaving as if surprised and very much vexed at the
idea that he might have been drinking to excess. He suggested that some
vague gossip about his being a user of alcoholic liquors might have started
because in the town of his birth, to which he had recently returned, one had
to go to disreputable places, extremely unsuitable to his own fastidious tastes
and frequented by rough and vulgar people, to get the occasional drink of
whiskey that any gentleman might want. His little difficulties with the law
about bad checks, swindling schemes, etc., he waived aside as if they had been
matters too small and too irrelevant for serious discussion. He showed plainly
that he considered himself of a type superior to the best people in town and
to his parents and dwelt at length on the rarefied social and intellectual
atmosphere in which he moved when away. Though assuming an air of condescension in speaking of his father, as if with the chivalrous intention to
deal lightly and generously with him, he admitted that he could not but resent his actions. He described his parents as meddling in his affairs and repeatedly interfering with the important plans he outlined for himself. His
manner was so convincing that the examining physician thought at first he
might really be, despite his bad record, a man of some attainment, since

he was plainly a man of intelligence. Had the parents been, perhaps, a little too quick and severe in their action? The social service report cleared up all doubt on these points. During study in the hospital he showed no technical evidence of psychosis or psychoneurosis. His disturbance was diagnosed as psychopathic personality, and he was discharged at the end of a month's observation.

On returning home, Walter continued in his old ways, losing each position obtained for him, wandering about the streets at night, or sometimes when drinking, falling maudlin and semistuporous in parks, coal yards, or on the riverbank. He was furnished with money to go to Boston, where he insisted opportunities now awaited him. He soon obtained a position as a salesman of radios and, despite irregularity at work, embarrassing behavior, and periodical sprees of drinking, seemed to do fairly well for a month or two. Then, complaining of discrimination against him at his office, he gave his employers a piece of his mind, threw up his position, and enlisted in the army. Four months later he suddenly deserted and, after wandering about the Midwest obtaining and losing various positions but chiefly making petty troubles for himself and others, came home to his parents. He was quickly discovered and taken into custody by army authorities.

He admitted that he knew what he was doing when he deserted, said that he had not been drinking at the time, and dismissed the whole matter with the supercilious remark that he left the army because he had some business that needed attention without delay. He was examined by physicians at this time. No evidence of a psychosis was found, but it was noted that he showed "ungratefulness, moral uselessness, a failure to profit by experience, utter irresponsibility, etc." He was judged unfit for military duties and, perhaps with some special leniency because of his wartime service, released without further punishment.

Some months later he was readmitted to the hospital after a series of misadventures in no way different from his earlier ones. He also had gonorrhea, which he was glad to have treated. He was at this time aloof and superior in his attitude, complained about being confined with psychotic patients, and professed himself disgusted at their table manners. He now admitted excessive drinking but attributed it and all his difficulties to his mother, saying little now about his father. He plainly considered himself a martyr to his mother's efforts to keep him out of jail and able to work. This he regarded as meddling and seemed to feel that it fully justified his own conduct. After six weeks he was discharged.

He was back again, however, after a short period of freedom by his father, who in the interval had continued his efforts to get the patient established. Several positions had been arranged for him in the city of his birth, and he had also been sent off and given financial assistance in an industrial center in the North. Always he failed, losing each position or giving it up and roaming the streets, getting into brawls or legal difficulties about debts, lying out in brothels or flophouses until rescued by the police or his father. This time he remained in the hospital for seven weeks.

When brought before the staff he was quite self-contained and spoke of his misconduct as though he were rather proud of it and considered it a humorous and fully justified sort of retaliation against his parents. He laughed and said that after having got pretty well drunk, he decided that his father might want to send him to the hospital and so continued drinking until this was inevitable. He admitted that his parents had suggested he drink at his own house with them as an alternative to his sodden sprees but could not see that this implied any tolerance on their part. He spoke with satisfaction about slipping away from them, taking the automobile, and, having loaded in several gallons of whiskey, heading out into the country where he would remain for four or five days, at times in thorough stupefaction.

His tone throughout the interview was brisk, self-assured, and somewhat pompous. He admitted verbally that the whole fault might not lie with his parents, but it was plain that this concession was made only for the purpose of showing his broadmindedness toward them. "Of course, there must be two sides to any question," he agreed with grudging deliberation, as if gratified and a bit surprised at his own generosity. It was obvious that no real conviction lay behind his words. The following samples are typical of his talk to the staff:

> Since I seem to end here anyway I thought I'd make a party of it. This has been going on for fifteen or twenty years, and I'm sick and tired of being dictated to. My father has a temper which has caused me considerable trouble at times. My career has not been perfect; nevertheless, I play the game on the level. I play it right on through. I was just matching my wits with my father. It just seems that there should be a stop put to this [his being sent to the hospital] because I'm satisfied I'm a kind of nuisance out here.

He then quoted his father as having expressed ideas of vengeance toward him in profane language and having gloated over his confinement at the hospital. Both the thought and the language were absurdly inconsistent with that grave man's despair about his son.

After six weeks he was taken out of the hospital on furlough. Five days later police brought the patient back, peevish, dictatorial, and uncontrollable. A few days later the father took him out again, only to have him escape.

167

Several days passed before he could be found, the police finally bringing him in from the abandoned stables behind an old unrented house where their attention had been drawn by midnight barking of stray dogs who had gathered and were thus saluting Walter as he fumbled about.

He was returned to the hospital, taken out again by his family, and sent back because of similar capers time after time. His father evidently hoped that the prospect of being confined indefinitely in a mental hospital would curb his activities and tried repeatedly to impress him by this means. Nothing, however, was accomplished, and after eight months spent on the wards and out on furloughs the attempt was abandoned. Walter left again to seek his fortune selling electric refrigerators in a large, distant city.

After losing a number of positions in various cities, spending many nights in jails over the country, and lying out in low dives or in the woods on prolonged solitary drinking sprees, he returned to his parents. He now began to make himself even more difficult than formerly. After uproarious, obscene, and threatening entrances into the house between midnight and dawn, he would sleep until the early afternoon, then, on arising, make a canvass of the city, calling chiefly on quiet old ladies, preferably close friends of his mother's, to wheedle money from them. Knowing that he would take whatever they furnished him and use it to make further trouble, these ladies, after giving him a few dollars, would, on the second or third visit, often send word by the servant that they were not at home. Thereupon he would become insistent, saying that his business was urgent, that he would wait until the lady returned. Growing particularly vehement, he sometimes accused the servants of lying, called in a loud voice up the stairs, and made such a commotion that his victim would have to come down and see him.

On several occasions he even disturbed these lifelong friends of his mother's from their beds, keeping up his calls until they came to the stairs and spoke with him. He did not readily take no for an answer but continued to beg after repeated refusals. His manner was supercilious and haughty, though his words were sometimes shamefully abject. During these interviews he outrageously and falsely criticized his parents, accusing them of the most fantastic mistreatment and laying all his difficulties at their door.

Few of his parents' friends escaped these embarrassing encounters. Respect and admiration for the parents prevented these people from calling the police to rid them of such a pest, and most would rather have suffered ten times such inconvenience than let it come to his parents' attention. Walter himself was a virtual stranger to these quiet old ladies, never having had much to do with respectable people since his childhood.

On one occasion he accosted the mother of a former playmate as she was walking down the street: "Hello, Aunt Maisie, hello!" he called in a loud, insistent voice from behind her. Superficially polite, but with a discernible swagger, he approached. She had not laid eyes on him for many years and scarcely recognized him. "I say, my car's just broken down up the street. Could you lend me a couple of dollars?"

Placing him after a moment, she regretfully said that she had only a little change in her purse. "Well, how much have you?" he countered briskly, smiling in a brittle sham of courtesy. As she opened the purse his eager hands flew to her assistance, mimicking still the action of a gentleman performing a small service for a lady. The few coins were scarcely in her palm before his fingers licked them up. With brief but extravagant words of thanks which had a peculiarly hollow ring, he was off.

Some months later he was readmitted to the hospital, coming from the police barracks. His father had become afraid that he might, in a fit of temper, actually harm his mother. Though he had often threatened both parents and once had even pulled his mother a few yards by the wrists, neither parent heretofore had seriously feared violence at his hands. He had brawled often in taverns, poolrooms, bars, and on the streets, but he had never shown sufficient violence to suggest that he was really dangerous. He had, however, recently adopted the habit of sleeping with a gallon of whiskey under his bed on which he laid a loaded revolver. His father did not want to take chances on his personal belief that Walter was unlikely to kill.

Let it be recorded here again that this patient's father showed no signs of being a victim of parental blindness, of foolish pride in his child, or of perceptible weakness in dealing with him. In discussing the case with physicians at the hospital, he spared no detail of the history, made no effort to whitewash the son's motives or to excuse him; as ugly as this situation was, he seemed to face it squarely at all times. There was no sign of vindictiveness or personal bitterness, but there was always complete frankness and remarkable insight. His grief and shame seemed almost, but not quite, too much for him. His unfailing devotion to his son as expressed in his actions became steadily more impressive to those who observed. Some of the physicians who dealt with the case felt that this man's understanding and his adequacy all but matched his son's spectacular opposite.

This time Walter stayed in the hospital for nearly three months. He was, as before, supercilious, full of quietly boastful innuendos, and totally unwilling to accept any of the responsibility for his maladjustment.

This time it was his mother who, by nagging at him and meddling with him, had got him into the hospital. At the staff meeting he came in rather like a lord. With chilly politeness not free from contempt he stated, in reply to a question, that he was an engineer, giving the term a pompous accent that showed his sense of superiority. This statement was based on his former work as a mechanic and was plainly not a delusion but a boastful exaggeration.

He was extremely dissatisfied on a ward with psychotic patients and incessantly demanded his release. Only the knowledge that his father would refer him at once to the police kept him from forcing the hospital to let him go. He seemed as out of place as any normal man would be, and he was no less impatient to gain his freedom. He was soon tried on parole. This did not last long, for he went off again and almost at once got into difficulties. After several such trials he was again discharged.

Soon afterward he went to the telephone one morning, called up a man he had known during his childhood, and said he was in trouble and needed help at once. The other man, though he remembered Walter as a child, had not seen him for a number of years. He was busy with pressing matters at the time in a cotton mill several miles from town where he held an important position.

"But I've got to see you at once," Walter insisted. "I tell you I'm in trouble." The other, becoming vexed at such insistence and at the high-handed, preemptory tone, explained that his own affairs were urgent also and asked to be told more about the matter. Walter would give no details. He became more demanding. "I tell you I want to see you. You come on down to 1321 Juniper Street. I'll be in front of the house. And if you've ever traveled fast in your life you travel fast now."

At this the other man became rebellious. He frankly stated that he could not and would not tear himself away from his own business at such a time on such an inscrutable errand. Walter then began to compromise and at last grudgingly agreed to a meeting in a few hours. His whole manner in the conversation was that of one who demands fulfillment of an obligation, not of one who requests a favor.

On arriving at the address given, the former acquaintance was at once beckoned by an abrupt jerk of the thumb to draw aside under a tree.

"I'm in a sort of jam," Walter said condescendingly. "Owe a man three dollars. I'd like for you to let me have that amount."

"I'm sorry," said the other, determined not to give anything after being so inconsiderately put upon, "I haven't got it on me."

Walter thereupon became insistent. Making it plain that he did not believe what the other man said, he continued as if demanding his rights, "Well, what have you in your pockets? Just give me what you have. That will be all right." Finally, uncomfortable at participating in this shameless demonstration, the other gave over some small change and left.

Walter continued on the same course, losing positions which his father obtained for him in other cities. Sometimes he worked for two or three months, but even during such periods he had many small social difficulties. He was sent to private institutions several times for whiskey cures and returned to take up immediately his well-known ways. Once he went to an evangelist's meeting, professed salvation, and assumed for a week or ten days an attitude of piety and spoke of carrying on the Lord's Work. Despite this period of propriety, he was in the police barracks about three or four times each month.

He disappeared again and was sought for several days by his anxious parents. A week later a friend of the family, on returning to her house which had been closed during her absence from the city, found him inside, stretched on the floor, snoring. He was disheveled and dirty. After a little shaking and shouting he aroused, blinked at her calmly, and acted as if he had been disturbed by some irresponsible person who must be treated as an indulgent grown person treats a child. In the house was also a half-dressed woman of frankly disreputable character whom he had brought with him. The rugs were stained with overturned drinks, and bottles and Mason jars were scattered over the floors. Unwashed dishes were piled in stacks or littered broken about the rooms. Several disarranged beds were heaped with stale sheets. Here and there furniture was overturned or burned with cigarettes. "Sorry," said Walter as if making a gallant apology for having accidentally jostled a lady in a crowd, "I am made so miserable at home that I had to come in."

He was sent again to the hospital by his father, following a series of misadventures somewhat more trying than usual. On arrival he was moderately influenced by drink but well aware of his actions. "Ask me no questions and I'll tell you no lies," he shouted gaily. "Yep, I've been drunk for five weeks. Drank a pint today. Carry it pretty well, don't I?"

He soon sobered up and insisted on leaving, stating that he had never done anything out of the ordinary and that he was sane and in the wrong place. He spoke convincingly of plans he had made to study air conditioning and of great engineering opportunities that awaited him in this field. Seeing him for the first time, it would have been easy to believe that he was a gifted and energetic young man whose ambitions were to be fulfilled as soon as he obtained his freedom.

Despite his many evasions and his opinions contrary to fact, no delusion, in the sense ordinarily understood by psychiatry, was ever found in Walter. After careful study and prolonged observation, he was again given the diagnosis of psychopathic personality. He was discharged at the end of five weeks as sane.

According to trustworthy reports he is continuing without any notable change in his former ways.

16

Joe

This patient came in the custody of two friends, both state officers in the American Legion, to apply for admission to the hospital. He had with him commitment papers showing that he had at his own request been declared incompetent.

Joe was alert and intelligent and conducted himself in a manner that suggested a person of poise, good judgment, and firm resolution. He was anything but the sort of figure that might come to mind in thinking of a patient sent for admission to such an institution.

He frankly admitted that he was not "insane" in the ordinary sense of the word and therefore was not eligible according to the letter of the law for admission into a hospital of this sort. He urged, however, that he be accepted, stating that for the last sixteen or seventeen years he had been drinking to great and foolish excess in periodic sprees. He seemed to be remarkably frank and straightforward, admitting that he had made an unholy mess of his life and caused misery untold for his wife, his parents, and his friends. At times he became much depressed, he said, when ruminating over the magnitude of his failure. He appeared earnest in his strongly expressed determination to pull himself together and make a fresh start.

A rather unusual and impressive sincerity seemed to distinguish this man from some with similar histories of psychopathic drinking and psychopathic failure. He did not promise to become a new man. He admitted that he knew it would be most difficult for him to change his ways and seemed to realize that his many collapses in the past after similar good intentions told against his present chances.

Records which accompanied him gave the information that three years previously Joe had attempted suicide by severing veins in both arms. Definite scars were visible four or five inches above the wrists. Since he had not played up this phase of his case, his statement that he had really tried to kill himself was particularly convincing. Though such patients, officially not psychotic and considered responsible for their own troubles and misdeeds, are not technically eligible, it was decided to take this man.

His history of a suicide attempt furnished plausible grounds for calling him an emergency, and his apparently desperate intention of escaping from the pattern of his past folly promised that treatment in a mental hospital might give him a chance to gain insight and forge new resolution which he would need in starting over again.

During the month of psychiatric study and constant observation that preceded diagnosis before the staff, this man proved to be a model patient. He was cheerful, convivial, alert, and energetic. He asked for work and at once made himself useful, checking out laundry, typing various lists, helping psychotic patients, and performing many other duties. Quick, accurate, and reliable, he seemed to take a real pleasure in all work that he could get and actually accomplished much more than an average man could.

He was at all times in perfect contact, reasonable, optimistic, and plainly intelligent. During examinations he told his story with a remarkable appearance of frankness and insight.

"I suppose, doctor, I am still a child emotionally," he admitted in explanation of the fifteen years during which he threw away many valuable positions, lost his wife, and went repeatedly to sanatoriums which offer whiskey cures and to mental hospitals. He seemed to realize that his conduct was extremely irrational and without reward, agreeing that he had been quite unhappy nearly all the time and a source of grief and despair to others.

Drinking, Joe said, was not in his opinion the cause of his trouble but merely a symptom of some obscure flaw in his makeup. This defect he found it hard to define or describe, although he spoke very intelligently and almost, it might be said, profoundly. He distinguished between his own case and the various psychoses, maintaining that he was entirely sane but admitting that, though sane, he had behaved more foolishly that a bona fide "lunatic," and for no purpose.

He mentioned the writings of Freud, Jung, Bleuler, and William A. White and showed unusual familiarity for a layman with psychiatric terminology as well as a slight acquaintance with the literature.

"I suppose I must be a constitutional psychopath," he concluded after describing his many opportunities, his many confident resolutions to adjust, and his inevitable, quick failures.

As in so many cases of this sort, drink, being a tangible and superficial activity, is often stressed by the family and the patient as if it were the major source of difficulty. Being at a loss to account for antisocial and self-damaging acts in terms of real purpose, it is customary for them to decide that these must have been carried out because some drinks had been taken. I do not share such a belief. This patient, like a good many others, was more inclined to discuss drinking than his more essential difficulties, so this at first was the chief topic.

"But why do you drink?" he was asked. "Why do you let yourself take the first drink, when you realize by now to what it will lead?" It was hard to say, he admitted. He felt he had not for many years obtained pleasure from the effects of whiskey. Even if there had been some extraordinary pleasure in drinking, he felt sure this would not have been worth even a small part of the price he had paid.

Perhaps habit was a factor, Joe suggested; perhaps he was emotionally conditioned to repeat this disastrous step, no matter how plainly reason warned him against it. He spoke of possible forces within his mind that might seek failure, unconscious tendencies to defeat himself. Desire to escape from the difficulties and failures of life, he felt, might influence him to seek intoxication. On the other hand, he believed the failure and difficulties would not occur if he did not drink. He was confident that drunkenness led to the many disastrous actions he had taken.

Joe emphasized his belief in a vicious cycle of sequences, the drink causing him to get in grave difficulty, to lose what he most wanted, and then his subsequent disappointments causing him to seek refuge in drink. Though some causal influence may lie in this, it is apparently secondary and superficial. When in extremely advantageous positions, in situations he described as ideal, without provocation or known purpose, he often acted in such a way as to lose all that he said he found desirable and to make failure inevitable and spectacular.

On being asked if he really found life worth while, if a normal life offered anything to him, he quickly answered that it did. He appeared frank in affirming that there was in him a strong and persistent will to succeed, an urge to get at the satisfactions of existence which most people choose in preference to the sort of career he had known with its almost fantastic and presumably frustrating reverses and maladjustments.

As Joe discussed the possibility that impulses unrecognized by him might play a part in his way of life, he seemed like one with an almost Socratic

174

respect for the depth and extent of the unknowable. It was entirely possible, he maintained, that he might be deceiving himself. Perhaps, he admitted, there were tendencies within, whose presence he did not suspect. As he continued, he spontaneously questioned his essential sincerity but in such a way as to make him seem even more sincere than heretofore.

This man's apparent insight, freedom from evasiveness, and willingness to admit himself responsible for his misfortunes are, it might be said, inconsistent with his history, which is typically that of a psychopath. In my opinion, however, none of these qualities which appeared to be so highly developed in him are real. It is perhaps more accurate to say that whatever reality there may be in these qualities it is not integrated into the person's functioning. It does not emerge objectively in the actuality of behavior.

In time, his insight comes to seem but a mimicry of insight. He uses the words which one who understood would use, but they do not have a corresponding meaning. He speaks with every evidence of conviction and sincerity, but when one studies him over a period of time, it becomes apparent finally that he is merely going through the motions, that he is not actually living the feelings he describes so well. His evasiveness, of almost Dostoevskian complexity, consists in an openness which is actually no openness at all. He freely gives up discrediting information about his weakness and his failures and appears to take them with ardent seriousness, to understand them, to regret them to the bottom of his heart, and to intend to learn and profit by them. But all the while he is, for the most part, merely using the words, the gestures, and the expressions without entering into the feeling and the understanding. We find ourselves dealing not so much with a genius at acting but with a person who, in the most important matters, has no capacity of distinguishing between what is acting and what is not.

Joe is not really facing facts now but only acting in a charade in which he faces imitation facts. He says he is responsible for his failures and seems to accept this responsibility honestly and to have normal regret for the pain he has caused others, but in studying him it becomes apparent that the regret is something quite different from what we have presumed he was talking about and that he is able to act as if it were profound only because he is utterly unaware of what real and serious regret is—because he does not experience real and serious emotions.

It is difficult to describe this impression without implying that the patient's reactions are being identified with deliberate fraud or with hypocrisy in its ordinary meaning. There is, however, a fundamental difference. Psychopaths notoriously deceive and falsify, with strict awareness of the intention and about any sort of situation.

Voluntary and quite conscious decisions to lie occur and are carried out in discussing the points on which we attempt to estimate insight, the genuineness of desire, grief, remorse, love, etc. In addition to such factors, however, we encounter misleading reports of another sort.

In all probability, Joe was often accurately describing his reactions insofar as he could. Something left out of his experience made it impossible for him to see that the words he used did not refer to such emotional actualities as they would in another. One might say this constitutes a kind of strange and paradoxical sincerity, something a little like the report of a color-blind man (without knowledge of his defect) who after investigation swears conscientiously that the horizon is gray, though it actually blazes with all colors of the sunset.

Such a comparison is, however, full of implications that may mislead us. It can also be said that this particular patient, when it suits his purposes, does not hesitate to falsify with full deliberation.

In time a typical glibness about the major social disasters of his life reveals itself, and one sees that this man has a sort of pride in the spectacular capers he has cut. He admits that he is to blame for his wife's having had to divorce him because of nonsupport, periods of desertion, and gross, repetitive, and almost publicly transacted acts of infidelity. Even now, while full of expressed intentions to change his ways, he shows no genuine concern for the fate of this former wife and little or none for his children. He admits his childishness, his failures in every undertaking, and his flagrant lack of consideration for others. He admits some dozen or two arrests in the last year and a half, for causing disorder in public and for unacceptable conduct while drinking. But he is very solemn in assuming that he is a *man of honor* in the most unqualified sense, despite what he confesses as his faults. He states that he will not break his word and that he has never committed an act against anyone else for which he should have been arrested. He admits that the alleged suicide attempt was a pure fraud and that he had made a false statement about it in order to get into the hospital. He had cut his arms only to frighten his wife and parents and to create a dramatic scene in order to gain his ends with them. He describes his exploit in detail, admitting its extreme childishness. He remembers that he took care to pull over a chair and to fall with a great thud and clatter so that he would attract sudden attention and become at once the center of an exciting scene.

This, for the sort of man he is known to be, is admitting a great deal. But he at once insists that he has always been a man of his word, ignoring the many incidents in his history to the contrary. He leaves out many well-established facts which would not fit in with the picture he now means to give of himself, as a man who has done many foolish and unpardonable things but who is still a "gentleman" fundamentally. He always insists that the many women with whom he has had relations were those who would obviously excite romantic feelings, though this is by no means true. He says repeatedly that sexual relations are no pleasure to him unless he gives the woman pleasure too, but one can see that this is an opinion he has picked up from reading and that it has nothing to do with the reality of his life. Actually his experiences with women have been casual, incomplete, and of so little real significance to him that he has been known to drink himself into a state of impotence rather than continue even the primary physical exercises of the relationship. Later he says that no woman among the many with whom he has had intercourse ever afforded anything of serious significance to him; but he feels that this is rather to his credit as a romantic lover. "I am in love with love!" he concludes tritely.

Joe speaks of his misadventures with what would pass for admirable humor, and this would have been real humor had there been a contrasting seriousness in his understanding to give it meaning. But his light touch in dealing with his own faults and his own follies loses significance when it becomes apparent that for him there is no tragic reality against which it is maintained.

Now 38 years of age, he is athletic, well groomed, and rather handsome. The story of his life as he gives it is in most of the outer facts identical with the story as given in social service reports and by his friends.

Joe's father was a prominent man in one of the largest cities in Alabama. High ambitions were entertained for this son, and he was given every educational opportunity. He feels that his mother had puritanical ideals of life and wished him to live according to them. He admits that he made no attempt to suppress his natural inclinations and says that he enjoyed sexual intercourse frequently since he was about 13 years of age. He was unusually bright in school and made rapid progress despite interruptions caused by pneumonia and typhoid fever. He was sent to a celebrated preparatory school in the East where he did well in his studies and achieved athletic prominence in football and tennis.

He then entered the state university but after two years transferred to Virginia Military Institute. Before graduating, he enlisted in the army. The war ended seven months later and he was discharged with the rank of corporal. He then entered law school at the state university and three years later graduated with high distinction, being named valedictorian for his class.

Joe had already begun to show irresponsibility, often walking out of class capriciously and ignoring serious duties as well as matters on which his own welfare depended. He had also on isolated occasions begun to show the tendency to behave outlandishly when he drank. He was very capable and successful in the practice of law when he gave his attention to it, but he soon lost interest and neglected his work. His father was, however, able to cover most of his deficiencies and keep him in an appearance of success. He often entertained big ideas but did little to put them into practice. He constantly made excuses and was full of highsounding promises, few of which he made any attempt to fulfill.

The patient himself accounts for his loss of interest in law as resulting from an idealistic outlook. He states that he entered his profession with the assumption that actual justice was the criterion of legal decisions; finding this to be far from true, he had little patience left for the law.

He was at this time settling down to serious drinking, as he expresses it. As a matter of fact, his essential untrustworthiness and his tendency to squander his resources and throw his responsibilities upon others stand out in his behavior while not drinking at all, although in his own account of his career he tends to cloak his more important aspects of maladjustment under the explanation of alcoholic influence.

Joe became interested in running for city council, threw himself with great energy into the race, and after a shrewd and active campaign was elected. According to the social service reports, most of his drinking was done alone, even at this time when he was in his early twenties. On occasions when he drank in company, he often misbehaved in most extraordinary and distressing ways.

Once when a guest at a formal dance held in a small town fifty miles away from his home, he threw a large crowd of respectable people into extreme consternation. After taking some drinks, he walked out on the dance floor, cut in on an attractive young lady who belonged to one of the best families in town, and joined with the crowd as it gave itself up to pleasant and seemly strains of a waltz.

Stopping brazenly in a semisecluded corner of the dancing area, Joe drew sudden attention from the chaperones, from the astonished eyes of a hundred waltzing couples, and from the musicians. These at first found it difficult to credit their perceptions or to act as they watched him jerk his partner's dress up over her head, set himself to work divesting her of her undergarments, and, despite her struggles and screams, commence on the first steps toward an attempt at sexual intercourse in these inauspicious surroundings. A tumult ensued. He was snatched from his victim and removed from the ballroom at once. Only the energetic intervention of his friends saved him from violence.

A year later he married. The wedding was delayed because Joe, about a month before the announced date, ran off with another girl, the respectable daughter of a professor in the university. He hid out with this partner in a cheap hotel to avoid pursuit by her parents but eventually, after many highly embarrassing and unseemly episodes, went off into maudlin or uproarious drunkenness and finally stupor, leaving his partner in illicit love to her own devices.

Joe's marriage was from the first a failure. He neglected his wife, lay out for days in drinking sprees, wandered off and spent the night in low dives, and availed himself of every opportunity to have casual intercourse with other women.

He made little pretense now of working, neglecting even his position on the city council which had cost him some shrewd planning and considerable effort to obtain. According to the opinion of those who know him, he was not interested in the position itself, that is to say, in anything he might accomplish thereby, but only in the petty fame it might bring him. He enjoyed stepping into various roles in which he played the big shot.

Joe's father, who is a very influential man, some time later got him appointed judge of a local court. This position paid an excellent salary and required only about an hour of work daily. This, however, was too much. He would not attend even to the barest minimum of his duties, refused to go to his office, wandered on pseudoadventures in distant cities without making any provision for his responsibilities to be met, often without letting his famly know he was going or informing them of his whereabouts. Despite the zeal of friends and relatives to make good his deficiencies, he lost this very valuable position.

His father bought him a house, leaving it encumbered with a small mortgage in order to stimulate the patient to use his funds constructively and free himself from his obligation. Although receiving an ample income to make these payments, he made no effort to do so but instead, as his father later discovered, took out another large mortgage and squandered this money as well as his income.

There seemed little incentive or definite purpose in the actions through which he destroyed his opportunities and squandered his and his parents' resources. One can discern no strong recognizable temptation, no formulated course of living, good or evil, for which be abandoned what others find so desirable.

Although his father supplied his wife and children with money (he has two daughters) and continued to give him opportunities to make an easy living at law, he worked little or not at all and spent his time getting in and out of police barracks, going time after time to hospitals where he remained for a few weeks or a month, only to return and take up at once his former practices.

After several years of such living he was sent to a federal psychiatric hospital in Mississippi for study and treatment. Nothing to suggest a psychosis or a psychoneurosis could be found. He showed himself to be highly intelligent and energetic but inclined to be domineering, especially toward his father, whom he would not allow to come on the ward and visit him. After five weeks he left against medical advice. He was classed as a case of psychopathic personality.

Three months later Joe set off in his car, sober and apparently enthusiastic about the prospect of his vacation, to join his wife and children who were spending a few weeks at a summer resort in the Tennessee mountains. On the way he picked up another woman, then after they had a few drinks together apparently lost interest in her. Stopping in a small town in northern Alabama, he left his companion in the car, making some excuse, and went to the railroad station, throwing away the keys to his car on the way in a gesture of careless bravado. At the station he stood before a timetable, closed his eyes, and put down his finger at random. Noting that he had by chance fallen on Tulsa, he bought a ticket and, bringing along a good supply of whiskey, left without more ado for that city.

Nothing was heard from him for several weeks. Leading the life of a bum or city tramp who lives by his wits, he was active at panhandling, petty fraud, and other schemes and tricks to pick up small sums. He fell more than once into the hands of the police. Always disarming and impressive, he cleverly talked himself out of the usual consequences.

At length an acquaintance of Joe's family ran across him in Texas and notified his father, who sent him funds at once by telegraph so that he could come home. Instead, he bought more whiskey and continued his rambles, drinking sometimes with chance acquaintances he found in saloons, occasionally drinking alone, and staggering about uninviting sections of town or out into the countryside.

After going up to Minneapolis, he wandered on an odd impulse into the tent where a celebrated evangelist was exhorting sinners. One of the evangelist's assistants happened on him and urged him to accept salvation and join the troupe. Although an unbeliever, he was attracted by the idea and, with a great show of enthusiasm, announced his intentions of devoting his life to the work.

Professing a lusty rebirth, he attached himself to the evangelist and went on to Chicago, where he was active and successful in bringing in the penitent and getting them out on the sawdust trail. He also showed himself extremely able and for a while industrious in running a mission where vagrants were fed. He told utterly false but dramatic and convincing stories of his life to the religious workers and seemed like one remarkably suited to his new calling.

Joe continued at these activities for several weeks, not drinking and enjoying himself fairly well. He maintains that he never entertained any serious belief in the doctrine of the evangelist or experienced any sensations of penitence or sanctity. "I just sold myself somehow on the idea of doing it," he says with a broad smile.

Meeting a red-haired girl, his thoughts inclined in another direction. Leaving the evangelist's party, he put up with her at a hotel where he briefly enjoyed her charms, then abandoned her as casually as he had begun the relationship.

For a while now he turned to alcohol, taking no interest in anything and summoning only enough energy to get the bottle and drink himself back to snoring oblivion. Shortly afterward he returned home, made a few brief gestures at working, but chiefly idled and drifted.

He continued in this fashion for a year, keeping his wife in misery and perplexity and his father active by day and night in efforts to get him out of jail, to bring him in from low resorts, or to whip up some interest in him to make a new start. Occasionally he spoke seriously of having obtained a new outlook and worked for a few weeks or a month, always showing excellent ability and succeeding with ease in all he attempted. No matter how bright were his prospects, he soon threw them up and went on another round of idle wanderings, self-defeating and apparently boring asocial or antisocial routines, or on mirthless and unhappy drinking bouts.

Finally Joe's wife divorced him and went to live with his father, who assumed full obligation for her support and that of the children, treating her with the greatest kindness and consideration.

Some time later the patient's father sent him to New York for another of his fresh starts. He had for years professed an interest in writing and during his sober interludes, had turned his hand occasionally to journalism. In New York he worked for several weeks and evidently was headed for some success, having already had a few articles accepted, one by a magazine of wide circulation.

Idle drifting among dull and delinquent groups, vagrancy, and sporadic drunkenness now intervened. He soon ceased all efforts to write and led very much the sort of life typical of men who have no opportunities left and (lacking an alternative) exist about large cities, lost to interest and incentive, in states often referred to as *being in the gutter*. Sometimes brawls in bar-rooms, quarrels about cheating in games of chance, etc., brought him into contact with the police. For several months he wandered in the slums of the city, often being brought in by the police or taken to Bellevue and other hospitals for brief periods of treatment.

On returning home, Joe's career began all over again at the point on which he had left off and continued until his present admission to this hospital. Though always cooperative, he was anxious to go before the staff for diagnosis as soon as possible, since he would only then become eligible for parole. Tactful and not obviously demanding, he did not at first press his requests but, after several delays had occurred, sent the following lines to the physician in charge of his case:

> Request is respectfully made
> By R———— number 6-7-3-0
> That his humble case may be laid
> Before a busy medico.
>
> Patient seldom hears the voices,*
> Never waxes vitriolic;
> Quite discerning in his choices
> For a chronic alcoholic.
>
> Quiet and cooperative,
> He is no wise sadistic;
> Records have it that his native
> Instincts are all altruistic
>
> A suicidal tendency
> Is foreign to his credo,
> Due to the marked ascendency
> Of exhibitionistic ego.
>
> Voluntarily committed,
> The patient can stand the gaff
> If only he were permitted
> Presentation to the Staff.
>
> Patient does not wish a discharge
> From this psychopathic knoll;
> He has no urge to roam at large,
> But he would like to have parole.
>
> And so, if it is convenient,
> Your call is respectfully urged;
> Hoping that you will be lenient
> When my rye psychosis is purged.

---

*This reference to hearing voices is, of course, made in jest. He has never experienced hallucinations.

There is little need to give in detail the record of his failures to adjust to these new responsibilities. His behavior was virtually the same as that already described in such patients while on parole status in psychiatric institutions in a similar situation. It was clear to him that freedom would be curtailed if irresponsible or antisocial actions occurred.

No matter how often he was brought in by police or hospital attendants or confined at the barracks for unacceptable behavior, always, in requesting restoration of parole, he seemed to have complete confidence in himself and to feel sure that others would feel likewise. His superficial charm, plausible explanations, and apparent sincerity enlisted the support of all who met him.

During his various periods on parole he met many women, some of whom he convinced he was being treated with incredible injustice at the hospital. Several intelligent and attractive women, persuaded that he was not understood, began to visit the hospital and intercede with authorities there whenever restriction of his privileges became necessary.

Even female employees of the hospital were not immune to his charm and found it difficult to believe he was anything but a wonderful and trustworthy fellow whose only difficulties arose from poor judgment or unfair attitudes on the part of his family or the physicians. Some of the nurses whose past experience with similar problems and direct observation of this subject would, one might think, make it impossible for them not to recognize his serious disorder seemed for a while inclined to believe that such an impressive man as this simply could not continue in failures so futile.*

At the weekly dances held for patients he intrigued and delighted large numbers of feminine visitors. Some of these devoted themselves to his cause, quickly convinced that sufficient sympathy and full demonstration of faith in his inherent manliness would resolve his difficulties.

At Joe's suggestion some of these admirers wrote to officials of veterans organizations and even to congressmen in Washington, insisting on special intervention in the case. On many occasions the patient violated the terms of his parole, returning several hours late from passes after being with some of these kind and zealous ladies who had become increasingly determined to mother him or perhaps to save him by more frankly exciting methods.

Despite all these efforts in his behalf, his behavior became worse and consequently his periods of parole briefer and less frequent. He soon demanded

---

*One of the most attractive and intelligent nurses in the hospital had, several years previously, married a patient whose disorder was diagnosed as psychopathic personality and who was much more obviously a poor marital risk than our present subject. The story of her experiences with him could not be adequately given without devoting our entire volume to it.

his discharge. His family emphasized the great and needless difficulties that would result and urged, in the name of common sense, that he not be released. Since the commitment furnished legal authorization, the medical staff kept him despite his protests.

At the suggestion of the chief of staff, who had consistently reacted to his failures with extraordinary patience, steps were taken that would lead to his soon regaining parole privileges. Just before these steps were completed, communications arrived from Washington citing bitter complaints about the hospital, quoting vicious and startling accusations against this patient's particular advocate, the chief of staff, who, in the opinion of many, had often gone too far in trying to meet his demands.

The patient had written to government officials, employing his cleverness, learning, and ingenuity in such a way as to make some people in high authority suspect that the most fantastic and implausible injustice had been done him. He had, furthermore, so used his father's standing in his home community and so manipulated the great respect in which his father was held that he evoked an extraordinary reaction. Some in Washington were so stirred and misled by his tactics that they apparently acted under the impression that the father's testimony supported that of the son.

When questioned about this surprising attack directed chiefly against the most lenient of all his physicians, Joe was supercilious and a little arrogant, insisted on skipping these subterfuges and getting down to brass tacks about the restoration of his parole. There seemed to be no sense of shame or dismay in this role or at having nothing at all to back up the serious charges he had made.

After being granted parole again, he so conducted himself that the police put him behind bars and notified the hospital of this fact. Shortly afterward he attempted to escape. The attempt was made soon after he had given his word, with all describable aspects of sincerity and with a clear demonstration that he fully understood his commitments and agreed to abide by them.

He became more and more difficult to deal with by the rules and procedures of a hospital set up for the ordinary type of psychotic patient. After a trying period for himself and his physicians, he called in an attorney. By legal procedures that followed the approved technicalities, he obtained his wishes.

Less than a week after Joe's departure from the hospital he returned in such a state that anyone could tell he needed shelter and assistance. At the outer gate of the hospital grounds he demanded that he be admitted. The physician on duty interviewed him and explained that legal steps had been taken which made it impossible for the hospital to readmit him. He begged and argued and brought forth the most cogent and practical and pertinent of reasons why he should be under supervision and treatment. The physician who talked with him agreed with all he said. But despite this agreement and common understanding, there was no means by which he could be taken back.

17

Milt

An incomplete account of this patient will be offered. His behavior and his apparent subjective reactions differ little from those of the patients already presented. He serves, however, as an example of the psychopath who resorts to no alcoholic beverage. Although drinking is sometimes prominent in a superficial appraisal of the clinical picture, nonalcoholic psychopaths are not so rare as the preceding accounts might lead one to believe. Since many observers still tend to explain such patients' essential difficulties as being caused by drinking and in legal matters stress is put upon this factor, it is, perhaps, worth while to consider this case.

At 19 years of age, Milt was admitted to a general hospital for psychiatric study. His mother and other relatives who had brought him from his home in a neighboring state expressed the greatest perplexity about his condition. The behavior which had resulted in his hospitalization became prominent about two years previously, but he was described as being sporadically unreliable and unresponsive since the early teens.

The patient's family were people of considerable means and had for many generations been prominent and highly respected in a city of approximately 100,000 inhabitants. His male antecedents had been judges, bank presidents, distinguished physicians, and brokers. The women on both sides of his family were almost uniformly charming and responsible members of the community. Four years prior to the boy's admission to the hospital, his father's business had failed, and in the consequent readjustment it was revealed that the father had disposed of large funds illegally. The family was able, however, to make arrangements which prevented serious legal action, and the father at present is established in another business. Except for this episode the father's career does not show any evidence of unusual or serious asocial behavior. Nothing at all in the father's activities can be found which would suggest the kind of behavior so prominent in the son. However indefensible the misappropriation of funds may be, it is an action based on motives which anyone can understand, though one may not approve of it. Sufficient income still existed for the family to live well. The patient's older brother, an older sister, and one younger brother were all regarded as normal and attractive young people. The two older siblings had finished college successfully.

The first thing which caused the parents worry was the patient's apparent failure to take anything seriously. Milt often became involved in adolescent pranks, but, unlike his playmates, he did not profit by his mistakes. If he, with other boys, destroyed property during the celebration after a high school football victory, he seemed unable to realize his responsibility for the damage. His verbal apologies were magnificent and he seemed in discussion to understand fully that he had been in the wrong. But he would soon repeat the same deed and, if apprehended, would express his regret with the same charming politeness but apparently without any awareness that the continued repetitions robbed his promises of conviction.

Milt's mother describes him as having become callous, saying that there seemed to be no way in which she could arouse any actual response. He agreed readily when rebuked, so readily, in fact, that the mother finally began to feel that the meaning of her words did not touch him.

An incident during the previous year illustrates this young man's specific indifference to stimuli accepted as basic by the ordinary person. His mother, who had just returned from the hospital after a major surgical operation, found it necessary to attend personally to an urgent matter of business. Our patient graciously volunteered to drive her on this mission in the family's automobile.

On the whole he had been thoughtful and attentive to her during the illness, and she had tried to grasp some shreds of encouragement from his apparent attitude on which to build hope again that favorable changes lay ahead. She had recovered sufficiently to sit up and to walk about a little but the surgeon had strongly prohibited any major physical exertion.

It was necessary to cross a long bridge over a river at the edge of town to reach their destination, and both the patient and his mother were vexed when the car stopped near the center of this bridge, leaving them inconveniently isolated. Milt, who was rather expert in such matters, soon found the cause of the trouble. A fuse had blown out. There being no extra fuse on hand and relatively little traffic at this hour, he offered to walk to a garage less than a half mile distant and bring back the simple article needed. Darkness was falling and it was difficult to estimate when another car might pass which could be utilized to expedite the trip to the garage. Most drivers crossed this bridge at high speed and there might be difficulty in flagging anyone down as darkness increased.

Bidding his mother an affectionate good-bye, Milt cheered her with the assurance that he would be back in less than fifteen minutes. Someone at the garage, he pointed out, would be glad to drive him back, so she would be left alone hardly more than a moment.

After a half hour, uneasiness developed in the mother as she waited and wondered about the possibilities of an accident having befallen her son. An occasional car racing across the bridge prompted dreadful speculations about hit-and-run drivers and the much publicized dangers of mutilation and death on the highways. When an hour had passed, Milt's mother, perhaps still more susceptible to stress than ordinary because of her recent operation, became desperate.

Her own situation was far from pleasant. The business she had to transact was important, and she had not regained sufficient strength to put up easily with this complication. Forbidden to walk any considerable distance, she found herself unhappily marooned in a spot where it was not unnatural for a woman left alone for an indefinite time to think of unpleasant possibilities, including robbery or personal molestation from night wanderers.

Her increasing worry about her son diverted her from preoccupation with her personal safety but finally brought her to a point little short of panic. After waiting a little longer, she got out, stood in the middle of the bridge, and at length succeeded in signalling a motorist who drove her home.

Almost frantic, she telephoned two hospitals to inquire at the emergency room about injured persons recently brought in from the road. She had already sent her younger son with a neighbor who offered assistance by automobile to inquire at the garage where Milt had told her he would get the needed fuse and to search that neighborhood. Before this expedition returned, Milt himself appeared.

He had, he explained, procured the fuse, started the car, and driven on home. During the next hour he by turns showed vexation at his mother for not having waited until he so belatedly got back and a bland immunity to any recognition that he had behaved irresponsibly or inconsiderately.

Milt had begun his trip to the garage with commendable haste. Shortly after leaving the bridge, he passed a cigar store. Noting that the afternoon's football scores were being posted on a blackboard, he lingered for ten or fifteen minutes to check results.

188

During this interval he recalled that a girl he knew lived a half block down a side street in this neighborhood and decided to drop in on her for a moment. She greeted him cordially and he spent approximately an hour in her company. There is no evidence that any sudden sexual urge or any other strongly tempting impulse diverted our patient. He had no special liking for the girl, and no attempt was made to gain even the mildest erotic favor.

Milt chatted with the girl amiably but desultorily about trifling matters. His departure followed the arrival of her date for the evening, whose rights to her company he acknowledged after a pleasant exchange of courtesies by bidding them good-bye and going on his way.

It is interesting to note that this conduct did not result from absentmindedness, from specific amnesia or confusion, or from some attraction so enthralling or distracting as to delay or divert a person from even a mildly serious mission. He was quite aware all through the episode of his mother waiting on the bridge and seems to have been free from any grudge or other impulse that would influence him deliberately to offend her or cause her hardship. Missing from his realization, apparently, was the evaluation of her emotional reactions that would in another have outweighed a whim so petty as that which in Milt gained easy ascendancy.

During his third year at high school he began to practice truancy, one or more times a week not going to school at all but hanging around poolrooms, going to motion pictures, or aimlessly wandering in the streets and parks. His absences were, of course, reported, and, as he could not have failed to foresee, became known each time to his parents. He often began by denying, simply and with the most thorough appearance of innocence, all charges of truancy. After the charges had been obviously demonstrated as true, he gave ingenious excuses. As these episodes continued, his excuses became more easily recognized as absurd or impossible. He always expressed regret, usually admitted himself at fault, and never failed to make convincing promises that the truancy would never recur. Efforts were made by various relatives, by physicians, and by scoutmasters to find out why the boy behaved as he did. He did not show a particular interest in any hobby or in any dissipation. All were at a loss in trying to discover what could possibly be his motivation. He was apparently frank with those who tried to investigate his reactions, seldom became sulky or evasive, and never showed anything that looked like genuine embarrassment or a realization that he had been caught in a lie. He always stated that he understood the necessity of attending school regularly and seemed from what he had to say about it actually to understand this better than the average boy of his years.

Meanwhile, he mixed freely with his contemporaries, attended dances, and played football. Sometimes he failed to attend football practice, deciding instead to loll about his room. He was, however, quite energetic when he chose to bestir himself. His ability was regarded as high by all his teachers, though his academic standing suffered from the gross neglect with which he treated his studies.

Not only his parents but also the two older siblings noted that he began to show less interest in companions of his own social status and to seek the company of boys and girls who were regarded by his friends as beneath him in taste and intelligence. Although many of his new associates were of questionable moral standing, they are described as being depressing or boring rather than actively depraved. He did not appear to be particularly driven by sexual urges for which he might be seeking fulfillment with these girls who were his so-called social inferiors. He did occasionally have intercourse but probably no more often than other boys of his age and class.

Now and then he failed to return to his home during the night, choosing to stay with some of his new acquaintances. He was never reported drunk and apparently did not use alcohol at all. When questioned about his absence, he usually made glib excuses. When his stories were broken down, he often showed pique and seemed to feel that he was being unjustly bothered. Sometimes he would admit his inconsiderateness with what seemed strong sincerity. But a week later his parents would pace the floor, telephone dozens of his acquaintances, and spend a miserable night of anxiety, only to see him appear the next day with some casual explanation.

Once after he had remained away for two full nights, the police were called. He was picked up at a dive where slot machines and other gambling devices furnished amusement to mill workers and rustics from the surrounding countryside. He had previously driven over to a nearby city with a casual acquaintance who had gone there in the course of his duties as a traveling salesman. The fact that he had not taken the trouble to inform his mother of his intentions seemed to him a trifle in comparison with what he indignantly regarded as the meddling of his family in asking the police to look for him.

He showed little regard for the convenience or the property of others, sometimes misappropriating things which he apparently did not mean to keep or sell but which he put to his own use without ordinary regard for the trouble inflicted on relatives, friends, or strangers. An example will illustrate.

Noting that a family in the neighborhood was on vacation, he tampered with the wiring of their car until he arranged connections by which he could start the motor without a key. Driving off to the house of a slightly younger friend, he explained that an uncle had given him the car and that he was leaving on a pleasure trip to New York. Another fellow, he said, who had planned to go with him had to give up the trip at the last moment. Our patient suggested that the friend come along.

Everything indicated that the situation was as represented. There was casual mention of details that suggested ample financial provision for all needs. Making hasty arrangements and telling his family of the fine opportunity, the friend joined in the expedition.

Our patient showed no signs of haste or uneasiness and the other boy's parents later regarded it as almost inconceivable that he could have been so self-assured under the circumstances.

Both travellers were surprised when they ran out of gasoline seventy or eighty miles away from town. The fuel gauge was out of order and had given misleading information.

The boy who had been persuaded to come along soon got other surprises. It became apparent that Milt had only a few dollars on him and was expecting his guest to contribute most of the expense for fuel. Suspecting a good deal now about the situation, the friend refused to give over what he had and decided not to go on.

Making his way to the nearest telephone, our patient called his family by long distance (reversing the charges) and told them of being stranded in this lonely spot, that he lacked sufficient funds to get back, and that he needed them to come for him at once.

Milt had apparently hoped to get some money from his companion at the beginning, then to sponge or panhandle along the way, to beat the bill at restaurants and filling stations, perhaps to get additional cash from time to time by playing slot machines or gambling in night spots or by misrepresentations or petty swindling. He thought, too, that, if it became necessary, he could sell the spare tire, a new spotlight, the radio, or other accessories from the car. The patient intended, it seems, not to dispose of the car itself but to return it surreptitiously after it had served his purpose.

It is interesting to contrast the ingenuity in some features of his plan with the injudiciousness of the general scheme. The talk of going all the way to New York with which he beguiled his companion probably represented a vague hope (if lucky breaks occurred, etc.) but the unlikelihood of getting that far did not deter the patient in his actions. Apparently Milt said to himself, well, if we don't make it all the way to New York, at least we'll have a good trip and see a lot of other places nearer at hand.

His parents, who had been deeply worried over his unexplained absence, drove through a hard rainstorm in haste and arrived exhausted and considerably upset. Milt was calm and full of ingenious explanations. His father arranged for the misappropriated automobile to be returned to its owner. The patient seemed not to understand why everyone got so upset and "nagged at him" about what had happened.

He did not seem to be prompted by strong yearning for adventure or any obvious, formulated, or purposeful criminal bent. Though he frequently stole small sums of money from his family, he did not engage in robbery or any regular and understandable misdemeanors while out on these jaunts.

He was at this stage sent off to a strict school in Virginia where discipline was stressed more than studies. After many misadventures he graduated satisfactorily. During his time at the preparatory school he showed no real or serious formulation of an aim and no encouraging tendency to change. When at home during vacations he continued his old practices. His family often sought to find out if he misunderstood or resented anything in their treatment of him. He was offered more freedom, a larger allowance, and other inducements to be more cooperative and considerate. He accepted these proposals but always continued to steal money from his mother's purse, to pawn objects from his home, or to go off for a day or two with the family car, sometimes damaging it or leaving it without gasoline.

After graduating from school, he entered a well-known military college in the East. For a year his progress in his studies was uneven. He was plainly bright, but he sometimes failed to attend an examination or to appear at drill. Occasionally he disappeared for longer periods. He gave various and very shrewd accounts of illness at home and of other emergencies. Since the college specialized in reshaping headstrong youths, unusual efforts were made to keep him despite his many irresponsible and absurd capers. He consistently cheated and lied but when rebuked denied all charges with astonishing suaveness and aplomb.

Shortly before his admission to the hospital he had been expelled, during his second year, from the military college. The events which led to the expulsion were typical of the psychopath. After a long series of irresponsible and often dishonest acts, Milt went downtown without permission when the cadet corps was assembling for a formal drill in celebration of the visit of a high military authority. He remained away all that afternoon and night but returned the next day, quite casual, and gave glib but hollow excuses for his absence. He had not been drinking and he knew perfectly well that he would have to face serious disciplinary action on his return. He was not a forgetful or absentminded person but appeared to be quite deliberate in his failures.

Shortly after this and while confined to barracks, Milt slipped away again and deliberately started a rumor that he had married a local prostitute. This story came to the school authorities and was for a time believed to be true. Later it was proved false, the patient having thought it a good joke to spread the report. While action on these matters was pending, he slipped out of his quarters again against the college regulations. Two other cadets, responsible in the matter, had to report him. He at once denied their report though the facts were plain and plainly showed him in falsehood. His family was informed that it had become impossible to persuade anyone to room with him and that the student body could not put up any further with him.

Milt arrived home apparently well pleased with himself. He admitted that he was sorry to leave college, for which he had voluntarily expressed a desire and to which he had never objected. He quickly placed all the blame for his expulsion on others and seemed to feel that nothing more should be said of it. What explanation he gave his parents centered about points of honor and principles which he let them know it was not modest or quite proper to speak of frankly and fully. He meant to promote the belief that he had, out of respect to the stoic traditions of honor in the school, sacrificed himself to protect another. There was not the slightest thread of truth in the skein of lies and false implications he built up about this, but it very naturally appealed to his parents.

Examination at the hospital showed a splendid figure of a young man slightly over 6 feet tall, weighing 180 pounds, and free from any sign of physical illness. Milt was neatly and becomingly dressed, distinguished in manner, alert, and intelligent. Although his politeness was unfailing, it was plain that he thought the psychiatric examination a bore. He confessed that he held it as nothing short of ridiculous for his parents to consider that there was any possibility of his having a personality disorder. He showed no interest in efforts to approach whatever emotional factors might lie behind his maladjustment and apparently was incapable of realizing that he had shown signs of maladjustment. His technical reasoning powers were excellent.

All the information about his past was discussed. Milt made many ingenious excuses, and if too much undeniable evidence was presented for him to persist in them, he dismissed the point. He would, in response to leading questions, state at times that phases of his situation seemed serious, but it was plain that he was not moved. No evidence of any substantial affective relation with his family, with girls, or with friends could be elicited. In discussing his expulsion from college, he maintained that he had been a victim of the military code of honor, allowing himself to be sacrificed instead of denying the report of the other cadets, which he calmly maintained was a falsehood.

"It had to be me or those boys. They were seniors, and it would have been harder on them than on me to be sent down."

A few days before entering the hospital he had been arrested for speeding after taking the family car without permission. He was given a summons but neglected to appear at court the next morning. The police found him and brought him to the barracks, where he telephoned his parents and indignantly demanded that they come at once and have him released. Hoping that the night in jail might be helpful, they refused to do so, carefully explaining their reasons. On being released, he showed plainly that he felt he had been seriously misused but condescendingly offered a cool forgiveness. Milt had no excuse for not answering his summons except to say that he had overslept. He had, however, been on the streets for several hours when the police arrested him at about noon.

This patient showed no sign at all of an ordinary psychosis. He was self-possessed, shrewd, and entirely calm except for a polite impatience to be gone from the hospital.

Milt was told frankly that everything indicated a serious condition and one that demanded his attention and his major efforts. He was bored with all efforts to approach him but agreed to undertake a detailed plan that was worked out. It was plain that he had no idea of doing so. On leaving the hospital, he continued exactly as he had been doing before.

The voice is Jacob's voice, but the hands are the hands of Esau.
— Genesis 27:22.

18

Degrees of disguise in essential pathology

The cases already reported are only a few among many hundreds whom I have observed. All of these people, when their records over the years are considered, strike one as remarkably similar. If the story of each could be told in detail, it is believed that the similarity would become more plain to any reader. It is the contention of the present argument that this personality disorder shapes and hardens into the outlines of a very definite clinical entity or reaction type, into a pattern of disorder quite as recognizable and as real as any listed in psychiatric nomenclature. When a large number of such patients are considered carefully, the vagueness with which they are often regarded lessens and the type emerges certainly not less sharp than that type on which is based the concept of schizophrenia. But vague as the concept of schizophrenia remains and various as its manifestations are, the schizophrenic, when recognized, is promptly called a patient with mental illness and treated as such. The psychopath, however, continues to be treated as a petty criminal at one moment, as mentally ill person at the next, and again as a well and normal human being—all without the slightest change in his condition having occurred. I do not have any dogmatic advice as to a final or even a satisfactory way of successfully rehabilitating these sociopaths but believe that it is important for some consistent attitude to be reached.

In the hope of letting major features of the clinical picture emerge more clearly, the following case reports are added. The persons already described are regarded as typical examples showing the disorder in its distinct clinical manifestations of disability. Many of them are plainly unsuited for life in any community; some are as thoroughly incapacitated, in my opinion, as most patients with unmistakable schizophrenic psychosis. Whether this is to be regarded as a more or less willful contrariness or as a sickness like schizophrenia, in which the patient is to be protected and looked after, may for the moment be put aside.

In the reports that follow, an effort has been made to present persons who are able to make some sort of adjustment in life and who may perhaps be regarded as less severely incapacitated, and in varying degrees. These patients are offered as examples showing, in some respects, indications of the same disorder seen in the others. In them, however, it may be regarded as milder or more limited. The psychopathologic process, the deviation (or the arrest), is, as with the others, a process affecting basic personal reactions; but here it has not altogether dominated the scene. It has not crowded ordinary successful functioning in the outer aspects of work and social relations entirely out of the picture.

Some of these patients I believe are definitely psychopaths but in a milder degree, just as a patient still living satisfactorily in a community may be clearly a schizophrenic but nevertheless able to maintain himself outside the shelter of a psychiatric hospital. Others might not deserve to be called psychopaths but seem to show strong, even if not consistent, tendencies and inner reactions characteristic of the group. They might be compared to the plain and complete manifestations of the psychopath as the schizoid personality might be compared to the schizophrenic patient who is obviously psychotic.

An example will perhaps make this comparison more concrete.

Some years ago I was consulted by a man 32 years of age whose only complaint was of a general listlessness which he had noticed for about a year. He was a tall, rather slender person, slightly brittle in manner, and gave a definite impression of being not very much worried about his complaint. He lived with his parents in a small town where he made an excellent salary as an expert in looking after electrical machinery in a large mill. He enjoyed the title of engineer though he had no formal education beyond that obtained in a rustic high school. Examination soon brought out the fact that he had never had sexual relations with a woman. He had, however, made the attempt not once but many times, the first attempt being twelve years ago. He succeeded in having erections but ejaculatio praecox always occurred, and he failed entirely to effect an entrance.

This situation, which most young men would find extremely distressing, he spoke about very casually. Questions concerning his attitudes toward love and women brought rather stereotyped answers. He denied ever having scruples about fornication. To him it was evidently neither good nor bad. His attempts to practice were, it would seem, made with a vague idea of doing what was the custom. He professed to be interested in overcoming his inability to perform intercourse and showed no embarrassment and little reticence about sexual questions but gave a strong impression of having only the shallowest interest. His entire emotional life seemed perfunctory and without warmth. Nothing in his experience could be elicited which brought forth any vividness or enthusiasm. He said that he was at present going with a girl whom he would like to marry, but his attitude toward her seemed without any tangible desire or eager anticipation. At times he gave a stilted, incongruous little laugh that sounded almost exactly like the manneristic laugh so familiar in actual schizophrenics. No delusions or hallucinations could be brought out. He had been leading an outwardly successful life and was a fairly conscientious and reliable member of society.

The man just mentioned could certainly not be called legally incompetent at present. Nor would he, by most psychiatrists, be classed as a case of schizophrenia, with all the practical implications of being adjudged psychotic. He is mentioned in order to compare him with the patient who is psychotic and who is frankly schizophrenic.

As an example of the developed schizophrenic, let us consider a former patient of mine who often sat for hours in a corner staring vacantly into space, his lips moving and silly, grimacing smiles flitting across his face. Sometimes this man would not answer questions, apparently not even hearing them, so absorbed was he in subjective contemplation. Again he would grin glassily and wink his eye or occasionally speak with passion about strange machinery in a distant city which enemies whom he referred to merely as "they" were using to inject queer colors into his thoughts and sometimes to make him ejaculate. This man at times suddenly attacked others. It was eminently necessary to keep him on a closed ward and under close supervision.

In some of the cases to be presented, such a comparison probably would not be justified. Some patients might more accurately be thought of as showing scattered indications of such a disorder, suggestions of a disturbance central in nature but well contained within an outer capsule of successful behavior much deeper that the merely logical and theoretical rationality of the fully disabled psychopath. In those who consistently support themselves and pass regularly as acceptable members of the social group, we can only be astonished at the difference between such technical outer adjustment and the indications of deeper pathologic features so similar to those found in the complete manifestation of the disorder.

There are many patients who show relatively circumscribed antisocial behavior or temporary episodes of gross, general delinquency, who have, I feel, much less in common with the obvious psychopath than those who make a better outward impression but who consistently show signs of inner subjective reactions typical of the clinically disabled patient.

These patients with temporary or circumscribed maladjustment or self-defeating behavior will be referred to later at greater length.* They are mentioned here to distinguish them not only from the fully manifested psychopath but also from those who, over the years, show more subtle indications of widespread and intractable defect or deviation in essential personal reactions and subjective evaluations.

The psychopathologic process, or state, which I believe is seriously disabling the patients already presented may be regarded as affecting in part and in varying degree those yet to be discussed. It may now be added that I believe that in these personalities designated as partially or inwardly affected, a very deepseated disorder often exists. The true difference between them and the psychopaths who continually go to jails or to psychiatric hospitals is that they keep up a far better and more consistent outward appearance of being normal. This outward appearance may include business or professional careers that continue in a sense successful, and which are truly successful when measured by financial reward or by the casual observer's opinion of real accomplishment. It must be remembered that even the most severely and obviously disabled psychopath presents a technical appearance of sanity, often one of high intellectual capacities, and not infrequently succeeds in business or professional activities for short periods, sometimes for considerable periods.

I maintain, however, that the actual but concealed pathology in some of the patients now to be described is in a deeper sense also far-reaching and profound. Although they occasionally appear on casual inspection as successful members of the community, as able lawyers, executives, or physicians, they do not, it seems, succeed in the sense of finding satisfaction or fulfillment in their accomplishments. Nor do they, when the full story is known, appear to find this in any other ordinary activity. By ordinary activity we do not need to postulate what is considered moral or decent by the aver-

*See. pp. 288 to 302.

age man but may include any type of asocial, or even criminal, activity so long as its motivation can be translated into terms of ordinary human striving, selfish or unselfish.

The chief difference between the patients already discussed and some of those to be mentioned lies perhaps in whether the mask or facade of psychobiologic health is extended into superficial material success. I believe that the relative state of this outward appearance is not necessarily consistent with the degree to which the person is really affected by the essential disorder. An analogy is at hand if we compare the catatonic schizophrenic, with his obvious psychosis, to the impressively intelligent paranoid patient who outwardly is much more normal and may even appear better adjusted than the average person. The catatonic schizophrenic is more likely to recover and, despite his appearance, is often less seriously disordered than the paranoiac.

It becomes difficult to imagine how much of the sham and hollowness which cynical commentators have immemorially pointed out in life may come from contact in serious issues with persons affected in some degree by the disorder we are trying to describe. The fake poet who really feels little; the painter who, despite his loftiness, had his eye chiefly on the lucrative fad of his day; the fashionable clergyman who, despite his burning eloquence or his lively castigation of the devil, is primarily concerned with his advancement; the flirt who can readily awaken love but cannot feel love or recognize its absence; parents who, despite smooth convictions that they have only the child's welfare at heart, actually reject him except as it suits their own petty or selfish aims: all these types, so familiar in literature and in anybody's experience, may be as they are because of a slight affliction with the personality disorder now under discussion. I believe it probable that many persons outwardly imposing yet actually of insignificant emotional import really are so affected.

Let us not, however, attempt to explain all pretense and all fraud on this basis. There are many other psychopathologic reactions besides the one with which we are now concerned. And some of these, too, are capable of producing such results. Let us be especially chary about assuming this limitation in our enemies or our neighbors. The mechanisms of reaction formation, projection, rationalization, and many other distorting influences work in all of us at the behest of envy, pique, or prejudice. It is not easy to estimate the degree of our neighbor's sincerity, the worth of an artist's production, or the clergyman's real motive.

Some of the episodes or symptoms mentioned in the brief sketches that follow may represent less profound inner disturbance than anything properly belonging with that of the real psychopath. Many of the acts might in isolation occur in the lives of people who at length achieve excellent adjustment not only externally but also within themselves. The material to follow is offered not primarily for the purpose of making a diagnosis of psychopathic personality but in illustration of features which specifically characterize the psychopath and which may, against a background of better general adjustment, emerge in sharper clarity. What can be learned from fantasy or dream in the normal person, from prejudice or many socially admired forms of self-renunciation, has been of value in psychiatric efforts to understand schizophrenia and other grave personality disorders. Many of the characteristics and reactions seen in extreme exaggeration among the psychotic appear sometimes to be utilized by those of great talent and excellent psychiatric status in the successful pursuit of valuable personal and social aims.[216] It is unlikely that the specific reactions of the psychopath can be directly utilized for important positive accomplishment. It is believed, however, that many persons in bewilderment and frustration temporarily fall into similar reactions and eventually, finding better means of adaptation, profit from what has been learned through the pathologic experiences.

The following accounts are given, then, for what light they may reflect on the serious clinical disorder manifested in the previous cases.

19

The psychopath as businessman

No attempt will be made to give a detailed history of this man. Suffice it to say that the incidents mentioned are not isolated experiences in the general life pattern but rather expressions of a motif which persistently recurs to interrupt the outward serenity.

He is now 50 years of age, and he has gone on to achieve considerable business success, being an equal partner in a wholesale grocery concern. As a businessman there is much to be said for him. Except for his periodic sprees, he works industriously. He has contributed foresight and ability to the business, whereas his partner has contributed the stability necessary to keep things going when he is out of action.

He is pleasant and affable during his normal phases, which make up the greater part of his time. One gets the impression, however, that ordinary life is not very full or rich, that strange gods are ever calling him, and that the call is far dearer to his heart than anything else. He is, perhaps, like a man who through necessity has given himself over to foreign ways for most of his hours and who goes on fairly patiently but without spontaneity until the time when he can throw it all aside for a while and go wholeheartedly at what he finds really to his taste.

These recesses are sometimes taken at intervals of a week; occasionally several months go by without one. They sometimes last merely a few days, sometimes a week or more.

He does not drink in groups with men and women whom he meets in the ordinary course of his life. It would never occur to him to have a cocktail party or to serve whiskey to friends in his own house. Apparently he can see no point in what might be called ordinary or normal drinking, in the sense, say, of taking several highballs to be warm and lively, to talk more gaily to pretty women and cut a finer figure in their eyes, to be more playful, to throw aside the routine problems of the day, and to express oneself a little more vividly.

If he drinks at all, it is to reach a state of roaring folly and perhaps to continue until he may fall limp. He frequently goes out of the city and, in some hotel of dubious standing, gathers a few coarse companions and begins to pour liquor into himself on such occasions. His associates are usually uninteresting drifters or vagrants ready to accept any handout. Sometimes obvious psychopaths are included. Often harlots are called into the room where this noisy group of fat, middle-aged men are already staggering about, sweaty in their undershirts or lying out half stupefied across the beds or on the floors.

The women are stripped or encouraged to strip themselves, and among those men still able to flounder about a great clamor arises. The women are chased about and fumbled over. Intercourse is accomplished by the more energetic ones, not in the privacy ordinarily considered desirable but in the presence of all and often on beds across which a more sodden member of the group lies snoring.

Men and women stumble about, the men pouring more and more whiskey into themselves, the women usually drinking little but occasionally picking their senseless companions' pockets. Daylight often finds a few of this jolly brotherhood still wobbling feebly or crawling about the room in search of more liquor.

During the next day some pull themselves together and depart, others remain drinking and cursing through the morning and afternoon. Consciousness and power to speak or sit erect come and go through the hours. During these more lucid intervals some find what they take as exceeding delight in sitting, naked and unsteady, on the edge of an untidy bed, staring at a companion, smiling inanely, and, in slurred, mushy tones, repeating for thirty minutes or more: "You old son of a bitch. You old son of a bitch, Jack. You old son of a bitch, you."

After such exploits the subject of our discussion returns home feeling pretty ill but apparently refreshed spiritually for his other kind of life. At other times his sprees will take the classic form already described, which consists in having a Negro boy drive him out into the woods where he drinks to semiconsciousness and, after lying out for a satisfactory period, allows the boy to drive him home.

Usually these extravaganzas take place without attracting general attention, but occasionally exuberance carries the play beyond its early secluded setting and the public is treated to puzzling displays. Returning from several days of ordinary lying out and still boisterous and maudlin by turns, this executive, disappointed in his wife's failure to greet him with proper enthusiasm, took a few more pulls from the bottle. Feeling suddenly much misused and sorry for himself, he rushed out on the lawn and began to bewail in thunderous tones the general injustice of his situation.

Since the time was high noon on Independence Day, he soon drew a fair-sized audience. Stimulated by this, he rushed to the dog's kennel and fumbled with the brass-studded collar of his big Doberman pinscher, who, patient-eyed, watched his frantic master. Gaining possession of the collar, he placed it around his own neck and, with the leash flying behind, set off at a lively pace through the neighborhood. Attempting to bark like a dog as he went and shaking his collar, he succeeded in conveying his conviction to the public. Not only was he, so to speak, "in the dog house" (in his wife's disfavor), but in vigorous canine outcries he registered his protest.

Trotting over the well-kept lawns and about the gardens, he was observed by many acquaintances who lived near him in this fashionable section of the city. Occasionally, in bursts of zeal, he practiced or mimicked the dog's well-known ritual in which eliminative and gregarious impulses blend. By the time he drew near the outskirts of town, he had a retinue of small boys in his wake. Realizing now that it was Independence Day, he led them to a small store where fireworks were sold and, roaring with wordy generosity, bought for them dozens of Roman candles, firecrackers, and skyrockets.

For a while his irrelevant shouts merged with the hissing and popping of fireworks but, becoming always more aggressive and purposeless, his efforts to direct his companions began to vex them. With the well-known callousness of small boys where mischief is concerned, they hit upon the idea that it would be more fun to direct their Roman candle barrages at or close about this comical stranger and to chase him.

As the skyrockets began to whiz by his wobbling head and the fiery balls from Roman candles began to play about his vicinity, he blundered into flight. With the shouting, joyous band behind, he made a zigzag progress which finally led him to the house of a friend.

This man has never been admitted to a psychiatric hospital. He has often spent a few days in general hospitals while sobering up and occasionally a week or more in retreats which advertise their success in *curing the liquor habit*.

For perhaps 80 or 90 per cent of his existence he has been a prosperous and respected member of his community and outwardly is not unlike other men of the same position.

20

The psychopath as man of the world

He comes from excellent stock and his educational background includes four years at a celebrated preparatory school and three at a well-known university. During his student days he took no interest whatsoever in any of his studies. His shrewdness, his skill at utilizing the work of his friends, from whose papers he usually patched together his own themes and essays, and his reliance on cheating in examinations enabled him to stay in the university through his junior year. His real interests during this period consisted in decking himself with fine clothes in which to saunter about, in presiding at social gatherings, and in flimsy but pretentious lovemaking with a large number of prominent young ladies. In the eyes of these and of their mothers he passed as a dashing beau, almost as an *arbiter elegantiarum.*

Among his fraternity brothers he was regarded with mixed feelings. Though better supplied with funds than most of his associates, he did not pay his dues and seldom his board at the fraternity house where he occupied the choice quarters. These shortcomings, however, were tolerated, if not entirely overlooked, because of the urbanity he lent to house parties, his impassioned speeches on the sacred mysteries of brotherhood, his eloquence and skill in inducing desirable freshmen to join his group, and the general air of *jeunesse dorée* which encompassed him. Some of his contemporaries, vexed at finding their dinner clothes or their favorite shoes always on this peacock at the very time they were most needed by the rightful owner and pressed to pay dues and other expenses which were higher for others because of his delinquencies, occasionally grumbled and cynically wondered if this glittering brother did not have special grounds for his fraternal zeal. His consecration in whipping up fraternity spirit in less ardent members was notable.

Space forbids a detailed survey of his career. It has been remarkably consistent. At nearly 50 years of age he finds no difficulty in having always at his beck and call several women who rush to comfort him and who work incessantly to find new positions for him each time he loses the last one. For long periods of his life he has been almost entirely supported by wealthy ladies who entertained him for weeks at fashionable house parties in summer and at winter resorts and who "lent" large sums of money to him time after time when he moaned his inability to make a fresh start in life.

He sometimes slept with the wives of his friends but, when a careful study is made of his life, it appears that he sought a mother-surrogate rather than a mistress or a real mate. Invariably the relation was one in which the woman served as protectress and support. His most effective means of winning the favor of these ladies consisted chiefly in becoming maudlin drunk, weeping like a baby, begging his companion to give him lethal drugs so that he could destroy himself, and quite generally indulging in theatrics familiar in spoiled children.

In his work as insurance agent, cotton broker, automobile dealer, advertising specialist, etc., he showed consistent and remarkable capacities for rest and casual disregard of primary responsibilities. It is true that he made valuable business associations at the country club, where he played golf or loitered a good part of each day. These associations often enabled him to make a good living for brief periods, but no matter how easy the work or how favorable the prospects, he had no serious difficulty in failing. Nor had he any more difficulty in arousing fresh enthusiasm in some tender-minded lady, or ladies, to raise money for a new venture or to find some easy position for him in the business of her friends or relatives.

He usually preferred women older than himself, becoming, in fact, a veritable lion among dowagers in his community. Young women also have sought to mother him. The large number of women who appear in his life story have this in common: they have consistently been of sober temperament and inclined toward domesticity rather than toward flirtatious, erotically passionate, or promiscuous behavior. This is true of the younger as well as of his older benefactresses.

Prominent in his plan of life are frequent sprees of drinking which he inaugurates by a few highballs in pleasant company but continues alone in his own quarters, in a hotel room, or perhaps in some bawdy house. These episodes sometimes occur without any objective precipitating cause but often follow some disappointment or reverse. He seldom fails to get word to the lady who is mothering him at the moment, giving dramatic utterance to his woe. Strenuous efforts are made to save him. Doctors are called, friends are sent to reason with him, and the ladies themselves plead. Despite all this attention, which he appears to relish keenly, he continues to drink, usually not incapacitating himself but taking enough to keep his protectors active. The spree often lasts for several days with our hero chiding and complaining, bursting into tears, and heaping his own self-pity upon the floods of pity which beat about him.

Frequently it has been necessary to send him to general hospitals and occasionally to psychiatric hospitals, where he finally settles down amidst all sorts of dramatics.

About ten years ago, before the period of these observations, no doubt perceiving his own advancing years, he married an extremely intelligent widow some years his elder who had for a decade tried to rehabilitate him and who was generally regarded as wealthy. Though casually unfaithful to her, he kept up a better front for the two years during which she lived. She spent money lavishly on him. In addition to this, her fortune was drastically reduced in a depression, and she died leaving him only enough for a few months of extravagance. The night after her funeral he spent in a cheap brothel, drinking and weeping and moaning, apparently for himself.

His ability to alarm and to draw out protective impulses in women is remarkable. Superficially he gives the impression when with them of a dashing and somewhat predatory male. He is not entirely without ambition as a lover and actually seduces some of his protectresses. His approach in seduction is, however, nearly always through pity.

On one of his recent sprees he called a young widow twenty years his junior and dramatically bemoaned his plight, insisting that only her influence kept him from blowing out his brains. Despite her earnest activities to cheer him up he continued to drink, calling her up from time to time to tell more of his sad state and how much worse he had become. That evening he came to her house and begged her to give him drugs with which to dispatch himself, then rushed off crying dramatically that he was en route to a notorious brothel. In the company of a male relative she followed him there and exhorted him to go home and sober up. As her pity and distress increased, his firmness in remaining hardened, and no doubt his pleasure also waxed sweeter.

This case well portrays the astonishing power that nearly all psychopaths and part-psychopaths have to win and to bind forever the devotion of women. Because of this they are often regarded as vigorous or romantic lovers, as men of peculiar virility. I believe, however, that they are seldom as well endowed in this way as the average man. Nor do they appear to be as much interested in really erotic aims as most men.

Such things are of course impossible to prove or to demonstrate, but the more intimately a large number of such people are studied, the stronger becomes the impression that it is chiefly woman's impulse to mother that they arouse. Feminine intuition senses that here, concealed beneath an appearance of maturity, is a baby or something very much like a helpless, crying little baby. Her deep instincts to nurse and to protect this winsome little darling are unconsciously called out. The superficial relationship of woman to her lover conceals this fundamental urge. She longs to take this defenseless creature, hold him to her breast, guard him, shape him, and let him grow up under her protection. Her feminine intuition, which so accurately divines the presence of the spiritual baby, fails, alas, to understand that it is a baby who will never grow up.

21

The psychopath as gentleman

This man, whom for convenience we may call W. R. L., first came to my attention professionally when seen strapped down during hydrotherapy in a continuous tub. There, surrounded by dozens of the most complete *madmen* an imaginative layman could conceive, he strained, cursed, bellowed, and hurled defiant imprecations at all about him.

Having seen him in the past occasionally at balls or garden parties in a Southern city famous for the amenities of life, I was astonished at the spectacle he now presented. He literally raved as he twisted and spat, damning his wife especially but sparing no one. Though quieter and less dramatic when he believed himself unobserved, he gave at this moment as good a superficial impression of honest madness as any of the psychotic patients among whom he writhed.

After a few minutes he quieted down enough to speak with some relevance and made it plain in vigorous terms that he held his wife entirely responsible for his plight. He admitted drinking; this was his wife's fault. He had, to be sure, derided and fought with the policemen. This would never have happened had his wife not called them to him for no good reason.

This man, 43 years of age, had been through several dozen such episodes during the last ten years. Belonging to a family widely known for its wealth since colonial times, his direct paternal ancestors included a general in the Continental Army during the Revolutionary War and two governors of a proud Southern state. His maternal background included a signer of the Declaration of Independence and a Confederate brigadier celebrated for his dashing and urbane personal qualities no less than for his valor at Antietam and Gettysburg.

W. R. L., when glimpsed at a garden party or when hailed in the street, seemed a proper and impressive scion of two such splendid strains, uniting in his person, it might be said, the rarest culture of two states. His courtesy was not only warm but distinguished, his manners so cordial that one felt better after greeting him. His general bearing combined the utmost dignity with perfect spontaneity, giving a deep conviction of one sophisticated, mellow, and commanding. But there were times when this impressive mask dropped and our gallant gentleman took on quite another color.

One of these incidents immediately preceded his admission to the hospital. After having eschewed strong drink utterly for a year and maintained, on the whole, his fine superficial front, he suddenly and for no discernible reason got pretty generously full. A bit wobbly but full of energy, he burst into the house, roundly cursed his wife, smashed a few vases, threatened to give her a thorough mauling, and departed for a roadhouse. Here he reveled for a few hours with more belligerence and buffoonery than gaiety or eroticism, then swept back in a passion to his house. He shook his wife out of bed, accused her of ruining his life and of unfairly taking possession of money which he had earned through shrewd speculation, and demanded a check for thousands.

Actually he had for many years been sustained financially by his wife's father, a high official in banking circles who not only kept his son-in-law employed in a respectable position at a local bank which he controlled but also furnished from time to time relatively stupendous sums to cover rash and disastrous losses at gambling and in speculation.

The patient's wife had a fairly large estate held in trust. The income from this was, however, not enough to cover the wants of the husband. W. R. L., at the time he married, was by no means dependent on his in-laws. His father had built up a stockbroker's business that fluctuated in value between one and several millions. W. brought his bride to a great Georgian mansion surrounded by lakes and gardens where a dozen servants often maintained scores of guests in spectacular comfort. Even before the death of the father, himself a rash but remarkably intuitive market plunger, the son had made heavy inroads into the family fortune. Afterward the other beneficiaries drew out their interests and stood aside while he doubled, halved, tripled, and finally lost outright his entire holdings. While gaining and while losing, he spent money with equal lavishness, chartering airplanes to fly to mistresses halfway across the continent, casually sending emeralds to chorus girls, or buying a yacht to cruise off the Florida keys.

210

Penniless, he resented bitterly the unwillingness of his father-in-law to let him throw his wife's fortune also into speculation. Stormy wrangles had been almost constant during the early years of this marriage. W., at intervals of a few weeks or a couple of months, went on hard sprees during which he sometimes tore off his wife's clothes or burst in on his father-in-law to threaten and to arraign him as the cause of his own financial decline and the common marital strife. The father-in-law, a man of much dignity and spirit, urged his daughter to leave W. and even threatened at times to cut off the ample income which he chiefly furnished them. After particularly outrageous episodes, the wife often agreed to quit, but W., once sober and aware of what he stood to lose, had no difficulty in appearing so earnest and penitent that he won her back. For a considerable time, pride kept the wife, the father-in-law, and others concerned from calling in policemen to quell the tempestuous and clamorous tumults that W. raised. Finally this step was taken, and it has now in fact become habitual.

On the occasion under discussion, Mrs. L. succeeded, after a struggle with her husband, in reaching headquarters by telephone. When the police arrived, they found her locked for protection in a downstairs room. W., boasting that he could not be taken alive, had knocked the wooden supports from the bannister railings and piled these, with chairs, coffee tables, and other furniture, into a barricade on the stairway.

Half naked above in the bathroom behind additional defenses, he challenged the law with magniloquent mock heroics to take him. For a while he waved a revolver as he hurled his obscene threats. Seeing that the policemen, who knew him well, came on despite his gestures, he laid this aside. Though making no serious attempt to injure his beseigers sufficiently to provoke painful retaliation, he wrestled with them, clawed with a fine show of violence, and was taken off cursing, grunting, and kicking.

Since short sojourns at the barracks in the past had done so little good, the family arranged to have him sent that very night as an emergency case to the psychiatric hospital. They probably had vague hopes that some remediable illness might be found as a cause for his conduct, but the stronger motive was hope that finding himself in what he regarded as the *lunatic asylum* might give him food for thought and possibly a taste for mending his ways.

After settling down sufficiently to permit an interview, he showed no ordinary evidence of a psychosis. He was charming superficially, dismissed his own deeds with lordly insouciance, bewailed his plight, for which he still blamed his wife, though he now spoke of her always with a show of gallantry and implied that her father and other relatives were responsible for her causing him all this trouble.

Though fundamentally childish and full of puerile self-pity, he was on the surface one of the most delightful persons I have ever seen. Something inimitably well-bred in his manner, a gracious and warming geniality which seemed, surely, to overlie great dignity and pride, caused all the personnel on the ward to treat him with particular deference. He all but became the pet of the hospital.

He immediately assumed that the physician was chiefly concerned in helping him get back into the good graces of his wife, who at present refused to accept him. He would have left the hospital at once but his in-laws and members of his own family had agreed for the police to take him if he did.

Persuaded by his apparent sincerity, his wife agreed after two days for him to come home on a pass for a few hours. She soon called the hospital and asked for attendants to be sent. He was brought in, mean and vehement, from a barroom where he had already drunk to excess after first creating a shocking uproar at his house.

The next day he agreed that he had conducted himself unwisely but laid his actions chiefly to his wife's failure to show complete confidence in him. Not a trace of anything like shame or remorse was discernible. Somewhat alarmed now that his wife might actually be persuaded to leave him, he bent all his efforts toward winning her over. She refused to visit him for several days. He spent hours writing letters to her. These he read proudly to his physician. They were of rather far-fetched eloquence and extravagant sentiment, and he read them with much oratorical gusto:

"What does any misunderstanding weigh against the immortal love I bear you? The carping and misguided influence of *others* should not be allowed to come between those united in such devotion as is ours. . . . My darling! My sweetheart! . . ." etc.

Wasn't this the best note to strike? he asked his physician. A politely subdued twinkle of pride and canniness came into his glance. He had succeeded so often that he was already confident. Nevertheless, he showed great vexation and restlessness at the delay, sighed and held his head in his hands, swearing that he could not stand it another hour. He very plainly showed and stated that he felt even one day in the hospital too severe a measure to take against such trivial indiscretions as his.

After three or four days his wife, a highly intelligent person, though far from confident that he would not continue in his ways, was won over sufficiently to take him home.

When last heard from several months later, he had given no further serious trouble. It is quite possible that he may continue the appearance of a fairly good adjustment for a year or two, but it must be remembered that he is supported in this by financial aid and by strong moral efforts on the part of his wife, his father-in-law, and others.

His history shows that he has remained as long as two years sober, fairly industrious, and nearly always in his mask of the grand and charming gentleman. It is important, however, not to give him access to substantial sums of money. Eventually, despite all efforts to protect him, his psychopathic tendencies come forward and he repeats with ingenious variations the theme of the episodes here described.

22

The psychopath as scientist

The limitations of space allow only a few highlights to be thrown on this man's interesting career. Though still in the late twenties, he was already a doctor of philosophy, and the co-author of several creditable papers on subjects in the general field of physics.

Although delayed by truancy and alcoholic escapades for a year in obtaining his degree, he always showed noteworthy ability in a technical sense so long as he applied himself. Now and then he was disabled for several days or a week, during which times he drank enough to remain semiconscious or climbed into trees, from which he hurled noisy defiance at his friends and later at policemen who attempted to get him down. He drank chiefly alone and sometimes urinated in bureau drawers, his own or his roommate's shoes, and indulged in other pranks of the same caliber.

Having obtained his degree, he had little difficulty in securing a satisfactory post on the faculty of a state university. He did not, however, enter upon these duties. Having taken up residence with an aunt in the university town several weeks before the beginning of classes, he at once proceeded to drink on weekends and to haunt public houses of unsavory reputation.

One night a few days before the formal beginning of the academic year, he made himself particularly disagreeable to his companions, who consisted of two prostitutes and a local derelict. In a mood of great irritability and arrogance he quit this group and joined another woman of the streets with whom he had frequently consorted but in whom he had never shown any special interest. During the next hour he drank little but spent his energy ridiculing and slandering his acquaintances in town, the faculty of the university, and particularly his aunt, who was his only local relative. At about 3 o'clock in the morning he astonished all present by announcing in imperious tones that he and his present companion would straightway join themselves in holy matrimony. Before leaving with such company as he could gather, he took pains to telephone his aunt and insist peremptorily that she attend the nuptials.

One may be left to imagine the consternation and confusion of the elderly and very circumspect lady as she sought first to understand and then to counsel her nephew.

On arriving at the residence of a justice of the peace, the aunt and friends whom she had brought left nothing undone in efforts to dissuade our subject from proceeding. In desperation they pointed out not only the defects of character so plain in the prospective bride but also her considerable age, her poorly made false teeth, and her unprepossessingly dyed hair. With oaths, obscenity, and a very artificial show of gaiety, these objections were waved aside, and the bridegroom fulfilled his aims.

The next day he condescendingly allowed his aunt to begin efforts to annul the marriage, but, while expressing his approval, he took very little active part. When earnestly questioned about his motivation, he casually averred that the whole affair was meant as a joke.

"But on whom is this joke?" an elderly friend of the family asked with some asperity.

"Why on me, I suppose," confessed the disinterested bridegroom, laughing with what appeared to be a calmness and lack of concern almost incredible under the circumstances. He never showed any signs of serious worry or of shame, although he glibly confessed to being in the wrong. The affair became widely known, and authorities in the university succeeded in obtaining their new instructor's resignation before he actually took up his duties.

He promptly abandoned the woman he had married, and his family made some settlement with her. After a financially successful year as an automobile salesman, in which he got into trouble somewhat less frequently than usual, he decided to return to the academic world.

He obtained several other good positions in universities where his work was fitful but promising. His personal life soon became so spectacularly designed to embarrass the institution that he had to be dropped. One of these positions he lost, after several minor efforts of the same sort, by the following bit of conduct:

After becoming drunk and conspicuously turbulent in his quarters, where efforts were being made to nurse him and to cajole him back to an appearance of what might be called sanity, he disappeared and could not be located for several days.

The authorities at the college remained in a state of considerable anxiety about his fate. This was terminated by a telephone call made by a local veterinarian to the professor in whose department he worked. The latter, a person of authentic and altogether unstudied dignity and a scholar of national importance, was probably the last man on earth whom a normal youth would desire to rouse out of bed at midnight and treat to a display of absurdity. Humor of no lesser order than his dignity characterized him. Though peaceful, unaggressive, and tolerant as a man can be, some deep subjective poise enabled him when prodded sufficiently to utter a quiet and ironic rebuke fit to unfrock a bishop.

The veterinarian informed this considerable personage that his missing research fellow was at present in the dog hospital and had insisted that this news be delivered to no other than himself, and at once. The bland, laconic lines of the professor's face subtly hardened. Pausing as he reached for his socks, he swore inaudibly.

On arriving at the dog hospital, he found his younger colleague sprawled in a large cage or cubicle used to house ailing Great Danes or St. Bernards. He at once yelled to the professor, announcing in glee that prophecies by the latter about his *going to the dogs* were now amply fulfilled—so what of it! His clamorous outcries rose above the din of barking dogs, who, aroused by the presence of so unusual a kennel-mate, gave voice vigorously and in unison.

The veterinarian explained that his new patient had come in some urgency and insisted on going to where the convalescent dogs were kept. Somewhat bewildered, but thinking perhaps that his visitor had good reason to inquire into the condition of some canine acquaintance, he promptly brought him to the kennels. The strange young man at once climbed into his present berth, defied the veterinarian to remove him, sang, shouted, cursed, and finally insisted that his superior be called.

Finally agreeing to come out, he remained generally obstreperous and at once began to blame a grave and gentle older colleague for his plight. The latter, who had been sincerely interested in trying to keep this promising young man from destroying himself, had, he said, set him off on the present spree by offering him a bottle of beer at lunch several days previously.

Despite many apparently self-imposed and purposeless obstacles in his career he continues to obtain positions, sometimes keeping them as long as a year. His family is called upon to see him through difficulties when they arise, and he continues to speak of those who assist him as if he considered them in a large measure responsible for his troubles.

23

The psychopath as physician

When first seen by me, he was still in his early forties. From the country town in which he was practicing medicine an inquiry came concerning his professional ability. Everyone regarded him as a brilliant man. His patients loved him, and while he was working regularly, his collections were more than adequate. It was often impossible to find him, for now and then, in the classic manner, he lay out in third-rate hotel rooms or in the fields semiconscious until he could be found and coaxed back home.

This was tolerantly accepted as one of his idiosyncrasies by the rustic folk he attended. It was inconvenient, but like drought and the boll weevil, what the devil could one do about it? The community, in which not only social drinking but even cardplaying and dances were generally regarded as devices of Satan, intuitively sensed that the Doc's doings had little or nothing in common with the proscribed gaieties or frivolities. Although a man known to drink cocktails for pleasure and even a woman who smoked cigarettes might have been ostracized, local deacons and town gossips made no concerted attack on the doctor.

The inquiry about his ability mentioned previously was prompted by the following incident.

A patient whom he had been attending off and on for several weeks had noticed that he occasionally seemed glassy-eyed and slightly irrelevant. Neither she nor her family, however, was prepared for such a bedside manner as was his on the last visit.

When the door was opened for the doctor, he swung in unsteadily with it, hanging desperately to the knob, which he apparently hesitated to relinquish. Breathing hard, he muttered inaudibly for a moment, winked inanely at three children who had withdrawn to a corner, gave several short, piercing cheers, and slipped to the floor. Retaining his instrument bag in one hand, he began, still prone, to crawl toward his patient's room. Switching his body from side to side, he made slow but spectacular progress, hesitating every few yards to give a series of hoarse, emphatic grunts or barks. This pantomime was taken by the family to represent an alligator slipping through a bog. In this manner he reached the bedside of the patient.

This man's history shows a great succession of purposeless follies dating from early manhood. He lost several valuable hospital appointments by lying out sodden or by bursting in on serious occasions with nonsensical uproar. He was once forced to relinquish a promising private practice because of the scandal and indignation which followed an escapade in a brothel where he had often lain out disconsolately for days at a time.

Accompanied by a friend who was also feeling some influence of drink, he swaggered into this favorite retreat and bellowed confidently for women. Congenially disposed in one room, the party of four called for highballs. For an hour or more only the crash of glasses, scattered oaths, and occasional thuds were heard. Then suddenly an earnest, piercing scream brought the proprietress and her servants racing into the chamber. One of the prostitutes lay prostrate, clasping a towel to her breast, yelling in agony. Through her wails and sobs she accused the subject of this report of having, in his injudicious blunderings, bitten off her nipple. An examination by those present showed that this unhappy dismemberment had, in fact, taken place. Although both men had at the moment been in bed with her, the entertainer had no doubt as to which one had done her the injury.

Feeling ran strong for a while, but, by paying a large sum of money as recompense for the professional disability and personal damage he had inflicted, the doctor avoided open prosecution. Before a settlement had been made, the guilty man attempted to persuade his companion to assume responsibility for the deed. It would be less serious for the other man, he argued, since his own prominence and professional standing made him a more vulnerable target for damaging courtroom dramatics and for slander. His companion, however, declined this opportunity for self-sacrifice with great firmness.

Less spectacular performances include locking himself in a hotel room alone where he would drink to stupefaction, arouse the management, break furniture, telephone his wife that he had decided to kill himself, drink more, and remain until taken by police or friends who broke open the door.

He also contributed vividly to the liveliness of a dance some years ago. His older brother, whom he was visiting in a New England town and who was an officer in a country club where the dance was in progress, remonstrated with him, urging him to leave because his loud and disorderly behavior, having already attracted unfavorable attention, was now beginning to cause consternation. Whooping in indignation, he at once grappled with his elder on the porch of the club where they stood.

The orchestra having stopped for intermission, a large number of ladies and gentlemen were strolling on the terrace below. Attracted by frantic outcries, reiterated curses, and the sound of scuffling above, these bystanders looked up to see the two brothers whirling dizzily in combat. The younger man, his strength finally prevailing, got the older against the banister and seemed about to throw him over. As observers ran to quell the tumult, our subject, having in his position of vantage breath to spare for oratory, caused the golf course to echo with his threats and insults.

"You bastard! You goddamned _____ bastard! You son of a bitch! I'll kill you, bastard and son of a bitch that you are!" he yelled, pushing his brother back farther over the banister as the echoes returned his violent words. One wonders if the brother was observant enough at the moment to note the two-edged nature of the term with which he was being so loudly reviled. Rescuers soon interrupted the performance. Our subject could very probably have thrown his brother over before they came, but his intention apparently was to make a scene rather than to inflict serious injury.

After one of his longest periods of regular work and apparently satisfactory adjustment, which lasted nearly a year, he attended the meeting of a regional medical society in a large city where an exploit brought him to the notice of local newspapers.

Found drunk on high altar of St. Philip's Church

A man listed as Dr. _____ _____ of _____ was arrested yesterday morning and charged with burglary when he was found asleep on the altar of St. Philip's Church. Officer J. G. Coates who made the arrest said that a painter engaged in painting St. Philip's dome found the door to the church open this morning and called him. Investigation revealed the man asleep on the altar. The officer quoted Dr. _____ as saying that someone else had been with him but that he could not remember who. The doctor seemed to be eminently rational but could give no adequate reason for his inopportune presence in such a place. While a charge of burglary had been placed, according to records at police barracks, a complete examination of the church property revealed the fact that nothing was missing.

He proved to the satisfaction of the authorities that he had entered the church with no intention of stealing or doing any other damage. I am indeed strongly convinced that this contention was correct. Finding a man in so preposterous a situation, the newspaper reporters had mistakenly, but understandably, assumed that some motive such as burglary must, of plain necessity, be responsible for his presence. What his purpose really was, we must admit, is difficult to explain in terms of ordinary human strivings.

He often swears off drinking and expresses the intention of devoting himself to constructive and regular occupation but, despite all the serious troubles that his conduct has brought him, he actually continues as before.

24

The psychopath as psychiatrist

In the group who show some fundamental characteristic of the typical psychopath but who make a good or fair superficial adjustment in society are sometimes found men who hold responsible positions. Lawyers, business executives, physicians, and engineers who show highly suggestive features of the disorder have been personally observed. Perhaps one would think that the psychiatrist, with good opportunity to observe the psychopath, would eschew all his ways. I believe, however, that a glimpse can be given of characteristics of the psychopath in such a person.

Let us first direct our attention to him many years ago when, as an author of some papers on psychiatric subjects, he attracted the interest of several inexperienced young physicians then at the beginning of their careers. The articles, it is true, were marred by grammatical errors and vulgarities in English a little disillusioning in view of the suave and pretentious style attempted by the author. At the time, however, they impressed this little group of naive admirers as having all the originality that the author so willingly allowed others to impute to them, and, as a matter of fact, implied not too subtly himself in every line of his work.

When seen later at a small medical meeting at which no experienced psychiatrists were present, this author seemed very grand indeed. The actual ideas expressed in his paper were, to be fair, culled from the primers of psychiatry and psychology, but he had an authoritative way of making them seem entirely his own, and marvelous, too. Despite his cool and somewhat commanding air, he succeeded in giving an impression of deep modesty.

Everything seemed to accentuate his relative youth which, in turn, hinted of precociousness and of great promise. The effect he had on his audience, most of whom were general practitioners from small towns, was tremendous. An opportunity to meet this splendid figure of a psychiatrist and to sit at his feet during the rest of the evening was avidly welcomed by several of his new admirers.

Dr. _____, though still in the middle thirties, enjoyed a wide and enviable reputation in a section of the country where psychiatrists were at the time almost unknown. After some work at hospitals in a distant state where he was born, he had come and set up as a specialist in his present habitat. He soon obtained a small institution in which he began to direct treatment of psychiatric patients. Reports indicate that it flourished and expanded greatly.

It was generally agreed that his learning and ability were chiefly responsible for his rapid rise to local prominence. Ephemeral rumors hinted that the idolized Dr. _____ made a practice of treating by expensive and doubtful procedures any patient of means whom he could obtain for as long as the money lasted and of then dismissing him or sending him promptly to a state hospital. It was also heard that with female patients he sometimes suggested, or even insisted on, activities (as therapy) which are specifically proscribed in the Hippocratic oath. But what physician has not had similar things said about him? The impressive bearing of the man and his reiterated and rather eloquent appeals for higher scientific consecration on the part of his colleagues snuffed out these feeble stirrings of adverse criticism which were almost universally ascribed to jealousy.

The lion of the evening seemed to put himself out in being gracious to his young admirers who were indeed nobodies on the fringe of the wonderful field which he seemed to dominate. His good fellowship was so hearty and yet so suave that one could scarcely bring himself to see the faint underlying note of condescension.

The privilege of driving this relatively great personage out to a country place where hospitality beckoned was seized by one of the young physicians. In the car an attempt was made to turn the conversation to psychiatric question which Dr. _____ had raised in his papers. He made a few stilted replies but soon drifted from the subject into talk that was hardly more than pompous gossip. His companion, fearing that such a learned man might be talking down to spare him the embarrassment of incomprehension, kept returning to psychiatry, trying to make it plain that no such embarrassment would discount the pleasure of hearing the master. Soon the replies of this admitted master left the young man in serious doubt not only as to the great one's knowledge, but even as to his interest in the subject.

Dr. _____, in his more popular talks and articles, as well as occasionally in those directed toward rustic medical groups, often gave psychiatric interpretations of literature and art. One of his more recent efforts in this line touched briefly but ambitiously on the works of Marcel Proust. Being then in the middle of an earnest pilgrimage among the psychopathologic wonders of *Remembrance of Things Past,* the fledgling psychiatrist, perhaps hoping to make a good impression but also eager for enlightenment, ventured a question on this subject.

The master at this time was calm and alert, but his remarks were so beside the point that his disciple wavered. Dr. _____ was perfectly self-assured, in fact politely pontifical, but the more he talked the clearer it became that he had not read the book at all. It finally became equally clear that even Proust's name was unfamiliar, and the disquieting suspicion dawned on his admirer that he had never encountered it except in the excerpt from some review which he had apparently come upon and used. He had not been sufficiently interested in what he had plagiarized even to retain the name and was now imputing it to some imaginary Viennese psychiatrist. He followed this pretension only for a moment, however, and only as a stepping stone to banalities with which he was familiar and about which he spoke with such deliberation and assurance that they almost seemed marvelous. Never in all this persiflage did he show the least sign of confusion or timidity. Apparently he felt that he had kept intact his impressive front. Even at this stage of the acquaintanceship it was hard to avoid suspicion that any important distinction between such a front and more substantial things was not in the orbit of his awareness.

With some remark about putting aside these grave and ponderous subjects, he sang a few lines of a surprisingly obscene ditty, clapped his companion on the back, and suggested with gusto: "When their social doings are over, let's you and I go get us a couple of good frisky chippies!"

Despite the conviviality implicit in this remark (and no less in his tone), in some way hard to describe he still maintained the attitude of one who means to insist on his distinct superiority even while for a moment generously waiving certain restrictions of caste and allowing his companion a more respectable footing. It was only a quasi-equality that he offered, however—an indulgence such as an adult might allow a child who on some special occasion is permitted to sit up and play that he is grown. The friendship he seemed to offer was at best a morganatic one.

His discourse during the rest of the drive, especially after he had stopped on the way for "a couple of quick ones," was coarse and humorless. It seemed impossible to strike a sincere idea from him on any subject.

On arriving at the host's place, a merry but entirely civilized company was found drinking highballs, singing around the piano, or talking enthusiastically in small groups. The singing was in key, and the talking was not loose or aimless. For the most part the gathering was composed of people who, though lively, had some interest in general ideas as contrasted with the trivia of daily life, and a few slowly ingested drinks brought out humorous and interesting conversation. The house was not very large or the furnishing spectacular, but the place, like the men and women present, gave a strong impression to the newcomer that he was in orderly surroundings, among people of dignity and good will.

A young, very good-looking married woman who had an amateur but genuine interest in psychiatric questions and who meant to be polite to the distinguished stranger, began talking to him with enthusiasm. He soon led her off into another room. A moment later, on passing through this room, one of the young physicians was hailed by a feminine voice and, responding, found the two in a nook, the lady pulling herself away from the doctor with some effort but with equanimity. It was plain that his crudely aggressive overtures were not welcome to her and she urged the other man, who was an old friend, to join them on the davenport. Apparently trying to start a conversation, she asked the celebrity about psychoanalysis, a subject on which he sometimes expounded to lay gatherings in such a way as to give the erroneous impression that he was a qualified analyst.

"If I could get you out in a car I'd psychoanalyze you right now," he muttered, low but loud enough to be overheard, accompanying his words with a confident leer. The savant had evidently misread the spirit of the party. The lady rose, smiled quickly at her other companion as if to say she knew a disagreeable fellow when she saw one, and quietly rejoined a group.

Dr. _____ now expressed the desire for straight liquor, making strong, derogatory remarks about highballs and those who drank them. Ordering his former disciple to come, he strode toward the kitchen. The former disciple, by this time feeling heavily responsible for the master, made haste to follow.

In the kitchen Dr. _____ began to order the servants about in profane and petulant fashion. He had gulped one or two small whiskeys when several men wandered in looking for ice. One of these, an eager intern, expressed interest in the important investigative work which Dr. _____ had begun now, in loud, boastful tones, to announce himself engaged in.

"If you want a job there, son, just lemme know," he thundered. Swaggering about, he made an all-embracing gesture. "At the _____ Institute I'm *it*. I'm the big cheese, I tell you." No one saw fit to dispute these claims.

He began then a tirade on the subject of his executive ability, his scientific standing, his knowledge of the stock market, his sexual power, and his political influence. Having delivered himself of this, he pushed his audience aside and sauntered back into the sitting room. There he recognized an old acquaintance, a physician who had formerly been on the resident staff with him at some hospital but in an inferior capacity. This man, a newcomer, was talking with the hostess in the midst of a small group of men and women.

"Why you old son of a bitch!" Dr. _____ shouted. "Come over here and set your goddamned a.. in this chair and talk to your chief."

It was no time for vacillation. The newcomer and the young physician who had accompanied Dr. _____ to the party caught each other's eye and quickly hurried the celebrity to the door. He pulled back at first but soon came along satisfactorily as both companions sought so earnestly to cajole him that the words of each were lost to the other. Turning to his companions just as the door was gained, he shouted:

"Chippies, did you say?"

On the way to his hotel he began to protest. He was by no means confused from drink.

"Be goddamned if I go there! What kind of dirty bastards are you anyway?"

He became insistent—nay, even defiant—about going where he could obtain women. The new member of the party, who had seen him through many such episodes and who, to the other escort's relief, kindly assumed charge of the case, advised that he be humored.

Dr. _____ himself, through an effervescence of obscene threats, muttered directions to the driver. Expecting to find an ordinary brothel, both of his companions were surprised to arrive at a large outdoor pavilion where an orderly dance was going on. Before a definite decision could be reached about what to do, Dr. _____ was out of the car.

"Luke! Luke!" he yelled imperiously.

A pleasant-looking man appeared.

"You've got to get us a good piece of t... and get it quick, boy!" he ordered. "We'll wait here and watch 'em dance by."

The man called Luke, so far as could be learned, was under serious obligations to Dr. _____ and apparently meant to obey him. He confided that he had stood by his friend and benefactor in many such sprees in this town. Luke had pleasant manners and was not drinking.

"God, that's one!" the savant muttered. "What an ---! Can you get that slut out here, Luke?" He was far enough away not to be overheard by the dancers. Luke smiled and shook his head. "There's one!" the doctor

225

commented again with enthusiasm. "She's rutting! That one's rutting! I can tell it." His subsequent remarks can hardly be suggested even in writing on a medical subject.

His two companions left him now in custody of Luke with instructions that he be brought back to the car when this was possible without violence. Luke had asked not to be left with sole responsibility.

Some time later the doctor returned. It was difficult to judge whether or not he had gained all the satisfaction he sought. He made it plain that he had found a companion but despite his boastful garrulousness did not give the final details of the encounter. In view of his windy frankness, this caused doubt as to how far he had succeeded in his aims. Beyond question he had made considerable progress. He announced this much loudly, holding up a finger, sniffing it as he did so, and making a comment of such ingenious distastefulness that even his brother physicians blenched with revulsion. The new disciple could not but ruminate about what appraisals of woman and of human relationships, what attitudes toward basic goals, prevailed beneath this successful man's ordinarily impressive exterior.

On the road back to his hotel he cursed truculently at other cars. He came in willingly. While going up on the elevator, he pinched the buttocks of the Negro girl who ran the machine, apparently oblivious of several passengers. There was no gaiety or human touch in these actions, only a sullen, derogatory aggressiveness. He uttered vague challenges and threats emphasizing his combative prowess and his readiness to fight anyone who might take issue with him on any question.

On entering his room, he immediately made for a whiskey bottle and began calling raucously for ice. He became loud and offensive when his companions sought to excuse themselves, banged the table with his fists, and offered grandiosely to fight and to fight at once. He was a tall, powerful man and by no means too drunk to put on a lively and embarrassing scene if crossed.

He cursed the bellboy, who had arrived meanwhile, with such foul oaths it was incredible that he took them. Pouring himself a quick drink, he called for careful attention from his companions.

Had he told them about his children? No. They must see pictures of them. He began to praise them extravagantly, to extol his love for them in sickening terms of pathos, or pseudopathos. He spoke of his plans for their future. His entire manner began to change, and it was plain that he had determined notions about keeping all his children what he called *pure*. A surprisingly moralistic aspect of this psychiatrist began to appear. Cheap expressions of sentimentality fairly gushed from him. In a loosely emotional strain he recited rhymes by Edgar A. Guest about the little ones. Then he momentarily broke down and blubbered. Tears ran down his cheeks.

The bellboy had brought ice and Dr. _____ insisted on pouring out drinks, swaggering about now in his earlier manner. When his companions insisted on leaving, he promptly announced that he would accompany them. He could not be persuaded to go to bed and quickly became overbearing when persuasion continued. Though he had, of course, taken a good deal of whiskey, he seemed to know perfectly what he was doing. In fact, he did not really seem drunk in the ordinary sense of the word. Both of his companions felt that this was not a person irresponsible for the moment who must be protected and prevented from doing things he would regret. On the contrary, one was strongly impressed that this was the man himself.

Going down on the elevator he renewed his practices on the polite Negro girl, becoming so annoying to her that his companions had to interfere. He called a taxi and insisted that all proceed at once to a brothel. Having had enough experience for one night in trying to be their brother's keeper, his companions were obdurate. He drove off, cursing them viciously as disgraceful specimens of humanity and making derogatory remarks about their virility.

"What's the matter with him?" asked the younger.

"Just a queer fellow that way," replied the one who knew him well. "He's cool and calculating, a good executive, and a rather pleasant man superficially during the week, though always a little arrogant. Even when on the job he's not to be trusted. Every time he gets a chance, he does just about what you've seen him do tonight. He keeps under wraps of outer dignity at the hospital and he's careful not to take them off under circumstances which would cause him to get in serious trouble. He passes as a great gentleman in polite but unsophisticated circles at home. But the cloak must be very uncomfortable. Almost every weekend he makes an opportunity to get it off, and he's always then just the man you saw tonight."

"But won't his reputation suffer from what he did tonight?"

"Probably not. He is a long way from home. Since the town is small, he evidently assumed that all the people he was thrown with tonight were country bumpkins who don't count for much and who would be overawed by him. He judges people only by superficial appearances of wealth and power, and he is seldom impressed except by gaudy display. He kept up a good front at the medical meeting. He is exceedingly shrewd, in a shallow sense, about where and when he behaves naturally. At home he often goes off into swamps with groups of men far beneath him in his own estimation and who are apparently flattered to be chosen. The trips are ostensibly to catch catfish or, in the winter, to shoot ducks; but actually it's merely to get rowdily drunk, boast and shout inanely, and sprawl about on the ground or in muddy boats around the camp. He wasn't drunk tonight. Out in the swamp he often passes through this obscene, blustering phase in an hour or two and reaches the sodden state that one might suspect is his goal.

"Sometimes he wants women. It doesn't matter what women or under what circumstances. Some of the people who know him say that he prefers low, unprepossessing partners, and especially illiterate Negresses, but it has always seemed to me that there was no preference at all, and I've seen him often. A beautiful woman means no more to him than an imbecilic harlot, but on the other hand the harlot means no more than the beautiful woman.

"Sometimes when the idea of sex is stirring him he gets too drunk to make much of his opportunities. I'll never forget one incident. It was about daybreak down in the swamps where we'd been fishing. He'd gone out on a sexual mission pretty drunk. We found him at a whitewashed shack. It was time to leave for home so another fellow and I rolled him off a fat Negro washerwoman. She must have weighed two hundred pounds!

" 'Sakes, Boss,' she muttered, 'he's far gone dis time. Ain't done nuthin' yet!' It was my last fishing trip with him."

The next morning with fresh sunlight streaming into the hotel, the youngest member of the group, having finished breakfast, met Dr. _____ in the lobby. He was emerging from a telephone booth. Tall, self-assured, clear-eyed, neat as a dandy, and fashionably dressed, he looked the fine figure of a man.

He spoke affably. With a disarming, boyish smile he made some reference to the previous evening. His polite expressions and poised tone made clear the implication that it had been a pleasant occasion and had cemented friendships. The inconspicuous trace of condescension first noted on meeting him was now more obvious, but this somehow tended to make his cordiality seem more precious. He was as sober as a man can be and showed no signs of *hangover*. Indeed, as his other companion of the night had said, he must have been drinking very moderately.

The former admirer of Dr. _____, who was an old friend of the lady whom he had offered to "psychoanalyze" in a parked car the night before, stopped at her house later in the day to say goodbye before leaving the city.

"Come in. I must speak to you," she said. There was some indignation in her tone but more mischief and merriment.

"What about your friend, the famous psychoanalyst?" she said, relishing, in all friendliness, the other's discomfiture. She was a person of some sophis-

228

tication and poise. Being also pretty, vital, and desirable to men, she knew well how to take care of herself in ordinary company. She had been married for several years and gave a strong impression of being happy and in love with her husband.

"Well," she continued, "I must tell you. You are interested in queer people."

"Early this morning the cook came and woke me up. 'It's the telephone,' she said. 'Damn the telephone, Lou!' I told her. 'Don't you know I was up till all hours last night?' 'Yes'm,' she answered, 'but the gentleman says you'll speak with *him,* and it's important business.'

"I picked up the phone.

" 'Good morning, Mary' said an unfamiliar, self-assured, masculine voice. I was wondering who it could be—knowing me well enough to use my first name and still so pompous. Then, just as I recognized the voice:

" 'Mary, this is Doctor ⸻.' From his tone you'd have judged he thought I ought to sing for joy!

" 'Yes indeed,' I said. He then baldly suggested that I make a date with him for this afternoon. He'd come out for me at 4 P.M. or, better still, he suggested, I could meet him at a drugstore downtown.

"Really, there was something so superior about him, a sort of indescribably cool insolence, or I don't know what . . . about his manner, I mean . . . and after last night! . . . not just the proposition itself . . . that I fairly turned white with rage.

"I wanted so much to blast him with scorn that I was at a loss for words. When you get that mad it's easy to lose your head. The calm and effective expression of indignation by which ladies in Victorian novels squelched 'insults' is hard to put into the idiom of today. Trying not to make myself unnecessarily ridiculous, but trusting the reply would register as final, I said:

" 'Is that so? *Sorry,* but I'm afraid I'll have to forego that pleasure.'

"He then insisted, not like a lover or even like one who's making any decent pretense of being a lover, but coolly, almost arrogantly, like a fake gentleman who's after a servant girl. I must have succeeded in making myself a little clearer by this time, for he resigned himself about this afternoon. But I wasn't done with him.

"He then began to say that he would be back in this city soon, probably every now and then. He'd like to see me on some of these occasions. He'd call me when he came. No, perhaps it would be better if he dropped me a note and let me know when he'd be here. Then I could call *him! I* was getting so vexed that I scarcely caught the implication that he didn't want to telephone and find George here.

"For a moment I couldn't answer. Then I suddenly remembered the way he announced himself: 'Mary, this is *Doctor* _____!' The overwhelming effrontery of the whole farce came over me. It was too much! 'Mary, this is *Doctor* _____!' That priceless ass calling me by my first name and referring to himself as 'Doctor _____!' And under such circumstances! Why, he probably pictured us having our little bout of 'love' in the same strain. 'You're so lovely, Mary, do let me take off your pants!' 'Oh, Doctor _____ (blushing), you're so genteel and handsome!'

"Can you beat it! I ask you as an old friend! The bumptious swine didn't even have enough delicacy in what he probably thought of as lovemaking to grant me the intimacy to call him Jack, or Harry, or Percival, or Happy Hooligan, or whatever else he's named. He's such an indescribable prig that he probably doesn't even allow *himself* to think of himself in terms of a first name.

"I just had time to get out the words which must have come with something of a lilt:

" 'Yes, you just *wait* until I call you!'

"I'm ashamed to confess they were almost lost in a burst of laughter. It wasn't ladylike at all the way I laughed. It was belly-shaking laughter. Homeric laughter. Rabelaisian laughter, maybe. I couldn't stop.

"Lou, the cook, came back in and asked what was the matter. 'I can't explain,' I told her and went on laughing.

"What sort of people are you psychiatrists anyway?" she now asked in her spirited, arch way, again enjoying her old friend's discomfiture which was now almost lost in wonder and amusement. "I bet that bat-house troubadour went away thinking I had become hysterical with delight at the opportunity he offered."

"That might not be absurd after all," the friend murmured, remembering the self-possession and happy assurance with which Dr. _____ had emerged from the telephone booth that morning.

This case is offered for what it may be worth. No diagnosis of psychopathic personality has been made. Occasional news of him over the next few years indicated that he was still outwardly well adjusted. I believe it likely that he continues to prosper and I have not the faintest notion that he will ever reach the wards of a psychiatric hospital except in the capacity of a physician and executive. He does not really succeed in impressing people of discernment, though he continues to think he succeeds in this. He impresses many people who are themselves essentially undiscriminating. He cannot tell these from others with sounder judgment and regards himself as a great success socially as well as financially.

Such a personality shows suggestions of an inner deviation qualitatively similar to what is found in the fully developed sociopath. The shrewdness is typical. Unlike others, such as Max, whose cleverness brings only momentary success in objective dealings with the world, this man's similar cleverness is applied with enough persistence for him to advance continuously. He advances financially and, within limits, even professionally. He is a smart fellow and, in a very superficial sense, has a glib facility in medical activities. In relations with the public he shows an excellent knack, an artful sense of showmanship.

For the more fundamental questions that immediately confront a person interested in psychiatry he apparently has no awareness, and therefore no concern. The problems of life that make up the chief and underlying interest for real psychiatrists do not exist for him. He is said to give many of his patients about what they feel they need. With relatively uncomplex and emotionally shallow persons his amazing self-confidence is perhaps more quickly effective than the deeper understanding, with its inevitable lack of certainties, that another sort of man would bring to his work.

His patients are reported to show improvement that compares favorably with that shown by most of the patients treated by physicians whose aims are more serious. We must not forget that pseudoscientific cultists frequently succeed in relieving psychoneurotic patients of their symptoms by absurd measures. These practitioners, if they work in accordance with the fundamental principles of their craft, have no awareness of the real problems underlying such symptoms and little or no ability to help patients understand and deal with these problems. Such a man as this appears to be similarly limited. If one imagines his attempting pertinent psychiatric study of a seriously motivated person, of a person whose world is quite foreign to him, the picture becomes farcical.

This man then, the traits already mentioned notwithstanding, is one who, unlike the obvious psychopath, succeeds over many years in his outer adjustment. Granting that the behavior just described is fairly typical and is persisted in, the conclusion follows that inwardly he is very poorly adjusted indeed. The quality of happiness he knows and the degree of reality in which he experiences so much that is major in human relations are such that, despite his superficial success, he must fail to participate very richly in life itself.

Let it be pointed out that the drunkenness, immature sex attitudes, execrable taste, and deceit are not in themselves the basis for suspecting that this man is affected in some measure with the same disorder that affects the patients presented previously. Many readers would perhaps dismiss all this with the thought that our man might be more properly called a bad fellow and his status left at that. The significant points are these:

His impulse to drink does not seem to be motivated by the hope of shared gaiety. His attitude in sexual aims is so self-centered as to give the impression that even when carrying out intercourse with women he is essentially solitary, isolated in evaluations so immature that what satisfaction he achieves must lie in concepts of a phallic damaging and despoiling of the female with simultaneous reassurances to puerile concepts of his own virility. Such confusing and fragmentary achievement, common enough in a groping boy of thirteen, is a poor and pathologic substitute for fulfillment compatible with deep personality integration and is inadequate for one even remotely as near adult as what is implied by this man's outer surface.

His lack of taste and judgment in human relationships seems inconsistent with his opportunity to learn and with his ability to learn in other modes of knowing where such values and meanings do not enter. His apparent hypocrisy is probably not a conscious element of behavior. At least he is unaware of how it would seem to others, even if he assumed all the facts were known to them. It has, perhaps, never occurred to him that there might be people in the world who had other fundamental aims than his own dominant aim to drop the disguise in which he has acted his part perhaps not too comfortably during the week, and plunge into what I would call activity more representative of perverse or disintegrative drives, of aims at sharp variance with everything his outer self seems to represent.

I am well aware that many basic impulses appear in forms not socially acceptable, that they might be called immoral, vulgar, or criminal or be described by other unpleasant words. The person here discussed, when seen without his mask, seems not to be directed in any consistent and purposive scheme by these socially unacceptable tendencies but largely to blunder about at their behest. In his outer front he functions in accordance with all the proprieties, large and small, but here the reality is thin and personal participation halfhearted. He is somewhat like a small boy who succeeds in maintaining decorum and even in getting a good mark for conduct while in the schoolroom under teacher's watchful eye. Though he looks attentive, he is only shrewdly compromising, biding his time to get at what is to him more important. When the bell rings and he escapes from what he finds to be an artificial situation, an area of formalities and polite pretenses, he becomes natural and plays in accordance with what he takes to be the actual rules and real aims of existence.

The small schoolboy learns eventually to reconcile what the classroom represented and what he sought in his hours of play. He finds in his work responsibilities, ways of celebrating, etc., much that is compatible, a core at least, that he can integrate into constructive, self-fulfilling, and, on the whole, harmonious expression of basic impulses.

In such a man as the one we are considering, little harmony of this sort appears. Unlike those presented as clinical psychopaths, he has learned to carry out the formalities rather consistently and appears as actually living in a constructive and socially adapted pattern. Actually this is a surface activity, a sort of ritual in which not much of himself enters. For his more natural and inwardly accepted impulses he has found nothing reconcilable with what he gives lip service to and must turn to patterns of behavior so immature and (subjectively) chaotic that they mock and deny all that his surface affirms.

The outer layers of socially acceptable functioning extend little deeper into affect than any other exercise empty of all but formality. He has apparently learned to carry out a lip service in matters that he finds unreal and tedious and to take pride in how well this is performed. As an alternative to the barren channels of formality, the inner man finds for the more valid fulfillment of real impulse only pathways or outlets that sharply deviate from the surface channels, that cannot in any way be integrated with them, and that in themselves remain relatively archaic, poorly organized, undirected toward any mature goal, and socially regressive or self-destructive.

It is confusing to interpret such a personality in terms of bad and good. From a psychiatric viewpoint, at least, such aspects of a maladjusted human being cannot be assessed authoritatively.

Years after the incidents recorded in this report, some news of the good doctor was received which I believe would stand as "Paradox in Paradise."

It was brought to the young psychiatrist who had accompanied Dr. _____ during the spree just cited by an earnest, middle-aged lady with a strong penchant for talking about psychology and psychiatry and psychoanalysis, about anything containing the prefix *psyche* for that matter. Striking at once for her hearer's closest interests, she began to talk about a wonderful lecture she had recently heard in a distant town at some woman's club or literary society which was fostering the cause of mental hygiene.

The lecturer was marvelous, she insisted. He stirred up such enthusiasm that half the ladies present had begun to study psychology. And his subject! He talked about the queerest people! They were not exactly *insane,* but they really did the most fantastic things! They were even harder to understand than lunatics themselves! But the lecturer understood them, though he confessed in all modesty that some points about them were a puzzle even to one of his own experience. He was a most impressive person—so poised and authoritative, yet always quiet-spoken. He was such an *intellectual* person. A man of wide and profound culture. And such a gentleman!

"I declare, I believe half of the women in our club wished they could exchange roles with his wife! With all that grasp of psychology, just imagine what a husband he must be!"

She would like to learn more about these people . . . psychopathic personalities or psychopaths the doctor had called them.

And the doctor's name. . . . She uttered it in hushed tones of admiration.

Cataloging the material

Part III

A clinical profile

25

Conceptual confusions which cloud the subject

While preparing the first edition of this volume, many years ago, I was impressed and sometimes astonished by the dearth of pertinent material about the psychopath in most psychiatric textbooks. It seems not only surprising but almost incredible to find how little space was devoted to this disorder. With psychopaths making up so large a proportion of the patients who must be dealt with, and their problems being so serious, it was indeed difficult to understand why they were almost ignored.

If the medical student, the resident physician, or the beginner in psychiatry could find little help from the textbooks, it would seem that he might obtain from monographs or special treatises the information he needed. Despite the existence of several large and scholarly volumes on the psychopathic personality, I was unable to discover anywhere a book that came to grips with the subject in such a way as to give real or practical assistance. There was, furthermore, relatively little published at the time in psychiatric journals that had much bearing on the urgent and major problems with which so many strove in helplessness and in confusion.

Through the literature of many decades pertinent articles were scattered. Some of these gave serious attention to the subject. Not always readily accessible to the average physician who dealt directly with these numerous patients, this largely buried but valuable material did not regularly influence methods or generally clarify the fundamental issues.

Surrounded by what almost seemed a conspiracy of silence, a desert of evasiveness or indifference, not only the relatives of the patients but also courts, physicians, and medical institutions had, it seemed, little to guide them in a task of the first order.

At present there are indications of more practical interest in the problem. Popular textbooks, it must be admitted, still have relatively little to say, but in their current treatment of the psychopath there is a happy departure from the once almost universal procedure of mixing the few pages or paragraphs on this subject with all manner of unrelated deficiencies, congenital organic brain diseases, etc.

The confusion and equivocation in which our subject has been all but lost can be better understood from a historical survey. Since the first edition of this book was prepared, Maughs[210] has published a thorough and valuable study of this sort. It is not practical here to do justice to the evolution of concepts which Maughs traces through more than a century and a half. A few points, however, have so much bearing on our central problem that they demand notice.

Early in the nineteenth century Pinel recorded his surprise in finding that many patients do not show the disordered reasoning assumed to be necessary for psychotic behavior. He is quoted by Maughs thus:

> I thought that madness was inseparable from delirium or delusion, and I was surprised to find many maniacs who at no period gave evidence of any lesion of the understanding. . . .*

Prichard's descriptions of a "moral insanity" and Benjamin Rush's beliefs about derangement of the "will" suggest that such patients as we now call sociopaths were observed and that the absence of delusion, irrationality of thought, etc. were noted. Maughs gives a most helpful account of the efforts to interpret such disorder in terms of disease that spares the intellect but attacks other "faculties" such as "moral affections," "will," "sense of Deity," "emotions," etc.[210]

It is most interesting to note that these earliest observers† not only recorded that serious personality disorder occurred in the absence of "a lesion of the intellect" but also that they were strongly inclined to recognize it as illness, to distinguish it from ordinary crime or depravity.

---

*From Maughs, Sidney: A concept of psychopathy and psychopathic personality—its evolution and historical development, Journal of Criminal Psychopathology 2:329-356, 465-499, 1941.

†Pinel, Esquirol, Rush, Woodward, Conolly, etc.[210]

Despite the fact that they dealt largely with philosophic abstractions and assumed various "faculties" which were treated as separate and established entities, their practical conclusions seem far more realistic than many subsequent concepts and perhaps more pertinent than those that now determine the medical and legal status of the psychopath.

Dr. Ordronaux, Professor of Medical Jurisprudence at Columbia University in 1873, expressed a contrary point of view that soon prevailed and, translated into other terms, represents rather accurately an attitude toward our problem that is still influential today. As quoted in part from Maughs, Ordronaux makes the following statement:

> Our moral nature is, like the mind, a special endowment. It feels, it is conscious. . . . Moral nature knows no alterations in rhythm, craves no rest, never sleeps voluntarily. The only disease to which moral nature is subject is sin.*

Though still assuming that "intellect" and "moral nature" are in actuality "things" as separate and independent as the words used to designate them, Ordronaux is quite sure that one, unlike the other, is not subject to any sort of disease.

At this point it might be helpful to ask ourselves a few questions. In psychiatry as in most other fields of human endeavor the belief in faculty psychology has long been abandoned. Primarily and chiefly through the persistent efforts of Adolf Meyer, nearly all medical workers agree today that we do not encounter a "mind" independently of a body, that we had best confine our attention to what we meet in experience, that is to say, a person who may show disorder in various aspects of his functioning. We reject the demand to deal separately with an "intellect," a "moral faculty," a "will," etc., as if they were, apart from the words, things that can be isolated for study or for treatment.[179,223,224,225]

In view of our generally avowed position in this matter, it is not a little surprising to find how concepts deeply rooted in the long-discarded faculty psychology enter, by the back door, and influence the attitudes and practices of today. A few of the many important points made by Korzybski are extremely pertinent here. Without attempting to go into the deep and general confusion, the ineffective procedure that can arise through the incompatibility of language and concept with fact, it is worth our while to consider for a moment what Korzybski and his co-workers refer to as consciousness of abstracting.[122,157,179]

*From Maughs, Sidney: A concept of psychopathy and psychopathic personality—its evolution and historical development, Journal of Criminal Psychopathology, 2:329-356, 465-499, 1941.

It is obvious to us today that what most psychiatrists and psychologists talked and wrote about some decades ago were verbal abstractions and that these were treated as if they referred to what can be met in experience. By juggling these verbal artifacts without realizing (and admitting) that they do not necessarily correspond to real and separate entities, logical and eloquent arguments can be made, but such philosophizing usually has little applicability to the world in which we live. In medical problems this method has been peculiarly unrewarding.*

If we grant that *mind* and *body, thinking* and *feeling, moral faculty* and *intellect,* and *character* and *personality* cannot, except in language, be split apart and dealt with as clear-cut entities, let us keep this fact clearly in mind. This is not to say that such terms must not be used. It is neither practicable nor possible to avoid them. They convey something that is important. When the relative of a patient asks, "It's not her mind, is it Doc?" and gets the reassuring answer, "No, it's just her nerves," he may receive useful and valid information (that she is not psychotic). On the other hand, he may receive a good deal of information that is not only misleading but sometimes distinctly harmful.[51] He may find himself automatically instructed to this effect:

1. His wife's trouble is confined to the peripheral nerves.
2. These nerves are weak (in the most literal sense) or perhaps frayed and a bit tangled.
3. The nerves have actually, as she has often told him, been jumping about in her body and knotting up in painful snarls.
4. She really has nothing wrong with her but is just putting on.
5. A little *active medicine* or a *nerve tonic* will cure the sickness, which is fortunately localized far from her "mind."
6. Since she got run down and developed nervous exhaustion, a lot of rest in bed is plainly the answer.

As psychiatrists it is no doubt clear to us that "nervous trouble" is a kind of "mental trouble," and we are not likely to be confused in such a way as the patient's husband. Nor are we likely, today, to believe that a neurosis is caused by toxins arising from sexual frustration or that it is some-

---

*In metaphysics or in personal formulations of religious conviction and other individualized value judgments, such concepts may be essential and necessary to human endeavor. Medicine (including psychiatry) has nothing to say against the value of methods and concepts that apply to the subject in dealing philosophically, theologically, or personally with matters beyond its bounds and from aspects impertinent to its task. The methods of medicine do not apply here. Such responsibilities do not belong to the doctor. He may work in metaphysics or mysticism but there is no evidence that by medical methods he can solve such problems.

thing essentially different from a psychoneurosis.[93,131] We are not likely to feel we are talking about a patient with ordinary psychosis ("mental illness") when we refer to a psychopath, despite the fact that our term unequivocally signifies illness of the "mind." To escape the unjustified implications of faculty psychology, we wisely avoid diagnosing "moral insanities," but we often turn to "neurotic character" as a term to indicate the same type of disorder.[11,88] If we use the current nomenclature, we may classify those usually called psychopaths under the general term *personality disorder* and the subtype *sociopathic personality disturbance.*[69] Whatever terms are used, it is important for us to retain full realization that we abstract in a term or concept some aspect of what we meet only as an integrated entity.

The early material cited and discussed by Maughs makes clear the difficulties encountered approximately one hundred or more years ago in trying to solve psychiatric problems on the assumptions of faculty psychology. Some believe that the chief medicolegal decisions today are determined almost entirely on the question of whether or not a "lesion of the intellect" can be demonstrated.

In more recent decades two tendencies particularly seem to have played a major and persistent role in isolating the sociopath from practical consideration and in concealing him in a strange and gratuitous confusion. One of these tendencies arose from efforts to group these patients with many other types by no means similar. The other seems to have proceeded from ambitious attempts to break down the psychopath's disorder by fine and largely imaginary distinctions, by all sorts of descriptive nuances and diagnostic legerdemain, into theoretical entities to be differentiated and classified under many subheadings.

These attempts at elaborate differentiation have been applied not to a distinguishable group having in common fundamental features that could be brought into conceptual focus but to an essentially heterogeneous referent. A good analogy would arise if someone set out to establish and list scores of inconsequential differences between Buicks, Oldsmobiles, Plymouths, Cadillacs, Lincolns, etc., by studying assiduously a general material in which automobiles, oxcarts, demolished freight cars, jet planes, rural woodsheds, and the village pump were undistinguished, embraced under a single term, and treated through such concepts as can be formed in such an approach. Would it not be wiser to put all our automobiles together in a field of reference before attempting to take further steps?

It is perhaps worth while to say here that the more types our writers enumerate and the more seriously they take these philosophic artifacts, the less likely is any relationship to be found between what is in the book and our direct experience with psychopaths. Before these fine distinctions can be made to any good purpose, there must first appear some recognition of the basic group that is to be further differentiated. This seems notably lacking where wordplay is most extensive and ambitious.

Either of the two practices just mentioned would in itself have introduced more than enough obscurity. Together they have worked to make a confusion unparalleled in the whole field of psychiatry.

As the psychoses were recognized and the psychoneuroses distinguished from these, it became increasingly popular to put virtually anything that failed to fit into these categories with the psychopath in a veritable diagnostic salad of incompatibles. The term *psychopathic personality,* of course, invites such practice with its literal applicability to all psychiatric disorders. The new official term *personality disorder* does not avoid similar implications of a very broad application.[69]

Early in the present century Meyer called attention to the importance of separating patients now generally called psychoneurotic from the heterogeneous conglomeration of types among which the pyschopath was then and is now officially placed.[221] Through persistent efforts the mental defective was also distinguished and today is considered apart.

Although mentally defective patients were undistinguished from the psychopath, many excellent observers found and reported physical abnormalities, stigmata of degeneration, and gross neural pathology in the general group. It is not remarkable to see that such findings became associated with (and regarded as characteristic of) not only the patients in whom they occurred but also the psychopath and other unrelated patients, all of whom were considered together as more or less identical examples of a constitutional defect state.[124] It is, however, truly remarkable that such errors have persisted through the years and decades. A good example is afforded by material from Sadler's popular textbook published in 1936.[257]

In this ponderous volume, totaling 1,231 pages of text, less than five pages are spared for our subject. After several descriptive statements that could apply accurately to the behavior of the real psychopath and that seem to indicate him as the subject under discussion, physical characteristics of "constitutional psychopathic inferiority" are given through an extensive quotation from another authority.[132] Some of these physical characteristics, presumably of the psychopath, deserve a moment of consideration:

> . . . The brain may be abnormally large or small or defective either in part or as a whole. The abnormalities may be due to defective development, injury, tumor, infection, or vascular accidents, such as cerebral hemorrhage, or to interference with the circulation of cerebro-

spinal fluid such as occurs in hydrocephalus. Associated with these abnormalities are weakness and paralyses of various parts of the body as well as varying degrees of intellectual defect. The spinal cord likewise may be affected with resulting weaknesses or paralyses. There may be gross physical defects in the development of the eyes, ears, nose, mouth, arms, hands, legs, feet, rectum, anus, and external urogenital organs. Minor physical defects sometimes referred to as stigmata of defective development include abnormalities of the cranium, malformations of the external ears, eyes, nose or mouth (abnormal spacing, position, or defective development of teeth; high-arched palate, harelip or cleft palate), webbing of fingers or toes, distorted or supernumerary digits, excessive amount or absence of hair, undescended testicles and infantile uterus.*

Just what bearing this curious compendium of deformities may have on the question of the psychopath I am scarcely prepared to say. A causal relation, to which Sadler[257] does not openly commit himself but seems somewhat evasively to imply, is scarcely to be assumed, even if it is not to be dismissed at once as fantastic. None of the many hundreds of psychopaths whom I have observed showed any such picture as one gets from reading this quotation in the context that is given. Although such stigmata and such gross brain changes are sometimes associated with mental deficiency, cerebral agenesis, and various organic diseases, they are certainly not regarded as characteristic of psychopathic personality. In fact, if such abnormalities as these were found in a patient, the diagnosis of organic brain disease, mental deficiency, or of some definite heredodegenerative condition would become inescapable and the diagnosis of psychopathic personality (or sociopathic personality disturbance) unlikely if not impossible.†

After other brief descriptions the author under discussion adds a statement which is all but incredible. Following the opinion that prognosis is hopeless for complete recovery, it is asserted that psychopaths are not likely to improve "unless a psychiatrist can take them in hand for six months to a year and teach them how to live."[257] Under these conditions great improvement is considered probable. It is quite clear that more than a few different and extremely unlike things are being considered. Though all these are grouped under one name, they do not thereby gain homogeneity. Nor does it seem helpful for purposes of description, study, or treatment to approach

---

*From Henry, George W.: Essentials of psychiatry, Baltimore, 1931, Williams & Wilkins Co. Cited in Sadler, William: Theory and practice of psychiatry, St. Louis, 1936, The C. V. Mosby Co., pp. 881-882.
†In Henry's original text from which the quotation was taken by Sadler, this list of physical deformities and organic brain and spinal cord diseases and abnormalities precedes a description of mental deficiency, to which it has pertinent application.[132]

either the psychopath or patients of these other types in such a manner.

A few paragraphs beyond the account of physical defects and gross neurologic abnormalities just quoted we find the description of a subtype, "the feebly inhibited," which includes these interesting statements:

> On the functional side these individuals are notoriously subject to "general nervousness." "Specifically, we find tremors, facial or other tics (habit spasms), abnormal movements of the eyes, headaches, little attacks of dizziness, enuresis, prolonged throughout childhood, and so on." The organs of the special senses are particularly apt to show signs of inferiority; defective vision is very common.*

Any person familiar with the psychopath as he is met in clinical experience will need no prompting to realize what confusion is likely to ensue if the medical student tries to reconcile books and facts at this point.

Let us give a little more attention to these statements. The book from which they are taken was published in 1936. The last quotation is to be found, repeated precisely to the last comma, in another volume by Sadler published in 1945.[258] It is of interest to note that the entire passage also appears in *The Individual Delinquent* (William Healy, 1915),[124] a work which expresses concepts widely accepted and congruent with the terminology at that time but at confusing variance with official standards in 1936† and long ago discarded by Healy. Though no longer representing the original author or the criteria of the American Psychiatric Association, we find this archaic concept carried verbatim in a textbook published twenty-one years later and in another published thirty years later.

And with all this we find other statements, some applicable to the real psychopath and apparently so directed but plainly incongruous, if not indeed fantastic, if we attempt to correlate them with the material just quoted from the same volume. For instance, it is said of these people that "they suffer from no physical or mental disease that would account for their deficiency." (What about those brains abnormally large or small and defective in part or as a whole? What about tumor, infection, cerebral hemorrhage? What about paralyses and "gross physical defects of the . . . nose . . . legs . . . anus," etc.?)[257]

The confusion about our subject as it is so often presented in psychiatric

---

*From Sadler, William: Theory and practice of psychiatry, St. Louis, 1936, The C. V. Mosby Co., p. 883.

†It is only proper to emphasize that Dr. Healy's subsequent writings do not suggest any identification of the type of patients we are discussing with other sorts of disorder related to organic brain disease. His work, on the contrary, stands out among the most valuable efforts of those who have helped clarify these matters.

textbooks should not be peremptorily attributed to carelessness or ignorance on the part of the authors. It is worth while for us to remember that these authors are attempting to treat many disparate and not a few distinctly incongruous matters under a single heading. Even today our officially approved standards demand that a good many different disorders be so treated.[69] Often we find much broader and more heterogeneous areas embraced, and such a motley conglomeration of diverse subjects appears under a single label that even the most sagacious author can say little without falling at once into paradox, error, and soon into absurdity. His statements may be sound, accurate, and entirely pertinent to the various subjects he, perchance, has in mind and at the same time ring loud with nonsense as they strike willy-nilly upon other and alien subjects all forced under a single identifying term that applies to nothing except in language.

The second tendency, already mentioned, is illustrated in the brief space (five pages) of the textbook we have been discussing.[257] Not only do we find many dissimilar subjects treated under one term, but also a record of ambitious attempts to devise subtypes on a superficially descriptive basis unrelated to the real and obvious differences (such as, for instance, between a patient with cerebral agenesis and a typical psychopath). We are given the various "types" as listed by Kraepelin, Schneider, and Partridge:

	Kraepelin		Schneider		Partridge
1.	The excitable	1.	The hyperthymic	1.	The delinquent
2.	The unstable	2.	The depressive	2.	The inadequate
3.	The impulsive	3.	The insecure	3.	Those with general
4.	The eccentric	4.	The fanatic		incompatibility
5.	The liars and swindlers	5.	The self-seeking		
6.	The antisocial	6.	The emotionally unstable		
7.	The quarrelsome	7.	The explosive		
		8.	The affectless		
		9.	The weak-willed		
		10.	The asthenic		

To these the author of the textbook adds his own list of types:
1. Kleptomania
2. Pathologic liars
3. Eccentrics
4. Sex abnormalities
5. The feebly inhibited[257]

Is it an exaggeration if we say that the difficulties confronting the psychiatrist who has to approach the psychopath through such a tangle of concepts (and it is our traditional method) are comparable with those that would be faced by a general practitioner discussing leukemia if this term meant also a broken leg, hemorrhoids, pregnancy, brain tumor, and the common cold? And if there were no other term available!

Throughout the second quarter of this century Kahn's treatise entitled *Psychopathic Personalities*[162] has, judging by references in textbooks and in the psychiatric journals, been generally regarded as the authoritative and the most useful source of information about our present subject. This I believe to be scarcely less unfortunate than paradoxical. Here we have a valuable and scholarly work by a distinguished psychiatrist, a large volume embodying the author's fundamental concepts of personality structure and psychopathology in general. But we find little or nothing in all this material that has any pertinent relation to our group of patients. We find, in fact, all the psychoneuroses treated under the heading "psychopathic personality" and a list of sixteen categories that seem occasionally to touch but never to clarify our subject. Kahn's use of the term *psychopathic personality* is, in my opinion, not only justifiable but more in accordance with its obvious literal meaning than our customary use. Such questions are, however, not particularly germane. The point that demands emphasis is that our chief scientific work generally regarded for a couple of decades as authoritative in the field turns out not to be a book about the psychopath but a careful and valuable study of other subjects. Among these subjects it is difficult to find material related to our problem.

In his work, which is primarily concerned with psychopathology in general, Kahn,* in accordance with established practice, lists types which have been almost universally quoted as characteristic subdivisions into which the psychopath can be classified:

1. The nervous	9. The affectively cold
2. The anxious	10. The weak-willed
3. The sensitive	11. The impulsive
4. The compulsive	12. The sexually perverse
5. The excitable	13. The hysterical
6. The hyperthymic	14. The fantastic
7. The depressive	15. The cranks
8. The moody	16. The eccentric

The authors whom we have quoted and briefly discussed are not respon-

---

*From Kahn, Eugen: Psychopathic personalities, New Haven, 1931, Yale University Press.

sible for the confusion that surrounds the psychopath. Such an approach to the subject is the traditional approach that has for decades prevailed in psychiatry. Even the most wise and painstaking efforts cannot clarify a subject unless the subject is available. Many of the works mentioned I hold in high respect. In them other subjects are handled in such a way that those who seek reliable information can find it without undue difficulty.

It is hoped that these points may help us keep in mind that in our attempts to understand the psychopath we must struggle not only with the intrinsic problem of trying to distinguish and evaluate a complex psychiatric disorder but also with an almost impregnable approach. To touch our subject itself we must somehow make our way through a surrounding zone dense with false or dubious assumptions, mined with terms that at the same time make sense and nonsense. The approach to our subject, is furthermore, skillfully camouflaged by traditional influences that may, before we know it, have us talking about two or four or seven other things, no matter how earnestly we strive to speak of one at a time. I have little doubt that the present attempt to discuss the psychopath will, like those of others, suffer from the general and intractable confusion.

26

Clarifying the approach

Despite the difficulties that have been discussed, efforts to study the psychopath have proceeded. No modification of the official psychiatric attitude has occurred, and no step has been taken to make it possible to deal with the disorder by medical methods. But information has been accumulating that may someday bring this about.

The studies of Partridge have been valuable in focusing attention on the type of patient who needs attention as a separate entity rather than in a confused group. In his writing can be found a discernible and well-presented clinical picture. Partridge's three general types include only psychopaths, and the relatively modest distinctions among them impress us as valid rather than imaginary. Here, too, we find a clear rejection of the time-honored assumption that psychopaths are marked by gross physical defects and "stigmata of degeneration" and that this disorder has been satisfactorily related to inborn defects. This valuable contribution, though largely ignored by many authorities, merits recognition today.[241,242,243,244]

Long ago, when the psychopath was, even more than at present, confusingly submerged in a nonspecific category (known only by terms applied also to a wide variety of gross physical defect states), Healy and those who worked with him began to emphasize the purposive or reactive nature of antisocial behavior.[9,125,126] Careful attention was given to the emotional deprivations and distortions of aim that lay behind maladapted acts, and evidence of influences essentially psychogenic were noted and evaluated.

In work with juvenile delinquents, Healy pointed out that under similar conditions of insecurity or emotional deprivation one child might show anxiety, passive withdrawal, etc., and another aggressive mischief, apparently in response to the personal stress. These observations have been helpful over the years in efforts to interpret and to deal with behavior disorder.

Although relatively neglected for a long period by those concerned with interpretive or causal as contrasted with simply descriptive formulations, the psychopath received attention from Alexander, who makes an interesting contrast between ordinary neurosis, in which repressed impulses find a symbolic or substitutive expression in subjectively unpleasant symptoms, and character neurosis, in which the unconscious drives appear in maladapted objective behavior. In both disorders unconscious conflict is postulated. In orthodox neurosis this conflict may give rise to conscious anxiety without visible source, or impulses (repressed and ungratified) may be manifested indirectly by displacement (as in obsessions, compulsions, etc.), or otherwise (as in conversion paralysis, anesthesia, etc.). In character neurosis, according to Alexander, unconcious impulses obtain a degree of fulfillment in another manner, by a pattern of pathologic behavior in which apparently purposeless and sometimes self-defeating antisocial acts are carried out persistently. This pattern is followed despite penalties and in the absence of adequate conscious incentive.[9,11,12] This formulation has attracted much popular interest.

Alexander and many of his followers maintain that the antisocial conduct often represents an unconscious but purposive effort to obtain punishment in order to expiate and gain relief from (unconscious) feelings of guilt. As a hypothesis this is indeed ingenious and appealing. It has attracted many adherents. I have not been able, however, to discover such a sense of guilt or remorse (conscious or unconscious) in any of the psychopaths I have studied. Nor have I seen any convincing evidence of such unconscious guilt revealed in the work of Alexander or of other observers who accept his formulation. Such guilt is often assumed but, so far as I know, never demonstrated. I must therefore remain skeptical of this popular interpretation, however pleasant it might be to solve the problem of the psychopath by an interpretation so simple and so graceful.

The more experience I have had with psychopaths, the stranger it has seemed to me that a theory should insist that they have such deep and influential unconscious feelings of guilt when they are at the same time so plainly callous and free from remorse about grievous wrongs and crimes that they clearly recognize as their own. It strikes me as a quaint fantasy to assume without real evidence that they unconsciously go to such pains to obtain punishment and win redemption for unknown sins when they plainly and glibly ignore responsibility for every known misdemeanor and felony and pride themselves in evading penalties and in flouting the basic principles of justice.

The term *neurotic character* adopted by Alexander to designate the psychopath, although it may be of value in suggesting belief in a psychogenic etiology, is not conducive to progress in dealing with our problem. This point has been well emphasized by Karl Menninger in a discussion of the practical need of a new official name for the psychopath.[214] As pointed out by Menninger, the word *character* in such a use offers possibilities of confusion. If one patient has a neurotic character and another a neurotic personality, then just what is a character? And just what is a personality? And just how do they differ? There is, we may emphasize again, a considerable possibility of arousing the ghosts of a faculty psychology in the use of these terms.

Menninger makes another point in speaking of neurotic character that I believe is of essential importance. "The condition" he writes, "is closer to a psychosis than to a neurosis and the term neurotic is, therefore, misleading."*

A helpful study of the psychopath by Henderson presented in the Salmon Lectures (1938) and subsequently published[129] calls attention to the seriousness of the problem. From this presentation the reader is able to get clear ideas about actual patients as they appear clinically and the need for better methods of handling them.

Over a period of several decades Karpman has called attention to the psychopath, pointing out how little serious effort has been made by psychiatrists to understand or to deal with the essential problem. He maintained that psychogenic factors are responsible for the behavior disorder in many instances and believed that most patients classified as psychopathic personality should be called neurotic. A small residue of patients for whom he proposed the term anethopath, are, in Karpman's opinion, essentially unlike the others in that they are disabled by intrinsic defect rather than by dynamic psychopathologic reactions.[166,167,168,169,170]

In these studies the very great egocentricity, the inability to form any important or binding attachment to another, the failure ever to realize and grasp the very meaning of responsibility, all features that I believe to be most essential, are emphasized by Karpman and made clear as seldom done in other literature on the psychopath. It is doubtful if anyone else has done more to elucidate this psychopathologic picture and similar antisocial behavior disorders.

In the system of classification that prevailed when the first two editions of this book were prepared, the diagnosis of psychopathic personality was

---

*From Menninger, Karl: Recognizing and renaming "psychopathic personalities," Bulletin of the Menninger Clinic, 5:150-156, 1941.

listed among those conditions considered as being "without mental disorder." The general term was subdivided as follows:

*Psychopathic personality**

With pathologic sexuality. Indicate symptomatic manifestations, e.g.: homosexuality, erotomania, sexual perversion, sexual immaturity.

With pathologic emotionality. Indicate symptomatic manifestations, e.g.: schizoid personality, cyclothymic personality, paranoid personality, emotional instability.

With asocial or amoral trends. Indicate symptomatic manifestations, e.g.: antisociality, pathologic mendacity, moral deficiency, vagabondage, misanthropy.

Mixed types.

The first division, *pathologic sexuality,* will be discussed later.[†] Suffice it to say here that only the last term, *sexual immaturity,* has been characteristic of our group.

In the second division, *pathologic emotionality,* the schizoid, cyclothymic, and paranoid personalities are regarded as relatively mild and relatively static deviations of the same types familiar in schizophrenia, manic-depressive psychosis, and paranoid psychosis. Their disorder or disability is very different clinically from that discussed in this volume. The typical psychopath shows little or no indication of suffering from a deviation in the directon of such a disorder as schizophrenia, manic-depressive psychosis, or paranoia but shows a disorder quite different. Characteristic schizoid or cyclothymic traits are not discernible features of the psychopath. Although psychopaths tend to blame their troubles on others, they do not, like patients with real paranoid deviation, organize and persistently follow out highly purposive plans or hold tenaciously to strong affective attitudes. Emotional instability is, in a shallow sense, applicable to the psychopath, but this quality scarcely seems an outstanding or fundamental deviation. Many, as a matter of fact, show less evidence of anxiety, uneasiness, etc., and other reactions implied by emotional instability than the average person.

The descriptive terms included in the third category apply in varying degrees to many of the patients discussed here, but these scarcely seem either broad enough or deep enough to be of value as diagnostic formulations.

Under one term, *psychopathic personality,* we find grouped here many types of disorder. These disorders have very little in common. One thing that

---

*From Outlines for psychiatric examinations, Albany, N. Y., 1943, The New York State Department of Mental Health.
†Pp. 303 to 323 and 394 to 399.

has been presumed about some of them, that is, that they are relatively trivial as contrasted with extremely disabling conditions, we grant, so far as schizoid personality, cyclothymic personality, and paranoid personality are concerned. This characteristic of being an incomplete degree of various sorts of disorder we deny as applying to the subject of this volume. Only by a manipulation of verbal abstractions can such disorders be identified with the specific disorder shown by those regularly called psychopaths.

In the current *Diagnostic and Statistical Manual*[69] we find the general term *personality disorders* used to designate all the various items formerly listed under *psychopathic personality*—all these and several more.

Personality disorders*
  Personality pattern disturbance
    Inadequate personality
    Schizoid personality
    Cyclothymic personality
    Paranoid personality
  Personality trait disturbance
    Emotionally unstable personality
    Passive-aggressive personality
    Compulsive personality
    Personality trait disturbance, other
  Sociopathic personality disturbance
    Antisocial reaction
    Dyssocial reaction
    Sexual deviation; specify supplementary term
    Addiction
      Alcoholism
      Drug addiction
  Special sympton reaction
    Learning disturbance
    Speech disturbance
    Enuresis
    Somnambulism
    Other

Transient situational personality disturbance*
  Gross stress reaction
  Adult situational reaction
  Adjustment reaction of infancy
  Adjustment reaction of childhood
    Habit disturbance
    Conduct disturbance
    Neurotic traits
  Adjustment reaction of adolescence
  Adjustment reaction of late life

---

*From Diagnostic and statistical manual, mental disorders, Washington, D. C., 1952, American Psychiatric Association Mental Hospital Service.

In this long list of items, *sociopathic personality disturbance, antisocial reaction,* is thus defined:

> This term refers to chronically antisocial individuals who are always in trouble, profiting neither from experience nor punishment, and maintaining no real loyalties to any person, group, or code. They are frequently callous and hedonistic, showing marked emotional immaturity, with lack of sense of responsibility, lack of judgment, and an ability to rationalize their behavior so that it appears warranted, reasonable, and justified.
>
> The term includes cases previously classified as "constitutional psychopathic state" and "psychopathic personality." As defined here the term is more limited, as well as more specific in its application.*

Here the familiar psychopath can be accurately and officially classified. It seems to me regrettably confusing that under the same general heading of *personality disorders* we find listed such astonishingly unallied minor difficulties as *learning disturbance, speech disturbance, enuresis,* and *somnambulism.*[69]

It is perhaps in silent recognition of the absurdities in our official categories that psychiatrists in practice still avail themselves of the more or less slang term which is a sort of nickname for our subject. When one psychiatrist on the staff of a state hospital, or at a meeting of the American Psychiatric Association, expresses to another some thought he has about the *psychopath,* it is immediately and plainly understood that he is not making reference to schizoid disorder or to sexual deviation *per se* but to a disorder nearly all psychiatrists recognize and recognize as distinct from the heterogeneous mess of unrelated disorders with which it is officially listed. The newer informal term *sociopath* has emerged as a synonym. Here the two words are used interchangeably. There is nothing vague about these patients clinically. Their course of conduct can be predicted with much greater accuracy than that of patients with defined psychoses.

Attempts to discuss this type of patient and to use the approved term *personality disorder* in its official meaning are likely to be neither clear nor accurate. In fact, it is difficult not to talk nonsense if any one bears in mind all the things that term is recognized as including.

What can be said correctly about a psychopath has little or no significance for many of the other conditions to which *personality disorder* also applies by its official definition. Any sensible plan for treatment or for handling psychopaths (as they have been presented in this volume and as they are gen-

---

*From Diagnostic and statistical manual, mental disorders, Washington, D. C., 1952, American Psychiatric Association Mental Hospital Service.

erally understood by working psychiatrists) would make little sense if applied to all the other kinds of disorder identified with them verbally by our old and discarded or by our current scheme of classification.

27

Purpose of this step

Some material has been presented in which manifestations of the disorder occur. It is our task to arrange it in such a way that its features can be seen clearly and compared with the features of other disorders. Such a step should be helpful in our efforts to recognize what we are dealing with and to evaluate it. Let us compare these patients known as psychopaths with others showing clinical illness and deviated reactions or patterns of living. Significant details should emerge, differentiation should become clearer, and distinguishing features of our subject should become more apparent.

The contrast with some surrounding types is so obvious that only a few points need be made. In discussing other disorders not so clearly defined and those traditionally confused with the psychopath, more extensive consideration is demanded. When there are important common characteristics between the two groups compared, it may be worth while to go into even more detail and bring out all features that can be helpful in delineating our subject. Only a few paragraphs or pages will be given to the discussion of some items that follow. To others which deserve it, a great deal more space will be devoted.

In Part II we shall consider the psychopath's relation to the following types:

1. The psychotic
2. Patients with deviations recognized as similar to the psychoses but regarded as incomplete or less severe reactions

3. The psychoneurotic
4. The mental defective
5. The ordinary criminal
6. Other character and behavior disorders, including delinquency, etc.
7. Specific homosexuality and other consistent sexual deviations
8. The erratic man of genius
9. The injudicious hedonist and some other drinkers
10. The clinical alcoholic
11. The malingerer
12. Fictional characters of psychiatric interest

28

The psychotic

For the sake of emphasis let us first contrast very briefly the psychopath with the general group of psychotic patients to which he is considered not to belong. These, if their disorder is well advanced, are usually recognized by the law as "insane" and by the man on the street as irrational, irresponsible, plainly unable to accept the general facts accepted by humanity at large, and, furthermore, unable to provide for themselves or to remain safely or conveniently at liberty among their fellows. Such people frequently have beliefs that are not only false but bizarre, inconsistent, and nearly always impossible to remove even by convincing demonstrations of their impossibility. Ready examples are the belief of a soda jerk that he is an emperor dead a thousand years ago, a belief still maintained although the patient admits he is living in the twentieth century and realizes that he is in a psychiatric hospital and that he grew up in the local slums, and the belief of an inconspicuous clerk that a worldwide organization has been formed to persecute him because of jealousy aroused by the fact that his testicles are pure radium.

Many of these patients hear voices speaking to them and cannot be made to see that these are imaginary. To the layman they are plainly not people to reason with or to be relied on but are obviously "demented." It is apparent that they do and say foolish or fantastic things because their reasoning processes, not to speak of their perceptions, are gravely disordered or misdirected. Their general personality outlines are often distorted or sometimes even appear to be destroyed.

Patients in whom a milder psychosis exists usually show some of these specific peculiarities and always show general personality deviations which enable the psychiatrist eventually to place them in their proper classification. These patients with milder disorder often are able to get along without serious difficulty in the community, just as a patient with mild influenza may not even go to bed whereas one with a severe attack may lie delirious, unable to sit up, and finally die. These milder degrees of psychosis, however, show the same type of disorder found in the more severe and obvious manifestations, just as the mild influenza attack is the same in type but not in degree as the serious one.

It is perhaps worth while to add here that not all those suffering from a typical psychosis, even when the disorder is serious in degree, give an obvious impression of derangement. Severe paranoid conditions, particularly those of the most malignant type, may exist for years in persons who lack all superficial signs that the layman often feels should be apparent to establish psychosis (insanity).[27,216]

Sometimes such people appear not only normal but brilliant, and their powers of reasoning in all areas except those dominated by delusion are intact. The delusions themselves may even be withheld when the excellent judgment of the subject discerns that they will not be accepted by others or may interfere with psychotic plans toward which he is assiduously and ingeniously working. "Why, if I'd let the public in on these facts, a lot of fools might have thought I was insane," one such patient explained. Another patient, who had for years been hearing imaginary voices which he accepted as real, admitted that he denied this to the draft board because, "They might have thought something was wrong with my mind." He had been doing a satisfactory job and, on the surface, making a good social adjustment in his community. He was accepted for service in the army.

Another man with clear-cut paranoid delusions prospered for years by selling stocks and bonds to opulent widows and to others in whom his enthusiastic optimism and shrewd reasoning powers worked marvelous conviction. He was indeed persuasive. To my definite knowledge he induced a friend to believe that serious mental disorder threatened him, or was perhaps already present. Offering to help the friend, who naturally became alarmed, the paranoiac made arrangements for his hospitalization and, accompanying the other, had him voluntarily admitted to a psychiatric institution. After a period of observation the friend was found to be free of any such trouble. Months later the real patient's delusional system was elicted and his commitment deemed necessary.

Even today one often encounters popular misconceptions of what constitutes psychosis or seriously disabling "mental disorder" that seem to belong

258

to earlier centuries. Even when patients are speaking frankly and continually about hearing voices from the next county (or the next world), relatives occasionally express surprise at the opinion that anything could be wrong with his *mind,"* insisting that he had been running the store as well as ever, adding up the accounts without error, and showing his usual common sense in daily affairs.

Fanatics and false prophets who show real but not so obvious signs of classic psychosis, as everyone must by now have learned, sometimes attract hundreds or thousands of followers who contribute large funds to projects founded on delusion. If news reports by many observers can be relied upon, even those showing plain evidence of very serious disorder, persons as fully psychotic as many on the wards of the state hospitals, also succeed in appearing to large groups not only as sage leaders or men with supernatural powers but also as God.[19,32]

The psychopath, on the other hand, is free of all technical signs of this sort. There are no demonstrable defects in theoretical reasoning. At least he is free of them in the same sense that the general run of men and women are free. He carries out his activities in what is regarded as ordinary awareness of the consequences and without the distorting influences of any demonstrable system of delusions. His personality outline is apparently or superficially intact and not obviously distorted.

The diagnostic formulation *psychosis with psychopathic personality,* listed in the nomenclature that was official until 1952, deserves attention. Such a psychosis was thus defined by the older *Statistical Manual:*

> The abnormal reactions which bring psychopathic personalities into the group of psychoses are varied in form but usually of an episodic character. Most prominent are attacks of irritability, excitement, depression, paranoid episodes, transient confused states, etc. . . . True prison psychoses belong in this group.
>
> A psychopathic personality with a manic-depressive attack should be classed in the manic-depressive group and likewise a psychopathic personality with a schizophrenic psychosis should go in the dementia praecox group. Psychopathic personalities without episodic mental attack or psychotic symptoms should be placed in the group "without psychosis."*

In agreement with Cruvant and Yochelson,[62] I cannot see that anything was gained through such a classification. If a psychopath develops some other disorder such as schizophrenia or affective psychosis, the additional disorder

---

*From Outlines for psychiatric examinations, Albany, N. Y., 1943, The New York State Department of Mental Hygiene.

can be listed properly without recourse to such an appellation as that just mentioned. So, too, if transient confusional states occur, they may be so classified in the psychopath as in others.

Such a category promoted confusion by implying the presence of a specific psychotic illness different from, and in addition to, the psychopath's essential disorder and that this, even if it is correctly listed as schizophrenia, paranoid psychosis, etc., needed the further qualification, "with psychopathic personality." The transient confusional states considered by some as a characteristic reaction of psychopaths to imprisonment are usually trivial (minor) additions to or complications of the very serious, incapacitating disorder that is fundamental. Such manifestations might be compared with those of a schizophrenic patient who by chance also develops temporary delirium.

If the psychopath develops major or minor disorder of a type classed among "the psychoses," it can be signified by addition of the usual term, just as if he had developed brain tumor or peptic ulcer. There seems to be neither need of nor warrant for a hybridizing concept which does nothing to clarify but a good deal to cloud the issues. I am not sure there was ever much more need for "psychosis with psychopathic personality" than for "psychosis with red hair" or "neurosis with a Ph.D. degree." The current nomenclature appears better designed to avoid unnecessary confusions of this sort.[69]

29

Deviations recognized as similar to the psychoses but regarded as incomplete or less severe reactions

As noted earlier, conditions resembling psychoses but appearing incomplete or less severe are still classified officially under the same general diagnostic term as the disorder to which this book is devoted. Such an arrangement has been approved by some as a means of placing together groups assumed to be on the border line of serious disorder with a genuine similarity in degree if not in type. There is another argument in favor of using one term to identify these diverse clinical realities. This arises from efforts to distinguish as active disease processes the psychoses and psychoneuroses from other conditions presumed to be circumscribed defect states or relatively static deviations. It is true that some genuine similarities can be discerned here among many of the diverse conditions listed under *personality disorders*. These similarities have, it seems to me, been given an undue importance.

It is far from proved that pathologic conditions which we call schizoid personality or paranoid personality begin at birth and remain unchanged throughout life. There is a vast range of difference in chronicity, reversibility, severity, prognosis, etc., throughout the schizoid disorders and, indeed, throughout the paranoid and affective disorders also. Much would be gained both logically and practically if in our official nomenclature we could place all essentially schizoid disorders in an appropriate category and then make what further distinctions are useful as to transiency, chronicity, degree, etc. Since schizoid manifestations vary from rapid processes to maladjustments apparently static, from relatively mild deviations and disabilities to total incapacity and maximum personality disintegration, let us then reflect these facts in our language. As a matter of fact, as every psychiatrist well knows, in many patients an initial disorder of slow or rapid progress (disease process) becomes static or relatively static at widely varying levels of deviation from the normal. So too, it seems, we should deal with affective and paranoid disorders. Without minimizing the fact that schizophrenia is an illness, it is perhaps more profitable to conceive of it as a complicated distortion of the life process (or, as has been said, *a way of life*, albeit an extremely pathologic way) than as a circumscribed external agency that selects and falls upon its victim. Active and progressive schizophrenic illness probably arises out of tendencies and influences not unlike those which underlie the milder and more static distortions we label as schizoid personality.

In many important respects it seems to me that the person who is called a psychopath or sociopath differs greatly from most people showing schizoid, paranoid, and cyclothymic disorder or deviation in degree short of psychosis and in whatever state of chronicity. Not only does the psychopath vary in type, but his specific disorder varies in severity from a mild or borderline degree up through great degrees of disability. There are also behavior patterns of this sort which prove to be temporary.

It will perhaps be worth while to consider briefly an example from the secondary group distinguished under various subheadings (schizoid, cyclothymic, etc.) and officially classed with the psychopath in a primary pigeon hole labeled *personality disorders*.

Well qualified for the diagnosis of schizoid personality is a 19-year-old boy whom I treated on several occasions. I would prefer to call his reaction one definitely schizoid in nature, very chronic and relatively static, and lacking most clinical features by which disorders otherwise similar are recognized as constituting "a psychosis." The first point that stands out in this patient is how obviously he differs from all psychopaths. On meeting him, it is immediately seen that he is a lonely person, one recognized as queer by all who encounter him. In discussing his recent attempt at suicide, he could give no good reason for his act. No evidence of depression was obtained. As if not knowing what else to say, he suggested he must have tried to kill himself "just out of curiosity." He had no positive convictions about a future life or interest in exploring such possibilities. He had been making good grades at college and he had no worries that he could express. His attempt at suicide had been authentic. Only by chance had he been discovered where he hung in a noose made by his belt. No evidence of delusions or hallucinations was ever elicited. A few excerpts from a report given by the college physician, who spent much time with him, are contributory:

> Oliver was recognized as a bit odd or eccentric since his coming here during the summer weeks of 19___. He worked quite willingly with sustained effort and application. Everyone liked him and although they protested his persistent pipe and untidy personal appearance (being unshaven, lax about clean garments, combed hair, etc.), they were amused and tolerant. He had the reputation of having superior intellectual capacity and that gave him the aura of a potential winner. The students included him in everything and he was a conflicting mixture of pathetic eagerness to be accepted as one of them and to be the lone wolf. He went through the motions of being one of the group but it all had to be within the boundaries of his own withdrawal pattern. Though unresponsive in regard to greetings and small talk, he would talk for hours about himself and his ideas and was eager for such expression.

> • • •

> Girls interested him less. Actually, though he protested that he had an average interest in the other sex, he had very few dates with them. However, very recently he groomed himself quite adequately and went to Foxbridge to visit a girl whom he used to date during his high school days and who is studying journalism there.

> • • •

> It was noted and accepted by everyone that Oliver would argue every point, in class and out, but much good-natured teasing caused him to restrain himself somewhat in this respect. However, I have noted in all my contacts with him a persistent negativistic attitude. He prided himself on always taking the opposite point of view and that his philosophy was quite peculiar to himself. He expressed a resentment of everything "expected" of him by way of the simplest courtesies and social amenities of any kind.

> • • •

> He is sure that there is nothing neurotic about himself and mentioned doctors and nurses other than yourself who have told him that they thought him to be all right. He exhibits an attitude toward his hospitalization quite similar to that toward his attempted suicide. His defense is thick and strong and he reacts with argument or denial to almost anything which is said which seems to imply that all is not quite as it should be with him. He said that you had told him that he would need some help and had better come to see me every few days. He thinks that is not necessary and I think he is right, for I can see no way to approach him even on the outskirts of his problem without

263

stimulating a negative reaction on his part. I noted that same lack of insight as you, and it is so complete as to bar any psychotherapeutic relation. I left the way open for him to come at any time and I will indeed help if I can.

This fragment from Oliver's personal notes also brings out something about his state that is difficult to describe:

Loneliness

By

Oliver _____, *Jr.*

It is now long after the hour of midnight. I am alone, except for my pipe and my ever-active mind, in one of the front rooms.

God has created many horrible things, but the greatest of all those monsters is that intolerable loneliness that man calls Love, Sex, Self-Pity, Comradeship, *und so weiter*. I trust that you, as an individual, shall be able to grasp some vague notion of what I, as a purely abstract thinking-apparatus, am trying to convey to you.

Nothing in a State of Nothingness. Can you imagine a more comforting place? No emotions of fear, love, hate, anger, sympathy, pity. No materiality! No spirituality! No mentality! Nothing!!! The Hell of the Bible! The Heaven of the Bible! Paradise! Purgatory! and the Inferno!—all One!! All nothing!!!

Have you ever really delved deeply into why, for what purpose you were born or why anyone was born? To bear children? Yes, but dogs can do that gracefully. To build? To make money? You must leave all behind when you depart. You are unable to carry it with you.

The epicureans had a good idea when they said, "Eat, drink and be merry, for tomorrow we may die." But why eat, drink, and be merry? Why should one live, or the animals which are so very close below us? There is no God; there is no Heaven; there is no Hell; these are the dreams of baby minds. The Church, the Bible, Science, Spiritualism, and on and on and on can offer not a solitary shred of evidence that there is a God, Heaven, Hell, Devil, Angels. They are but wistful thinkers—the Church, the Bible, and Spiritualism. They are the idealists. Scientists are the realists, but they study nature. Why build machines? What can it matter to you personally one hundred years from now? You will be nothing. Nothing.

Am I insane? They say I am because I ask, "Why?" and there is no answer to that by anyone. "What?" can be answered. So can "When?" "Where?" "Who?" "How?" et cetera, but not "Why?" Healthy minds do not ask, "Why?" Normal people sleep and love, eat and drink, breathe and excrete, work and, perhaps, think—think, but only a little and only within the bounds of conventionality.

—Oliver

This boy frequently writes letters to the newspapers commenting on politics, art, religion, history, etc. There is usually a bitterness in his comments and a kind of wit that seems to leaven his isolation. The brittle strangeness of manner, the inadequateness and inappropriateness of his affective reactions can only be appreciated in direct contact. An excerpt follows:

It was just a fairly good "B" picture. There was nothing in it that I had not seen numbers of times before at the cinema. I did not think it dirty. I thought it to be just what it was—a literally cheap movie. Artists only would have banned it. On the other hand, I found the decidedly wicked picture, "The Outlaw," to be the funniest screened attraction I'd ever seen (I saw it on my return trip in Atlanta). It caused more laughs than "Kiss and Tell."

Miss Smith, please find your glasses! My morals are evaporating!

Oliver _____, Jr.

At the end of a letter to his father he signs himself,

With a heart of gold (hard and yellow), I close,

Your oldest son,
Oliver _____, Jr.

This is a person who, despite his superior intelligence and his awkward gestures at being sociable, is recognized at once as extremely eccentric, if not indeed bizarre, by his classmates as well as by the expert. Evidence of his psychiatric trouble is apparent, and no trained observer would confuse him with the psychopath. A history is not necessary to surmise that he has had difficulties and that further difficulties lie ahead. Although his personality is not outwardly fragmented, it immediately gives clues to the fact that here experience is not what others find it. Such a patient sometimes gives the impression that through him one comes in closer touch with what is most specific and inexplicable in schizophrenia, what is usually blurred or hidden in the chaos of the overt psychosis. Superficially nothing could be more different from what he presents than the socially smooth psychopath who has an explanation for everything, an easy cordiality for everyone. His bitterly authentic seriousness and his capacity for hurt and suffering also contrast with the psychopath.

In many patients the disturbance classed as schizoid personality might be more accurately regarded as masked schizophrenia or, as has been sometimes said, "ambulatory" schizophrenia. Although the more gross technical signs of psychosis are not evident on the surface, many of these patients have very serious disorder within. The tendency to call their condition schizoid personality (and therefore label them as definitely "sane") sometimes results in their being incorrectly treated. Very dangerous tendencies, well concealed, may emerge into tragic acts.

Some years ago a young woman regarded as seclusive, a bit queer, and withdrawn by her acquaintances called a big-league baseball player to her hotel room on the pretext of grave and urgent business. The business was not what might be expected from such a call by a young woman to a man whom she had never met personally but had seemed to admire, hero-worship, and brood over for a long time in yearning fantasies. According to newspaper accounts, the girl, with no explanation or reason she could explain afterward, shot the ballplayer in a genuine attempt to kill him and one which barely failed to do so.

I cannot offer a diagnosis on this patient whom I have never seen. Her behavior and her personal characteristics as disclosed in the press are, however, entirely typical of patients with masked but real and serious schizoid disorder. Such patients are more accurately indicated by the term "masked schizophrenia" than by "schizoid personality," which may, artifically and unrealistically, ignore the true state of very ill and dangerous persons and classify them with those presumably deviated in mild degree.

Some patients of this sort eventually show themselves to be psychotic, and it then becomes apparent that a serious inner disorder has, perhaps for many years, been masked by the minor overt peculiarities that constitute what is generally regarded as schizoid personality. Sometimes in patients with masked schizophrenia the serious inner pathology is so well concealed that the patient may be almost indistinguishable from the typical psychopath. It is important to keep in mind that the excellence of the superficial aspect of the patient (whether he be called a masked schizophrenic or a psychopath) gives no reliable indication of how serious the inner, concealed, and at the time undemonstrable pathology may prove to be or how disastrously and unpredictably it may be expressed when it erupts into antisocial (psychotic) behavior. Like the very dangerous and profoundly ill ambulatory schizophrenic patient whose central disorder is well masked and not yet demonstrable, the psychopath has a concealed but very real and grave pathology. Unlike other types of masked psychosis, the central personality "lesions" of the psychopath are covered over not by peripheral or surface functioning suggestive of some eccentricity or peculiarity of personality or typical of another and lesser disorder but by a perfect mask of genuine sanity, a flawless surface indicative in every respect of robust mental health.

The example of schizoid personality or masked schizophrenia just presented under the pseudonym *Oliver* is obviously distinguishable from the psychopath. His outer aspect contrasts vividly with the smooth and deceptive disguise of the typical psychopath. There are, however, other masked schizophrenics who resemble the typical psychopath much more closely. I have seen a number of patients who were classified by able and experienced psychiatrists as typical psychopaths (sociopaths) and by others, equally able, as very well-masked schizophrenics. About these patients the difference of judgment lay in estimates of how effectively the surface function masked the inner disorder and gave an appearance of full health. There was usually no disagreement in the conclusion by all the psychiatrists that an underlying disorder was severe and maximally disabling. The deceptive qualities of the excellent disguise, the perfection of the mask, afford no reliable indication that the true condition is mild or moderate and no assurance that it may not be far more serious than the disability of some patients in whom auditory hallucinations and bizarre delusions can be readily demonstrated.

It is perhaps pertinent to mention here that there are other disguises behind which other serious personality disorders mislead us. Chamberlain[53] has ably emphasized what he refers to as cryptic depression. Patients so affected may complain only of headache, nausea, a pain in the back, weakness, etc. On repeated questioning, some will admit depression as a minor element in the situation. Others will deny it convincingly and show no evidence of it. I have seen many such patients in whom the history of previous depressive psychosis, many details of the patient's personality, and the prompt response to electric shock therapy give indirect but convincing evidence of the invisible illness. Here it might be said that the potentially more serious condition appears only in a substituted reaction that seems to constitute a compromise or a disguise.

Under the term *pseudoneurotic schizophrenia,* Hoch and Polatin[139] discuss what every psychiatrist has often encountered—the patient who gives one the feeling that he must be a schizophrenic but in whom none of the specifically characteristic features of psychosis can be demonstrated. Often the only complaints are of vague or minor physical discomforts. Sometimes other features that literally indicate a psychoneurosis, and this only, constitute all that can be brought out. Such patients do not express delusions. They deny hallucinations and show no disorder of thinking as this is ordinarily described and no mannerisms or bizarre overt attitudes. They are never grossly irrational in what they express. The history does not show them psychotically deviated in their general behavior until, perhaps, some irreparable psychotic act occurs. Their lack of insight (broader and more profound than in the psychoneurotic patient) and a peculiar emotional deficit and distortion make the examiner realize, without being able to prove it, that he is dealing with schizophrenia. At length the examiner becomes convinced that these patients do not normally experience and evaluate the basic issues of life and that this difference is of the sort and degree not found except in schizophrenia. Some of these people eventually develop delusions and hallucinations, but many go on year after year fully masked by the psychoneurotic facade.

The patient who is seriously schizophrenic but whose basic disorder is masked by the outer appearance of neurosis or by what seem to be only minor eccentricities or schizoid traits can nearly always be readily distinguished from the true psychopath. As mentioned previously, however, there are sometimes masked schizophrenics whose outer appearance is more like that of the true psychopath.

Guttmacher discusses these patients in a very interesting paper and designates them by the term *pseudopsychopathic schizophrenia*.[111] The type of patient discussed by Guttmacher may appear for many years to be a typical psychopath and show all the features in his behavior that are characteristic. Some of these patients do not show the outer eccentricities and oddnesses that usually distinguish the masked schizophrenic. Indeed, they may be as outgoing, charming in manner, and free from apparent abnormality as the classic psychopath. As pointed out by Guttmacher, sometimes such a patient will eventually develop a full-blown and obvious schizophrenic psychosis.

It might be argued that the psychosis has developed independently of the psychopathic defect, but I think it much more likely that a serious central disorder was present all the time and that eventually it has become manifest through the disruption of the formerly perfect superficial function and outer appearance. Such developments as these lead me to believe not only that the central disorder in the psychopath may perhaps be similar in degree to that in schizophrenia but also that there may be more similarity in quality than is generally recognized.

An interesting comparison between thoroughly masked schizophrenia and the disorder of the psychopath can be found in the fictional characters Judd Steiner and Artie Straus as they are presented by Meyer Levin in his novel *Compulsion*.[186] Judd Steiner, the fictional representative of Nathan Leopold, gives a strong impression of deep schizoid disorder masked by generally sane behavior and great intellectual brilliance. Artie Straus, who is modelled on the novelist's conception of Loeb, emerges in the book as a remarkably well-drawn figure of the classic psychopath. The author admits that his fictional characters are not necessarily true interpretations of the actual characters whose utterly unprovoked sensational murder of a teenaged boy startled and horrified the world approximately forty years ago. This long-deliberated and ingeniously planned murder for a thrill suggests a callousness and cynicism that are difficult to describe and still astonishing to contemplate. Both the similarities and the differences between Judd and

Artie are wonderfully and convincingly conveyed by Levin in his book and should stimulate interest in everyone concerned with the basic problems of psychiatry.

There is little point in devoting space to detailed accounts of paranoid or cyclothymic personalities. In some degree such characteristics can be seen among anyone's acquaintances, and to name a quantitative point at which they warrant a diagnosis is not easy. Nor is it possible to lay down specifications that will enable one to delineate confidently where paranoid personality ceases and paranoid state or paranoid psychosis begins. So it is with depressions. Where the depth of negative affect permissible to a cyclothmic personality ceases and that of "neurotic depression" begins is perhaps even more difficult to define than where, at greater depths, the disorder should properly be pronounced depressive psychosis. There is about all this much to suggest that traditional concepts have attributed to our terms a good deal more authority than clinical facts uphold.

I find it helpful to consider all schizoid reactions, of whatever degree or course of development, as qualitatively similar, whether or not they are sufficiently disabling to merit such a term as psychosis. So, too, the affective and paranoid reactions seem to fall naturally each into its primary group rather than into other pigeonholes (on the basis of degree) which may give rise to confusion.

The characteristic disorder of the psychopath is usually not difficult to distinguish from these other disorders, but like all of them, it, too, is seen in the widest variations of degree, in manifestations ranging from isolated character traits in a successful person, or brief episodes of delinquency in adolescence, to disability far greater than that shown by many of the psychotic patients committed to institutions.

30

The psychoneurotic

People who suffer from personality disorders which cause them to be anxious, restless, unhappy, and obsessed with thoughts they themselves recognize as absurd but who are, in the lay sense, altogether sane have for years been classed as psychoneurotic. They recognize reason in general, often admit that their symptoms arise from emotional conflicts, and are free from delusions and hallucinations.

Sometimes their complaints are chiefly physical, of fatigue, of numbness, of indigestion, even of paralysis. Often they will not admit that this numbness or indigestion or paralysis could possibly be related to emotional difficulty and indeed they themselves may be unaware of conflict. They are often resistant to reasoning but more in the sense of a person with strong prejudices than of one with delusions or with intellectual dilapidation. Sometimes they feel strong fears that they may carry out acts which they dread and which would indeed be tragic or criminal, but they recognize the nature of these acts and do not carry them out. Other acts, apparently senseless but relatively harmless, they do carry out, recognizing the absurdity of feeling that they must do so but becoming anxious if they resist the impulse.

In general, psychoneurotic people recognize objective reality and try to adapt themselves like most others to the ways of society. In general it may be said that patients with traditional psychoneurosis are not characterized by antisocial activity or by striking inability to pursue ordinary goals. Their symptoms handicap them often, but in a way we readily understand. Anxiety, for instance, can make special difficulties for a salesman or obsessive manifestations can handicap a banker, a scholar, or a housewife. These patients as a group are sharply characterized by anxiety and by the various symptomatic schemes that apparently arise from the anxiety and that look as if they were measures employed in reaction to the anxiety and in efforts to relieve it.

It is true that many patients with conversion symptoms do not show what is ordinarily conveyed by the word *anxiety* or by *tension, fear, distress,* and similar terms. Many psychiatrists believe that in such instances the paralysis (or the blindness) may be a substitute for conscious anxiety and probably a defense against it, a means of preventing it or controlling it. The rather remarkable calmness shown by such patients has often been pointed out. Not a few psychopathologists maintain that there is an "unconscious anxiety" or what might be thought of as something embryonic, underlying, or incipient that would be anxiety if not converted into the physical manifestation.

Certainly it may be said about psychoneurosis, as the term is officially used and most widely accepted, that patients with this kind of disorder find their symptoms unpleasant, consciously suffer from them, and complain.

On the contrary, those called psychopaths are very sharply characterized by the lack of anxiety (remorse, uneasy anticipation, apprehensive scrupulousness, the sense of being under stress or strain) and, less than the average person, show what is widely regarded as basic in the neurotic. It is very true that Alexander[9,11] and others[88,215] who use his terminology and accept his interpretations refer to behavior disorders as character neuroses. Karpman[170] feels that most (but not all) patients who are classed as psychopaths should be grouped with the neurotic or the psychotic group. So far as its implication of causal factors is concerned, the term neurotic has undeniably valuable applications; but its tendency otherwise to identify the psychopath with hysteria, anxiety reactions, or ordinary obsessive-compulsive disorders is likely to cause confusion and make for practical difficulties.

If the psychopath (or most of those so diagnosed) really has a neurosis, it is a neurosis that is manifested in a fundamentally different life-pattern from classic neurosis, manifested, one might say, in a pattern that is not only different but opposite. Alexander and others have made this quite clear, and the interpretation of the psychopath's behavior as symptomatic "acting out" against his surroundings, in contrast with the development of anxiety or headache or obsession is, it seems to me, an interesting formulation. It is of obvious importance to respect this polar difference between how the psychopath is going to behave socially and what can be expected of patients with somatization, conversion, etc. I do not believe that psychopaths should be identified with the psychoneurotic group, for this would imply that they possess full social and legal competency, that they are capable of handling adequately their own affairs, and that they are earnestly seeking relief from unpleasant symptoms.

There are disorders in which the two diverse types of reaction (developing subjectively unpleasant symptoms versus callously carrying out socially destructive acts) seem to exist in the same symptom. The so-called pyromaniac (and kleptomaniac) often seems motivated by forces similar to the classic obsessive-compulsive patient who corrects the alignment of objects on the bureau forty times a day and who is painfully and overscrupulously preoccupied with fears that he may harm his child. The latter detests the acts he carries out as a sort of ritual to mitigate his subjective distress and is by no means likely to harm the child. He is, in fact, horrified by these thoughts (fears) and is nearly always conscientious to an excessive degree.

On the other hand, as Fenichel has pointed out, the patient abnormally impelled to commit arson or theft (or sex murder) is not committing an act in which scrupulous feelings play a direct or major role and (despite possible ambivalence) gains excitement and consciously satisfies strong drives. The distinction emphasized by Fenichel between ego-syntonic and ego-alien motivations (compulsive acts of caution versus so-called "compulsive" antisocial acts) is a fundamental point and brings out a distinction not merely of degree but of quality. Behavior that Fenichel classifies as impulse neurosis seems to lie in an area where the unlike (and, as a rule, mutually exclusive) manifestations of the psychopath and the classic obsessive-compulsive patient both play a part together, the two customary opposites approaching and perhaps merging, paradoxically, in the antisocial act.[88,262]

This particular mingling of influences (or merging of pictures) ordinarily quite different (and mutually exclusive) is not unique in psychiatry. Is there any one who has not seen patients manifesting genuine manic and genuine catatonic features? Has any psychiatrist failed to note obsessive reactions that are colored with genuine delusion?

Despite any confusions that arise in arguments about psychopathology (dynamic or descriptive) in regard to the psychopath, all, I believe, will agree that his clinical manifestations are easily distinguished from the syndromes now classified as psychoneurosis. It is doubtful if in the whole of medicine any other two reactions stand out in clearer contrast.

The true psychopaths personally observed have usually been free, or as free as the general run of humanity, from real symptoms of psychoneurosis. The psychoneurotic patient, furthermore, is usually anxious to get over his symptoms, while the psychopath does not show sincere evidence of regretting his conduct or of intending to change it.

Caldwell[38] has effectively set down outstanding differences between these two clinical pictures in a brief tabulation. Our point can be clarified by quoting it*:

	Feeling	Thinking	Acting
1. Ego-enhancement (psychopathic)	Hedonistic Callous Emotionally immature	Irresponsible Rationalistic	Antisocial Impulsive Defiant Explosive

2. Ego-depreciation (neurotic)	Apprehensive
	Anxious
	Fearful
	Depressed
	Helpless
	Inferior
	Jealous
		Stereotyped in
		  fantasies
		Preoccupied with
		  moral and
		  religious ideas
		Obsessive
			Antisocial
			Asocial
			Shy, sensitive
			Hesitant
			Indecisive
			Suggestible
			Overly protective
			Sexually
			  conditioned
			Timorous
			Passive

Some observers believe that the presence of what has long been known as psychoneurosis is sufficient reason for questioning the diagnosis of psychopathic personality. In the study just referred to, Caldwell reports neurotic manifestations in patients whose chief features were plainly those of the psychopath. I believe that the two types of reaction are not characteristically seen together but that there are no two pathologic syndromes in psychiatry, however distinct, that do not sometimes overlap.

---

*From Caldwell, John M.: Neurotic components in psychopathic behavior, Journal of Nervous and Mental Disease **99**:134-148, 1944.

31

The mental defective

The mental defective often behaves foolishly or ineffectively and, if the defectiveness is great, may show prolonged and serious maladjustment in ordinary surroundings. In contrast with the psychopath, however, the mental defective is obviously stupid and his follies may be understood readily as depending on his lack of intelligence, a handicap that is easily demonstrated. This can be measured with some accuracy in psychometric examinations. Many low-grade defectives show developmental deficiencies or other organic changes in their actual brain structure. The psychopath, on the other hand, is often, if not usually, of superior intelligence when measured scientifically. Some of his accomplishments also indicate that he has ability that is average or better when he is using it. He often gives the impression in conversation of excellent intellect and is plainly a very different person from the mental defective. Though in England the psychopathic personality is still sometimes referred to by the expressive term, *moral imbecile,* the distinction from intellectual imbecility has always been clearly recognized.[129]

Serious defects in ordinary intelligence naturally handicap a subject, naturally make it difficult for him to learn complicated relationships between cause and effect, and limit his critical ability in choosing wisely among the many courses of conduct offered every day. The defective is likely to be susceptible to false counsel and prone to overlook the more remote and subtle consequences that may follow the gratification of a petty impulse. Unlike the psychopath, mental defectives show limitations of judgment in theoretical situations. They are often unable to express adequate comprehension of mistakes they have made or wrongs they have done. They seldom outline, even verbally, ingenious plans for the future or discuss their total situation in such a way as to give a convincing impression of wisdom and reliability or of deep contrition, purpose, and understanding, unless such qualities are actually present. The badly handicapped mental defective may repeat time after time acts which result in loss or harm to others and to himself. His limitation in reasoning about facts that play a part in such consequences usually offers a satisfactory explanation of his disability.

This disability is considered by courts before which the defective may be tried for misdemeanors or felonies and which may be called upon in efforts to hospitalize him or in other ways to safeguard and help him. It is not only admitted that intellectual defect diminishes judgment and legal responsibility, but varying degrees of defect are recognized and, for practical purposes, accepted as implying degrees of competency.

If a high-grade moron commits murder, his relatively slight defect will be regarded as slight by the jury. The idiot or the imbecile will, however, be properly considered as one with a disability that may have played a major part in such an act. So, too, there is no difficulty in having the idiot committed (if necessary, against his own will and judgment) to a medical institution where he can be protected and cared for. No jury, however, not even a jury of morons, would deprive of his legal freedom a man showing no more defect than what is customary with an I.Q. of 70.

It is important for us to note that particularly in the question of commitment for a mental defective, varying degrees of disability are recognized and are regarded as affecting competency in varying degrees. In determining the presence of disability and its degree, the record of the defective's actual behavior is not ignored. Psychometric tests furnish evidence which helps the psychiatrist to classify patients properly as idiots, imbeciles, or morons, and this evidence contributes to medicolegal decisions concerning competency. The need for institutionalization in a defective is, however, demonstrated more effectively by his acts than by his I.Q. In contrast, we find that no matter how much evidence of incompetency emerges in the psychopath's record, this classification alone is (officially) regarded as establishing complete sanity, absolute competency.

32

The ordinary criminal

Although efforts have been made to interpret criminalism as a form of mental disorder and many criminal careers have been expounded as reactions to emotional conflict,[11,12] the sort of person described here shows the following important points of distinction from the typical criminal:

1. The criminal usually works consistently and with what abilities are at his command toward obtaining his own ends. He sometimes succeeds in amassing a large fortune and may manage successfully and to his own profit a racket as complicated as a big business. The psychopath very seldom takes much advantage of what he gains and almost never works consistently in crime or in anything else to achieve a permanent position of power or wealth or security. Mercier has made the following statement:

> There are persons who indulge in vice with such persistence, at a cost of punishment so heavy, so certain, and so prompt, who incur their punishment for the sake of pleasure so trifling and so transient, that they are by common consent considered insane although they exhibit no other indication of insanity.*

The man who is essentially criminal may then be regarded as consistently purposive, whereas the psychopath seems hardly purposive at all in comparison. To say the least, the pattern of his actions over any fairly long range of time indicates little that the observer can understand as what a

---

*From Mercier: In Henderson, D. K.: Psychopathic states, New York, 1939, W. W. Norton & Co., Inc.

human being would consciously choose. The patient himself sometimes convincingly denies any particular temptation driving him toward the situations to which his behavior repeatedly leads.

2. The criminal ends, though perhaps condemned, can usually be understood by the average man. The impulse to take money, even unlawfully, in order to have luxuries or power otherwise unobtainable, is not hard to grasp. The criminal, in short, is usually trying to get something we all want, although he uses methods we shun. On the other hand, the psychopath, if he steals or defrauds, seems to do so for a much more obscure purpose. He will repeatedly jeopardize and sometimes even deliberately throw away so much in order to seek what is very trivial (by his own evaluation) and very ephemeral. He does not utilize his gains as the criminal does. Often his antisocial acts are quite incomprehensible and are not done for any material gain at all.[50]

3. The criminal usually spares himself as much as possible and harms others. The psychopath, though he incidentally causes sorrow and trouble for others, usually puts himself also in a position that would be shameful and most uncomfortable for the ordinary man or for the typical criminal. In fact, his most serious damage to others is often largely through their concern for him and their efforts to help him.

4. The typical psychopath, as I have seen him, usually does not commit murder or other offenses that demand major prison sentences. This is true of the disorder as we present it in what we consider a pure culture. A large part of his antisocial activity might be interpreted as purposively designed to harm himself if one notices the painful results that so quickly overtake him. Of course I am aware of the fact that persons showing the characteristics of those here described do commit major crimes and crimes of maximal violence. There are so many, however, who do not, that such tendencies should be regarded as the exception rather than as the rule, perhaps, as a pathologic trait independent, to a considerable degree, of the other manifestations which we regard as fundamental. It is, of course, granted that when serious criminal tendencies do emerge in the psychopath, they gain ready expression, and that no punishment can discourage them. Psychopaths who commit physically brutal acts upon others often seem to ignore the consequences. Unlike the ordinary shrewd criminal, they carry out an antisocial act and even repeat it many times, although it may be plainly apparent that they will be discovered and that they must suffer the consequences.

Many people, perhaps most, who commit violent and serious crimes fail to show the chief characteristics which so consistently appear in the cases we have considered. Many, in fact, show features that make it very difficult to identify them with this group. The term psychopath (or sociopath) as it is applied by various psychiatrists and hospital staffs sometimes becomes so broad that it might be applied to almost any criminal. Granting the essential vagueness of the term, and disputing no one's right to it, I (who am using it only for convenience) maintain that the large group of maladjusted personalities whom I have personally studied and to whom this diagnosis has been consistently applied differs distinctly from ordinary criminals. The essential reactive pattern appears to be in many important respects unlike the ordinary criminal's simpler and better organized revolt against society and to be something far more subtly pathologic. It is my opinion that when the typical psychopath, in the sense with which this term is here used, occasionally commits a deed of violence, it is usually a casual act done not from tremendous passion or as a result of plans persistently followed with earnest compelling fervor. There is less to indicate excessively violent rage than a relatively weak emotion breaking through even weaker restraints. The psychopath is not volcanically explosive, at the mercy of irresistible drives and overwhelming rage of temper. Often he seems scarcely wholehearted, even in wrath or "wickedness." Jenkins,[153] in making distinctions between the dyssocial type of sociopathic personality and the antisocial type, brings out important points. Criminals, despite the fact that they break the laws of society, are often loyal to each other and can sometimes pursue a common cause consistently. Jenkins distinguishes these as dyssocial personalities from the truly antisocial personalities who cannot maintain loyalty even to each other in a common defiance of society or in any consistent revolt.

A few brief examples may illustrate important distinctions:

A bright and attractive young man who for some years now has shown typical features of the psychopath obtained a new job. As so often in the past, he began almost at once to succeed and to excel his fellow salesmen. Soon he was regarded by the company as the best man in his line, full of promise for much greater tasks and opportunities in the near future. He regularly earned a good deal more than any of the other salesmen, had an ample income for his family, and seemed on the sure road to high success.

His sales records, already surpassing all competitors, soon began to increase still more, finally becoming almost unbelievable. A short time later it became evident that something was wrong. His apparent straightforwardness and his confident explanations kept the company confused for a while longer. His ingenious methods delayed discovery that, in dealing with a less brilliant and resourceful man, would have been made much earlier.

278

It was eventually established that he had been selling the commodities with which he dealt at prices below cost. Thus he had sold widely and on a vast scale, and his commissions had increased proportionately. By intricate and exceedingly well-planned tactics, both in the field and at the central office, he had covered up all discrepancies until the company had to sustain a heavy loss in setting matters right.

To a man far less clever and scheming than this one, the virtually inevitable discovery and the consequent personal loss to himself would be easily discernible. The factual aspects were not simply overlooked in his reasoning, but something about them failed, however, to enter into his reactions, something that would not have failed to make the ordinary criminal (or the average man) behave otherwise. Such incidents abound in the histories of these patients. They do not seem to be seeking punishment or retribution to allay feelings of guilt. I can find no real evidence to support the assumption that these people are burdened with profound remorse of which they are unconscious.

* * *

A few more brief episodes deserve attention:

A boy in his teens comes into the office. He has been there a number of times before and realizes that much of his story is known to the physician. On being asked how he has spent his time, he replies in the most natural manner that he has been reading Dickens.

As the subject is developed he says that he has devoted most of his leisure time during the summer months to this literary recreation. He has found it interesting as well as useful and stimulating. After a good deal more discussion, in which he gives not the slightest sign of pretense or of uneasiness, he says that he has about completed all the novels Dickens wrote.

It is very easy to demonstrate by specific questions that he never read one volume, that he only recalls two or three titles and has no firsthand acquaintance with any of the material. On being confronted with his idle and unnecessary fabrication, he casually admits it but seems to feel no need to account for such a falsehood. He showed no indications of even slight shame or of particular chagrin at being detected.

* * *

A man almost 30 years of age whose wife has seriously threatened to divorce him many times in the past but who has been brought back by his eloquent and extremely convincing expressions of rare, romantic love, of devotion beyond the experience of most couples, is now succeeding in his work and apparently has given up all the old habits which made life with him unbearable.

His duties take him out of town for a number of days each week. It eventually becomes apparent that he has married a girl in one of the cities to which his business takes him. Great difficulties arise and violent feelings in the girl's family are demonstrated. He had represented himself to her as divorced long ago from a shrew who mistreated him, made off with his property, and who left his heart hungry for real love. He spoke so casually and convincingly of many things nonexistent that one might say the new bride knew his entire life in every detail except one—that nothing he had told her was factual!

Before this bigamy and its serious complications can be settled, evidence emerges that he has also married another young lady in still another city where he spent time each week. Unbelievable as it may appear, a third bride, also legally married, soon comes into the picture. All three of these had been wooed with what seemed touching sincerity and wed within the course of a single month. None of these four women found him a man of intense sexual passion or judged him as one who might seek so many wives because of more than ordinary erotic needs. An intentional "despoiler of women" of the familiar type (perhaps with masked homosexuality) would probably have seduced the wives of others but scarcely would have let himself be caught with four ladies legally married to him at one time.

• • •

A boy expelled from prep school for many antisocial and delinquent acts is talking with his father. Where, the father asks, are the clothes which were taken to school but are not now to be found in his baggage? The son, with no hesitation but with indications of regret and apology, explains that his baggage fell off the bus while crossing a bridge. Efforts to regain the baggage were successful, despite the current, etc., but the suitcases had come open from the fall and all the clothes were lost.

The father has already received information from the school explaining that his son sold the rather valuable clothing from time to time and often for ridiculously inadequate sums. The boy had no particular visible need for the money he got. Sometimes this was squandered on treating a crowd of fellow students to soft drinks, candy bars, etc. He did not, however, seem either especially generous or eager to establish himself in the good graces of the others.

I have tried to emphasize the point that many typical psychopaths, despite their continually repeated transgressions against the law and the rights of others and their apparent lack of moral compunction, often avoid murder and other grave felonies that might remove them from free activity in the social group. Most of these people carry out antisocial acts that would seem to make it likely for them to be confined indefinitely in penal institutions but often succeed, through the efforts of their families or through their equivocal medicolegal status, in escaping punishment altogether or in being released long before the expiration of ordinary terms of confinement. It should be emphasized, nevertheless, that there are other typical psychopaths (sociopaths) who, in addition to the usual and familiar pattern of incompetent maladjustment and deliberate folly, proceed to carry out crimes of the greatest magnitude, including premeditated, unprovoked, and trivially motivated murder.

When such crimes are committed and he is convicted of them, the real psychopath usually seems as free of remorse, as unperturbed, and as secure in a callous equanimity as when he has been detected in forgery, theft, adultery, or perjury—or after he has squandered in some idle and transient whim all the funds upon which his wife and children are depending to keep them from hardship and bitter poverty over the next few years.

The reactions of a young man convicted of murder some years ago are illustrative. The reports indicate that he had enjoyed the advantages of wealth and a highly respectable family background but suggest that he had shown capricious irresponsibility and repetitious, unprovoked, antisocial activities over a long period.

After learning that his mother was going to take a trip by airplane, he made some careful and rather elaborate plans. These included taking out flight insurance on her life for a considerable sum of money and payable to himself. He also succeeded in placing a time bomb in his mother's luggage and set it to explode during the flight. His efforts were successful. The plane was demolished and all persons aboard, including his mother, were killed. Some of this young man's reactions, as reported by the press, suggest that the chance of obtaining the insurance money was perhaps less stimulating to him than what he took to be the sporting qualities and challenges of the exploit. He apparently had no grudge against his mother or other reason to wish her ill.

Accounts in newspapers and magazines of this young man's trial suggest an insouciance and easy equanimity under circumstances that would naturally evoke extreme remorse, dread, and other desperately serious emotions. He often seemed to be enjoying his role and to delight in having the opportunity to be at the focal point of so much attention and publicity. He appeared to be entirely free of sorrow over the death of his mother and also free of shame at being proved guilty of such a horrible and unprovoked mass murder.

In *Newsweek* magazine the following items were reported.

> At times, he watched the proceedings with wide, staring eyes that showed no emotion; at other times he read a book, *The Mask of Sanity,* by Dr. Hervey Cleckley.
>
> When the verdict was announced he bit his lower lip, but otherwise remained impassive. His wife, Gloria, 22, the mother of his two small children, broke down and sobbed hysterically.*

Some accounts of this trial lead one to feel that the murderer might have found amusement in what he regarded as an important and dramatic role and one in which he could display himself to advantage.

Some psychiatrists might say that this young man's apparent nonchalance under these circumstances should be taken as indicating that he was motivated by an unconscious sense of guilt which he now found satisfaction in expiating. Perhaps so. But I remain skeptical of this hypothesis until I see some concrete evidence of its validity. Evidence, let us remember, cannot be obtained by free surmises and interpretations based on the projection of mere assumptions into a theoretically constructed but still invisible unconscious. The attitude of this young man toward his brutal and senseless crime and toward the death of his mother, it seems to me, is consistent with the amazing lack of capacity for love and normal human feelings that is typical of the psychopath. His amusement and apparent satisfaction in his prominent role in court also impress me as typical of the psychopath's egocentricity, his relish for many of his uninviting and antisocial deeds, and his feeling of petty satisfaction in cleverly carrying out acts that would overwhelm others with tragic sorrow and humiliation.

If there is no positive motivation toward major goals, no adequate inhibition by revulsion from what is horrible or sordid, it is perhaps more understandable that the rudderless and chartless facsimile of a full human being may flounder about in trivialities or in tragic blunders and see little distinction between them.

---

*From Newsweek, May 14, 1956, p. 38.

33

Other character and behavior disorders, including delinquency, etc.

Those who repeatedly commit antisocial acts or continue to carry out behavior in other ways unacceptable to the group and incompatible with good standing among one's fellows are often referred to as delinquents. Truly felonious deeds are not regarded as characteristic of delinquency so much as repetitiveness in misdemeanor or impropriety. In contrast with the orthodox criminal and to some degree like the psychopath, the delinquent often shows lack of sufficient conscious motivation to account for his conduct. Though delinquency is not a diagnostic term, it has value in that it indicates character and behavior disorders lying between the criminal and psychopathic extremes. Transient episodes of poorly adapted behavior, particularly in the juvenile, are included. Many of the things which the psychopath does are typical of the delinquent but seem to constitute only a part of his life expression, perhaps a relatively small part. Motivation also can often be discovered in the delinquent. Such motivation may be imperfectly understood by the patient and may arise indirectly from circumstances, within and without, which he fails to recognize or to evaluate properly.

Ordinary delinquency might be thought of as a relatively mild disorder with fair prognosis similar in its outer clinical manifestations to the malignant and sweeping disorder found in the full-blown psychopath. As a pathologic reaction, as a kind of maladaptation, there are important resemblances and correlations. Hysterical dissociation and the sort of personality dissociation or disintegration found in schizophrenia have something in common as well as important differences.

In one, the distintegrative process is more superficial and self-limited, often of brief duration; in the other, this process may continue until the entire personality is fragmented and no longer recognizable and the organism is incapable of functioning even at the lower levels accepted as characteristic of a human being. In repetitive delinquent behavior the subject often seems to be going a certain distance along the course that a full psychopath follows to the end. In the less severe disorder, antisocial or self-defeating activities are frequently more circumscribed and may stand out against a larger background of successful adaptation. The border lines between chronic delinquency and what we have called the psychopath merge in this area. Although anxiety, remorse, shame, and other consciously painful subjective responses to undesirable consequences are deficient in both as compared with the normal, this callousness or apathy is far deeper in the psychopath.

It is worth while to emphasize that many who, as they mature, become well-adjusted people and happy and distinguished citizens can look back to incidents of unprovoked misconduct which, if habitual, might constitute delinquency. If such isolated fragments not only persisted but took precedence in the entire life scheme, and became in fact the major expression of the personality, behavior would emerge having much in common with the case histories given in this book.

Many stable and productive adults are known by me (and others, no doubt, by the reader) who can be clearly identified earlier in life as members of destructive gangs which, on Halloween or on other special occasions, carried out raids in the residential section, hurling brickbats about, smashing windows, removing wrought-iron gates, puncturing automobile tires, and shooting about rather wildly with air guns or small-caliber rifles. Some remembered as special leaders in these activities, as well as in half-serious plans to derail trains or wreck trolley cars by thoroughly oiling the hillside tracks, are now properly respected bankers, Rotarians, physicians, deacons, professors, attorneys, and scout masters.

A happy husband and father who is also an outstanding civic leader recalls with some retroactive bewilderment his membership in a select club at college in which the chief topic at meetings consisted of obscenely boastful accounts of recent enterprises in miscegenation. In this particular setting, that of an isolated rural community in the South, such relations in themselves implied a maximum of scatalogic contempt for the partner, a peculiarly derogatory aim in the act, that even the language customarily used in such reminiscences could not adequately convey.

284

Another conventional and well-adjusted adult recalls an incident after a beer party following the last football game of the season when a fair proportion of the celebrants went out together to a pasture and there pursued and constrained a number of cows in efforts to achieve sexual relations with the patient but reluctant animals.

A kindly and eminently responsible medical colleague reports numerous episodes from his adolescent days in a farming community. Among many other fumbling and confused ventures in the masculine approach, he remembers finding amusement and delight in joining with other boys to make the rounds of outlying primitive toilets where young ladies, like all other local people, in response to natural demands, exposed to those strategically placed the most secret regions of the body through familiar apertures. Those who lay in wait now made stealthy use of bamboo switches or small branches to titillate the relatively immobilized and vulnerable ladies at this vividly inopportune moment. Strange girls visiting in the community gave special impetus to these gross but hilarious improprieties.

Numerous instances come to mind of young girls who, after episodes of damaging promiscuity not accounted for by erotic passion, achieve a better evaluation of such acts and, as they mature, integrate their impulses in such a way as to find security, personal fulfillment, and adequate sexual response in stable and faithful marriages. A transient episode in a woman about 30 years of age is also pertinent to the discussion.

Despite very unhappy marital relations she had scrupulously refrained from indulging in any sexual activity except with her husband until shortly after their divorce. Then, for reasons she could not explain, she found herself susceptible to almost any overture, and, in fact, made it all too plain that she was cheaply available. There occurred a series of unrewarding sexual relations with strangers who casually picked her up, with some salesmen who happened to appear at the door, and with acquaintances of long standing (some of whom she considered distinctly unattractive). After some months of this behavior she reoriented herself and has since then been leading her customary conventional life.

Temporary periods of distinctly delinquent behavior are apparently not uncommon even in careers on the whole successful and constructive. More protracted or habitual reactions of this sort result in disordered patterns that approach in varying degrees the pattern of the psychopath.

Confused manifestations of revolt or self-expression are, as everyone knows, more likely to produce unacceptable behavior during childhood and adolescence than in adult life. Sometimes persistent traits and tendencies of this sort and inadequate emotional responses indicate the picture of the sociopath early in his career. Sometimes, however, the child or the adolescent will for a while behave in a way that would seem scarcely possible to anyone but the true psychopath and later change, becoming a normal and useful member of society. Such cases put a serious responsibility on the psychiatrist.

A patient I once saw affords an excellent example. A 15-year-old high school boy, the son of respectable and God-fearing parents, attacked with considerable violence and apparently tried to rape a 9-year-old girl. When interviewed, he showed indifference, despite the fact that the girl's father had threatened him with death and tried to seize him. He denied actual rape and spoke calmly of the whole affair as if it were a minor matter, such as, for instance, breaking a neighbor's window. He later tried to excuse himself by inventing a palpably absurd story about being drugged with marihuana given him in the form of cigarettes by a Mephistophelian stranger. This boy's parents were severely pious and strait-laced. Much of his teaching had apparently implied that a minor oath or any preoccupation with thoughts of sex should be regarded as soul-devouring. He seemed indeed much like a psychopath, but might his conduct not have been the result of an ordinary adolescent drive emerging in a mind relatively without restraining principles partly because of the very fact that absurd trifles had been so magnified by his teaching that he saw all prohibited things at a level of importance and had dismissed all as absurd because so many indeed were? In such a case I feel that the child should be given benefit of the doubt until evidence of a persistent pattern is thoroughly established.

A 16-year-old boy was sent to jail for stealing a valuable watch. Though apparently gay and untouched by his situation, after a few questions were asked he began to seem more like a child who feels the unpleasantness of his position. He confessed that he had worried much about masturbation, saying he had been threatened and punished severely for it and told that it would cause him to become "insane."

He also said no one liked him, that he talked and yelled too much, and that no one would play with him. While speaking of this he seemed to echo a real worry, to reenact a former attitude to a perplexity and trouble that he once felt. At the moment this boy seemed accessible and it was felt his problem might be understood, as many of the behavior problems of children and adolescents can be understood. In the next moment, however, hope faded, and it became apparent that the boy was not now taking seriously what he might once have taken seriously. I could not reach a level of any inward reality. There remained only the mimicry of feeling that, if it ever existed, had now vanished. Of course, it cannot be stated positively that there was no genuine feeling. It cannot be known that a schizophrenic who fails to turn his head when told of a tragedy fails to suffer. We often feel with strong conviction, however, that the schizophrenic does not appreciate such events in the ordinary sense and as people who are not schizophrenic appreciate them. With similar conviction I believe that this boy was no longer aware of conflict or suffering or humiliation either about masturbation, about his present status in jail, or about the almost unbelievable series of absurd, shameful, and fruitless acts that had occupied him for years. He was entirely rational in the ordinary sense and of average intellectual capacity.

He admitted having broken into his mother's jewelry box and stolen a watch valued at $150.00. He calmly related that he exchanged the watch for 15 cents' worth of ice cream and seemed entirely satisfied with what he had done. He readily admitted that his act was wrong, used the proper words to express his intention to cause no further trouble, and, when asked, said that he would like very much to get out of jail.

He stated that he loved his mother devotedly. "I just kiss her and kiss her ten or twelve times when she comes to see me!" he exclaimed with shallow zeal. These manifestations of affection were so artificial, and, one might even say, unconsciously artificial, that few laymen would be convinced that any feeling, in the ordinary sense, lay in them. Nor was his mother convinced.

A few weeks before this boy was sent to jail, he displayed to his mother some rifle cartridges. When asked what he wanted with them, he explained that they would fit the rifle in a nearby closet. "I've tried them," he announced. And in a lively tone added, "Why, I could put them in the gun and shoot you. You would fall right over!" He laughed and his eyes shone with a small but real impulse.

This might be considered merely childish jest. A normal child might, of course, say such a thing, and in a normal child it would be merely a jest. I believe that this boy also spoke in jest, but I fear that he might carry out the jest, not with bitterness or hate in the ordinary sense but merely because the fancy struck him and because the death of his mother would mean so little to him that it cannot be counted in the ordinary terms of human emotion.

This boy's history showed, over a period of several years, dozens of episodes similar to the present. His misdeeds were apparently without purpose. He gained nothing, took little or no precaution against detection, and seemed to be unmoved by punishment. He is mentioned here because I could not help but wonder if a few years earlier he perhaps did feel shame and insecurity and might have been amenable to teaching. It was difficult to say whether his behavior disorder would tend to improve or be substantially modified by ordinary treatment or whether this was an early stage of the psychopath's career.[50]

34

A case showing circumscribed behavior disorder

When behavior disorder is circumscribed, in a child or in an adult, one may sometimes feel that symptomatically the patient resembles a psychopath but that a different sort of personality lies behind the manifestation. Instead of essential indifference to the pathologic situation, we sometimes see genuine zeal to avoid the faulty and self-damaging acts. It is not rare to find relatively normal attitudes to most aspects of life and sometimes healthy and admirable personality features.

In such patients, unlike psychopaths, it is more often possible to bring out valid responses and to learn about experiences and relations that have been influential over years and that may have played an important part in causing the poorly adapted behavior. Strong indications can sometimes be found that inner and poorly understood emotional confusions and conflicts are provoking repetitive rebellious and ineffective antisocial conduct.

A brief discussion of one such patient may be germane:

This young woman in her middle twenties voluntarily sought help from an internist widely known for his interest in personality problems; he referred her for psychiatric treatment. Her spontaneous complaint was of sexual promiscuity which she feared would damage her socially. She expressed the opinion that, aside from what these doings might cause others to think of her, she herself deemed them wrong and highly undesirable.

A virgin until approximately two years earlier, she had since that time had full sexual relations with over twenty different men. She denied any personal attachment or romantic attitudes toward these partners, to whom she had yielded casually, promptly, and apparently without conflict or indecision. She had obtained pleasant reactions from the physical contact and after the first few ventures began to respond regularly with genital orgasm. She had never entertained illusions to the effect that any of this considerable group of men were enamored of her and said she had no desire to bring out such feelings in them. Her appearance was distinctly attractive and her figure particularly well endowed with anatomic features likely to arouse and enhance erotic interest.

An articulate and apparently a candid girl, she showed little reluctance to discuss either her sexual adventures or any other material. In most respects she showed evidence of better than ordinary maturity and a considerable sophistication without affectedness. Her general intelligence was even better than might have been expected from her good record at college and subsequent success in her work.

In journalism she had made rapid progress as a writer of advertisements and of feature articles on the daily paper in one of the largest cities in her state. She did not, as many newspaperwomen do, write for the society columns or deal chiefly with material considered of special interest to women. She often discussed politics, scientific developments, and economic problems. Nothing in her appearance or manner, however, suggested masculine characteristics, tastes, or attitudes. She dressed in such a way as to make the most of her looks and had interests and hobbies predominantly feminine.

Although the excitement of physical relations seemed to have been genuine and full vaginal orgasm occurred and left her without the feeling that anything might be lacking, the experiences reported impressed the examiner, in some important respects, as relatively shallow. She gave as her reason or motive for doing what she regarded as wrong (and as unwise) a mounting sense of tension and a specific desire that she found too strong to resist. It seemed likely that she was really influenced by natural feelings of this sort but not to any unusual degree.

In fact, it was chiefly the matter of relieving a trivial or, at most, a rather moderate need than of being driven by intense passions or allured by breathtaking or exquisite possibilities of fulfillment.

Although she had made her charms fully available to so many men, she usually permitted only a single encounter of this sort. Shortly after the beginning of her promiscuity she had continued with one partner through three dates at intervals of several days, and a few months later she equaled this record with another man. Several other times she had repeated her adventure with the same partner through two sessions.

The rule for many months had, however, been one night with almost anybody but two with none. Considering her physical attributes and personal attractiveness, it is not surprising that those who had been so generously treated, often on the first date, wished to continue. She felt not only an aversion for this but also for seeing or having anything further to do with the partner. She realized that after such full and prompt compliance or cooperation at the beginning it would be difficult indeed to keep matters more or less platonic thereafter.

She was cognizant of the old analogy between getting the first olive out of a bottle and getting the first kiss and of its even greater applicability to what she had offered without even initial delay or any impediment whatsoever.

This did not, however, appear to be the chief factor in her breaking off relations. There was a primary loss of interest in the partner. No evidence emerged of an appreciable sense of shame on her part or of uneasiness about meeting unflattering attitudes and appraisals that might develop toward a girl who lets herself be taken so readily.

Nor did she worry about perhaps drawing out strong feelings in the partner, about his developing a binding attachment that might cause him distress. She was not, so far as she was aware, designing her conduct so as to enjoy the frustration or disappointment of all these men by cutting them off so abruptly from a quite lively pleasure they had reason to hope would remain available.

Completion of the sexual act was not followed by remorse or self-recrimination. Relieved and pleased, she had no wish for any sort of personal closeness or intimacy with her companion but, on the other hand, she did not feel strong revulsion. She had not sought personal intimacy in the beginning, and nothing happened, despite rather delightful somatic sensations, that gave incentives in this direction. After satisfaction occurred, she did not react with negative feelings toward sexuality or promiscuity as she might had there been strong conscious conflict between an intensely passionate yearning and the ordinary resistances to such conduct under such conditions. She evaluated her behavior as wrong, dangerous, and puzzling, but this evaluation was steady. Her attitude did not lead to a fierce struggle against the impulses toward such behavior, succumb temporarily to overpowering passions, and then arise to invoke shame and bitter regret.

She did not feel impelled by any special need for variety in changing her partners so promptly and in embracing so many, nor did she have the mistaken idea, so commonly encountered in problems of female promiscuity, that she was proving her charms and sex appeal by the fact that so many men had relations with her. She had been popular with men for a long time before her present habits began, and she realized better than most women that almost any female, even one of distinctly mediocre attractions, would not have trouble in getting seduced by practically any number of males alert for opportunities of free entertainment of this sort.

Though sometimes succumbing with almost unparalleled rapidity as soon as her date began his advances, she often pretended to be reluctant and made him go through a good many overtures, both verbally and with caresses, before cooperating.

She could not, however, recall having even once, since over a year previously, failed in full cooperation on the man's initial attempt. Although not unresponsive sensually to kisses and caresses, it was not the heightening or prolongation of ecstatic pleasure that prompted her to hold out for a while and allow these preliminaries to run their course.

She expressed, in fact, a preference for "going on, getting to it, and getting it over with." She distinctly enjoyed observing with skepticism a man's efforts to pretend he might be taking her seriously, his tactics in going through rituals of deception so common and sometimes rather elaborate, which the predatory male uses to get his way with the ladies. She was not conscious, during early discussion of these matters, of any real hate or contempt but admitted it made her feel that by seeing through these hypocritical ruses and pseudoemotional maneuvers she was getting the better of the man in their encounter.

It had not occurred to her that this would be regarded by most as an almost fantastically inaccurate way of scoring in such a contest, since the adversary never failed to gain all his ends. She admitted awareness that men would be inclined to take her lightly, to say the least, on finding that she could be so casually induced to have intercourse, and by so many. She seemed to regret this and to show some concern about it, but hardly to do so in ordinary or adequate degree.

She admitted that the feeling of satisfaction and superiority she attained through her prompt recognition of the date's concealed intentions and through inwardly mocking him in the steps he took to work the situation toward seduction while pretending other attitudes was distinctly pleasant to her and that she valued it highly.

The more this was discussed, the larger part she estimated it to have played in her motivations. She did not recognize any deeply derogatory attitude in this but found in it something more like the thrill of a game in which one enjoys outwitting and defeating, according to fair rules of the contest, an opponent who is not disliked or despised because of this. She did not feel tempted to show that she saw through the date's pretenses by her manner and attitude, by so telling him, or by making him fail to achieve his obvious aims with her.

As about other matters, she entered frankly into the discussion of relations she had previously maintained with an older woman. The patient voluntarily brought up this subject and did not seem to have had any intention to evade it.

Shortly after moving to the city where she now worked, she had met this woman, who immediately showed warm cordiality and treated her with attention that suggested both affection and admiration. This new friend, although almost fifteen years older than the patient, was youthful in appearance and in spirit, attractive to men, and extremely intelligent. She and her husband also were on the faculty of a local college. This woman, whose knowledge of literature, music, and of many other matters was considerable, seemed to the patient distinctly the most delightful and understanding person encountered in all her life.

A tremendous new interest was aroused in our patient, who found in fiction, poetry, psychological books, etc., and in almost all the activities of life, meaning and delight she never before discovered or deemed possible.

She felt uniquely understood and really cared for in a way that made everything she had regarded in the past as understanding and love seem perfunctory and trivial. For the first time she felt very close to someone and was thus able, for the first time, to realize that this had heretofore been missing.

The patient had been popular with both girls and boys and had never considered herself as lonely or isolated. Her friendship with other girls had, she now discovered, been relatively superficial. She realized more clearly also how little her popularity with boys had led to any personal intimacy or valuable shared understanding. She learned far more in a short time from this new friend than she had during all the years at college, and what she learned filled life with interest, humor, and all sorts of marvelous pleasures and goals.

She found confirmation of attitudes she had developed toward many of the conventional and uninspiring ideas, demands, limitations, and expectations she had encountered in her family. Achieving what she felt was new and real understanding which she could apply to conflicts and uncertainties that had troubled her as long as she could remember, she now felt secure, independent, and almost triumphantly eager for the future and its opportunities.

Soon her friend's husband had to go elsewhere for several months of work on a research project. She welcomed the opportunity to give up her own quarters and stay in the house of this wonderful and inspiring guide and benefactress. Despite the complications and interruptions of her hostess's two small children (whom the patient seemed to enjoy playing with and to love), there were greater opportunities for listening together to symphonies, for reading aloud Shakespearean plays, and for discussion over a few highballs until long past midnight.

She shared her friend's room and soon was sleeping in the same twin bed with her, both finding the nearness and the contact delightful. Lying together in the dark, thrilled with evidences of being understood and loved, she liked to talk and to listen and to have close physical contact with her idol. Both women made lively and articulate by highballs and by delight, found it easy to murmur to each other all sorts of things concerning admiration and love and what each meant to the other.

From close embraces, to kisses, to mutual masturbation, things proceeded without our patient's giving very distinct thought to whether or not there was anything homosexual, anything perverse or queer about such practices. The older and more sophisticated of the two was the other's symbol of the ideal. What she approved and considered natural and delightful was almost automatically accepted by the other.

Furthermore, she got the strangest new delights from what happened while they were in bed together. She had, as a matter of fact, not only erotically exciting sensations but distinct orgasms from the digital caresses and stimulations of the other. She did not think of herself and the other woman as something equivalent to husband and wife or as one pretending to be a man and the other acting the part of a woman under such circumstances. Both were women, in the patient's feelings, but there were wonderful and unforeseen revelations, sensual as well as intellectual and otherwise, in all this prized experience.

She was not preoccupied with resentment toward the absent husband. Without quite knowing why, she would not have wanted him to know every detail about what she and his wife did. But he did not loom in her concepts as a distinct rival, nor did their mutual masturbation seem to intrude distinctly into the areas supposedly reserved for husbands and wives. She was more concerned about the fact that her main source of happiness would be curtailed, that she could not be so often with this wonderful person after the husband returned and she went back to her regular quarters.

The sensuous feelings and the startlingly delightful and new experience of orgasm were all tied in with her affection and love and unstinted admiration for the wonderful person who had brought so much to her. She had learned something about homosexuality not only from books but from her efforts several years earlier as president of a students' honorary society at college to help a freshman who had shown what seemed to her serious and regrettable tendencies of this sort. It sometimes occurred to her that what she and the totally wise friend did might be regarded as perverse or like the misdeeds of that girl at college, but such thoughts had little more force in her evaluation of the acts than some farfetched philosophic abstraction which might be literally true in syllogisms but without relation to actualities of experience. These sexual activities were a private and secret delight, one part of the many things they shared and into which no one else entered.

As she discussed this matter, freely and without hedging or apparent shame, she seemed to have little or no fear that she might be homosexual. I also felt that she was probably not what this term indicates in its reference to full and fixed lesbian women. Her physically erotic relations with the other woman had been in some respects a substitutive practice, though what it might stand for was not well formulated among her goals. Her reaction, in certain aspects, seemed akin to what a normal, adolescent boy might experience in masturbating while immersed in vivid fantasies of intercourse with the image of the girl he has chosen as a sweetheart and wants someday to marry.

There was, however, an important difference. She had no definite referential imagery in which a male figure could be located as the personally and fully embraced partner in the world of delightful feelings that were evoked. There was no channellized structure, as in the example of the romantically masturbating boy, to conduct her aspirations toward a real and well-defined goal. Although there were resemblances, her experience apparently lacked features essential to the malignant pattern of true homosexuality. In the first rewarding intimacy she had experienced with another human being, this delightful and exciting physical contact seemed wonderful, and she found it in no way disturbing or objectionable.

Such a situation could scarcely have arisen for a man under similar circumstances without vastly more pathologic actualities and consequences, for in the virgin male genital aims are nearly always clearer and less ambiguously merged in general and nonsexual personal relations.

After some months of what had been the most delightful time in our patient's life, her beloved friend and idol announced that their relations must be terminated. The young girl could not conceive of any valid reason for such a decision. The articulateness of her preceptor failed at the task of making clear or acceptable what was, nevertheless, made final. Soon afterward this indescribably wise and wonderful being moved away, her husband having been given a position much to his advantage at a university in another section of the country.

The young lady we are concerned with was puzzled, sad, and hurt beyond anything that she could express or explain. After having for the first time in her life exposed and offered her intimacy, love, adoration, longings, and everything else that she had heretofore automatically and fearfully guarded, she found herself rejected. Her emotional commitment had led to loneliness and frustration and to the shame and hurt of being discarded.

It was not difficult for this intelligent girl to begin discovering that without knowing it she had for some time been deliberately and actively engaged in the process of throwing herself away. She had been thrown away by the only person to whom she had offered and fully given herself. Unable to make verbal comment on her hurt and betrayal, she formulated and, in another way, expressed comment in behavior that spoke with more authority than any language. She began to understand that by so damaging herself she was, not in the mere light symbols of language but in terms more concrete, trying to explain to the one who had rejected her how much this rejection hurt. This could not be adequately conveyed without pain also to the one her desperate message must reach. The banishment inflicted by this other, she had already found, constituted a wall that could be penetrated, if at all, only by an emotional projectile of great traumatic force.

Going back a little farther, let us consider the situation of this girl prior to her meeting with the older woman. Since she could first remember, it had seemed obvious to her that civilization was devised in such a way as to give the human male many undeserved advantages over the human female. Little boys could wander off on tree-climbing, hiking, or other adventures, but little girls were more restricted. Boys became airplane pilots, surgeons, generals, etc., whereas nearly all women, as she saw it, became wives who day after day performed routine household tasks, washed dishes, nursed babies, and seldom got out to have any fun, even at night.

Furthermore, husbands did not seem to find them attractive. Even the funny papers joked about how dull a wife was as compared to the stenographer and showed husbands on every possible occasion gleefully slipping away from prosaic and dowdy figures at home to get "a night out with the boys." As her life progressed, she had steadily encountered facts to corroborate the implications of an old saying fairly common in her childhood, "Why you can't get any more lift out of that than out of kissing your own wife."

When she had wanted to be a general or a cowboy leader in those early games in the park, the others laughed at her and said she was only a girl. Facts such as her being able to run faster and climb better than some of the boys did not matter. No, the decisions were all determined by the irrelevant point about her being a girl.

She had to stay at home sometimes and help her mother with the dishes or other tasks. Daddy, after reading the morning paper, went off and stayed the whole day among all the excitements of town. There is no need to give much from the thousands of incidents, real and familiar to anyone, which she encountered and from which she logically derived her convictions that active and exciting lives are open to men whereas wives are expected to live in the circumscribed orbit of a house, carrying out repetitious tasks and dull, petty, routines and often becoming creatures of convention, careless of their looks, shapeless, and uninspiring.

In her reactions to these formulations she did not derive envy and admiration for man as compared with woman. It was not through any real virtue or superiority that these males had all the interesting work and freedom and fun. It was because of conventions and rules, based not on facts but on tradition, that men had this advantage.

They were often smug enough and biased enough to think they deserved such a break. Women, not taking the trouble to think things through, placidly accepted such an arrangement. She did not want to be a man or more like a man, but she was determined to evade as much as possible these artificial impediments. Instead of throwing her life away in a meek gesture to empty conventions, she would go after the interesting things. The success and independence she might achieve, the fun she might have, would, aside from their intrinsic value, be a comment on the fallacies she had detected and would oppose.

Under hypnosis and narcosis as well as in unaltered awareness, she gave much detail that filled in a convincing picture of her childhood environment. Hundreds of memory items emerged to disclose her father not as cruel but as an arbitrary and moody disciplinarian in small matters. Her parents did not (to her) seem to find intimacy, fulfillment, or very much real fun together in their marriage.

The mother (in her eyes) lived in trivial activities and was bored, boring, and fretful but unaware of the reasons. The patient's outlook and aims had slowly taken form in reaction to the model of marriage she found in her home. As she grew, she discovered in her general surroundings thousands of items which supported and further shaped opinion and inclination.

It should not be assumed that the marriage of these parents was all that it appeared to the little girl. Details of it which she encountered at susceptible moments might be accurate without being representative of the whole. So, too, as she grew and observed the world about her, she found facts which continued to confirm her early evaluations.

Anyone can find dull housewives and distant, bored husbands. Everyone knows that the immature male takes advantage of the "double standard" and often tries to see how far he can get with girls under the pretense of love, only to react with the precise and unflattering opposite of love in degree proportionate to their acquiescence. During an early discussion of the disadvantages of marriage for girls, the patient cited as evidence two young couples who often went together on automobile trips, the two husbands sitting together in front, the wives ignored on the rear seat. All the observations given as evidence by the patient seemed to be true and accurate. Her interpretations also seemed, for the specific instances she cited, correct.

If a man and a woman value so much the opportunity to be together on dates, why should they almost immediately after marriage so change as to choose even a person of the same sex to sit by in preference to the mate? Custom or courtesy might suggest that, as in seating arrangements at dinner parties, husbands and wives, in this limited sense, be swapped about. But can anything except the absence of basic sexual and personal interest make men turn regularly to men and women to women on occasions when married couples gather? The patient found in scores of incidents she had observed indications that these couples were not particularly close to each other or having much fun together.

Among other examples she pointed out how often at parties the husbands drifted or sometimes almost raced for the kitchen, where, in purely male company, they spent most of the evening, frankly oblivious of the wives stranded together in the living room.

I could not but agree with her that such behavior was consistent with and might indicate serious attrition, if not indeed the unhappy and untimely death, of what it is natural to seek in heterosexual love relations. Her basic concept can, perhaps, be conveyed by a joke she told. It is an old joke, but expressive:

A husband who habitually paid little attention to his wife did not even look up from his paper when she came down one day in a new and breathtaking dress. She tried in vain to make him notice and admire it. She was a good-looking and voluptuous woman and resented being ignored. Not succeeding in getting the husband to raise his eyes even momentarily to regard her, she ran back upstairs. Resolved to shake him from his lethargy, she stripped and came down again, completely naked. Announcing she was on her way downtown to shop, she paused for his appraisal. Finally she succeeded in getting him to glance up from the paper. Before returning to peruse it, he indifferently remarked, "Umph! Need a shave, don't you."

Among her married friends she had observed many wives who received strict allowances dealt out to them as if they were children or servants by husbands who would not even divulge to their mates and reputed equals any fundamental information about the family's finances. Everything concerning their business affairs, to which these husbands seemed to devote most of their lives and interest, was withheld from wives who were, the patient felt, appraised as too inconsequential or undeserving to share in these matters sacred to the male world.

Many of her conclusions might apply correctly to the specific cases from which she drew them. She had, apparently, with precocious accuracy, sensed and ferreted out negative points in specific husbands and specific wives that others, accepting more optimistic generalizations, would have overlooked. Her ideologies and the general shaping of her aims and actions had been strongly conditioned by the implicit assumption that all marriage was necessarily what she had seen it to be in many instances. Argument with her about this overgeneralization would scarcely have altered her fundamental outlook.

In the course of time, however, as she brought up the concrete details of experience with increasing amounts of affect, she became aware of distortions and evasions formerly screened by her dogmatic ideologies. Eventually she could see (and feel) that it was her mother (or the image she had made of her mother as a child) which she had rejected and that this did not demand rejection of the feminine role itself. She could see also that while she had determined not to accept all the limitations she believed inherent in woman's status sociologically, this distortion had not extended into deeper biologic levels. She had not, in turning from the mother, identified herself with her father and determined to *be* a man. Had this occurred, far more serious problems might have arisen for this girl.

Marriage was very strongly rejected as an ambition. Reactions to her mother and to her father apparently combined in this negative force and contributed to a distorted response to this major feminine role. She examined again and felt again the effects upon her of her older brother. It was he for whom money had to be saved so that he could go to medical school. She recalled that at first she had been very fond of him and proud of him. As she continued to reorient herself to what had appeared to be preference on the parents' part for his ambitions, while deprivations were demanded of her so that he could attain the independence of being a physician, she became better able to see these things in the general context of her life.

Incidents scorned at the time and since then neglected, when now recalled and reappraised, indicated parental pride in her also. It became possible for her to see that this had not been sufficiently valued by her because it was pride in her as a girl and for qualities unlike those she specifically needed for competition with her brother.

It is impossible to set down here all the myriad events that came up for this girl's reappraisal or the affective reactions and shaping of attitudes that, seen as a whole, seemed to account for her rejection of marriage and fear to give herself in any deep, personal intimacy with men. Nothing that is said as a generalization about her life pattern can convey what emerged as she reproduced it in the concrete form of innumerable incidents. Nor would any explanation in general terms have been useful in her efforts to reorient herself as were the explanations she herself gradually arrived at.

The sexual relations with men, begun several months after the break with her lesbian partner, soon convinced her of something she had not wanted to admit at the time—that the sexual organs of man and woman are appropriately designed for contact and work together in such a way as to get better sensual results than anything possible with two female bodies, which are not anatomically equipped for such a feat. She was forced to admit this although she continued to deny all possibility of other genuine and happy relations between man and woman.

This at first was a blow to her, for she sought to preserve in idealized perfection her concept of the relation with the other woman as being in every respect superior to anything possible between woman and man. She had jealously guarded those feelings and impulses which, in being bestowed, constitute falling in love. In her sexual activities with the series of men she went to unusual lengths in trying to keep all relations and contacts of any importance to herself and to let her sensations remain confined, localized, and impersonal. Capacities to love another, to give genuine intimacy (herself) to another, drawn out initially by the homosexual partner, were less deeply buried than heretofore and hence demanded more vigilant protection from arousal by man.

In having intercourse with men she continued also her old competition with the other sex, rejecting them as lovers or needed complements to herself in personal matters, but seeking to outwit them or to find some basis, however farfetched and flimsy, on which she could mock them in their sexual tactics.

Her promiscuous relations appeared eventually to the patient as having been used to carry out several purposes simultaneously:
1. They satisfied a need for sensual pleasure and orgasm that had, since her experiences with the woman, become clearer and more urgent.
2. By cheapening herself as a sexual object, she expressed reproach and criticism of one who had discarded her and made a protest against being so treated.
3. She reaffirmed her rejection of woman's role in marriage by carica-

turing in her own attitude the personal relations of the heterosexual act.

4. She found an aspect of the situation, however farcical and insubstantial, by which she could think of herself as mocking the man (his not realizing she knew what he was after).

5. She tried to ensure her freedom from any need of marrying by getting localized genital pleasures and relief while keeping distinctly withdrawn from all personal relations.

6. By changing partners on each occasion, she expressed her freedom from attachment, her disdain for any important relationship in connection with the act. This practice also made it impossible for an attachment to develop and threaten the sort of lonely security she had built up over so many years.

It took her much less time and effort to reach the foregoing conclusions than to realize emotionally that she had, without suspecting it, been very much influenced by a need (not admitted) to find something she had never realized was desirable and necessary until she had sensed a misleading clue to it in her close personal relations with the older woman.

It was more difficult still for her to accept the possibility that anything of this nature might be worth seeking in a man. This possibility did not become acceptable to her so much through its direct examination or continuing reappraisal of what she had experienced with the woman, but chiefly, it seemed, through the relation of present and recent matters, to aims, attitudes, and reactions recognizable in her childhood and, under varying aspects, in the year-by-year pattern of her life. She at first brought out material with little affective reaction to it. Later her feelings about incidents already mentioned were allowed expression.

It was less difficult for her to give up her sexual promiscuity than to alter her attitude toward marriage. Even the possibility that male and female have personality features and resources for erotic relations with each other comparable to the situation anatomically (which she had found so superior to the deviated homosexual experience) was a possibility it took her much time to accept.

The fear, born in her childhood, of losing that freedom which would enable her to escape the fate she saw as inevitable for every housewife, strove long and stubbornly against the recognition of anything that might modify her concepts and her affective reactions to them. These concepts, warning her perpetually from within, had, it seems, blocked many nascent impulses that might have led her years ago into experiences which could not but modify her basic fear. Not by reasoning alone but only by experiencing something directly, something directly between herself and man, was it likely that sufficient modification could occur for her to continue improvement.

From a small and very reluctant beginning, such experiences develop, and with them came changes of attitude extending much deeper than the presence or absence of the symptoms she had once expressed in her behavior.

No attempt has been made to bring out anything very deep or remarkable about this patient. She illustrates, however, several points useful for our purpose. The outlandishly promiscuous and poorly motivated sexual activity that constituted the objective clinical manifestation of her trouble was entirely typical of what we find in the real psychopath. Her conduct in this respect would seem to argue well for that diagnosis. The lack of adequate conscious purpose, of anything resembling irresistible passion or even strong ordinary temptation, to account for such inappropriate and unrewarding behavior seems even more characteristic than the bare deeds.

Important distinctions can be made, however, between this localized expression and the similar but generalized malfunctioning that distorts the psychopath in all his serious performances. Not only was this young lady consistently successful and purposive in her work and in all other social relations, but her emotional attitudes and responses in almost every situation except those centering about sexual aims were normal and adequate. In the erotic situation she not only behaved unwisely and unsuccessfully but also showed evidence of distorted evaluations, of affective confusion, and of serious deficit. In a crude analogy it might be said that her pathology compared with the widespread pathology of the psychopath somewhat as a carbuncle caused by a staphylococcic infection compares to staphylococcic septicemia.

Despite many superficial resemblances to serious and predominant homosexual reactivity and life patterning, she had retained, beneath the surface, biologic and fundamental heterosexual potentiality. Her experiences with the seriously deviated woman awakened or liberated needs and capacities for close, devoted, and understanding human relations. In the framework of this broad awakening, genital impulses were also stimulated, though misdirected. For the patient, it appears that she found in the experience with the older woman expression for much that she had missed long ago in parental relations as well as in friendships and the usual heterosexual gropings of adolescence.

The somewhat clarified and freed genital impulses did not seem to be integrated into the broader pattern of personal arousal in such a way as to constitute real and firmly fixed homosexuality, but rather, they appeared to accompany, in a confusing but additive sense, the other and surrounding affective capacities and urges as all emerged. In a confusion which she could not evaluate, reacting to several important needs or urges, she hit upon the maladapted behavior pattern in which she presented herself.

Her personality as a whole remained sufficiently intact or normally functional for her to give to the physician and to herself an account of earlier experiences and her reactions to them sufficiently valid for plausible explanation of the disordered behavior to emerge. The awareness of important influences shaping the pattern of behavior made available to the patient (as well as to the observer) some understanding of this pattern. On the basis of this, slowly but progressively, helpful modifications were made by the patient in her evaluations and in her adaptation.

It is quite possible that in the fully disordered psychopath similar but far more complicated causative influences exist behind the clinical manifestations. In the real psychopath a gross lack of sincerity and insight seriously impedes all efforts to obtain information essential to interpretation. We must also consider the possibility that the psychopath may be born with a biologic defect that leaves him without the capacity to feel and appreciate the major issues of life or to react to them in a normal and adequate manner.

35

Homosexuality and other consistent sexual deviations

It has been a popular custom in psychiatric writing to use such terms as *sexual psychopath, sexual psychopathy,* etc., and this custom has had authoritative sanction in the nomenclature. In the last revision of our official terminology, the term *psychopathic personality* was discarded entirely. Under the new term *sociopathic personality reaction* we still find, as in the old system of classification, the well-known psychopath (antisocial reaction) listed in the same general category with the various forms of sexual aberration.[69] It is true that many sexual deviates show additional pathologic features. Sometimes these features include those typical of the psychopath. This does not, however, seem an adequate reason for identifying the two groups under a single term as if they were merely two types of the same disorder.

No one is more ready than I to agree that the real psychopath's sexuality is abnormal. The schizophrenic, the paretic, the paranoid, and many other types of psychiatric patients also carry out deviated sexual activity, and in those who do not are often found many indications of extremely pathologic attitudes about the basic erotic orientations. Yet we would not find it profitable to give up our distinguishing terms for these disorders and merge them as types under a general term that also embraces the sexual disorders. Such a scheme would, no doubt, tend in time to blur our concepts about what we are dealing with.

It impresses me as inaccurate to assume that homosexuals as a class show the general life pattern of gratuitous folly and purposelessness so typical of the psychopath. The Kinsey Report offers statistics which have been interpreted by many as virtually proving that one-third of all American men engage in homosexual activities.[173] Bergler, among others, has in his significant paper, "The Myth of a New National Disease," emphasized some of the obvious fallacies in such interpretations.[20] Aside from other points made by Bergler, it seems plain that many of the items tabulated by Kinsey represent essentially masturbatory acts in childhood or during puberty rather than specifically homosexual deviations. Although it is my belief that the Kinsey Report grossly overestimates the proportion of male homosexuals in the nation, it seems obvious that they are far from rare in almost any community. Although some deviates of this sort also show the more generalized and even the typical maladjustment seen in the psychopath, the two groups, neither in medical practice nor in a survey of the community, seem to coincide. There is, indeed, some overlapping, but this is true of most psychiatric conditions.

During recent years a tendency among some psychiatric writers to redefine the term homosexuality has promoted regrettable confusion among the laity and also, I believe, within our professional group. Since it is desirable in any discussion for both parties to be reasonably aware of the subject under consideration, let us briefly examine this confusion in the hope of avoiding it. In their *Psychiatric Dictionary,* Hinsie and Campbell give the following definition:

> **"Homosexuality** The state of being in love with one belonging to to the same sex. Until the early part of the 20th century, this generally meant a form of sexual perversion. With the development of psychoanalysis, however, there came to be laid less emphasis on sex proper and a correspondingly broader connotation assigned to the term sexual. In current usage, overt homosexuality is used to refer to physical, sexual contact between members of the same sex, while latent homosexuality is used to refer to impulses and desires toward a member of the same sex which are unconscious or, if conscious, are not openly expressed. Some writers differentiate between homogenitality (genital relations); homosexuality (sexual relationship, but not expressed genitally); and homoerotism (erotic relationship which is well sublimated)."*

During the period when nationwide concern was aroused over reports that many homosexuals occupied positions of high responsibility in the

---

*From Hinsie, L. E., and Campbell, Robert J.: Psychiatric dictionary, New York, 1960, Oxford University Press.

State Department, a number of psychiatrists felt it would be desirable to give the public "some very simple and elementary scientific opinions" on homosexuality. Some of the statements proposed are the following:

> The term "homosexuality" is usually interpreted by the average lay-man to mean genital stimulation between two individuals of the same sex. Because sexuality is so closely linked with morals in our culture and since "homosexuality" is officially a crime in most states and considered a sin by some religious orders, this subject arouses great emotional feeling.

> .   .   .

> In contrast to this lay point of view, the psychiatrist most often uses the term "homosexuality" to refer to one stage in the psychological and social growth of the individual. It is used broadly to refer to the interest felt by all persons in other persons of the same sex. In the course of normal development every child passes through a stage during the period of adolescence when his major interest is focussed upon persons of the same sex. It is during this period that youth organizations thrive as expressions of this normal stage of development. The normal individual progresses through and beyond this stage to a preference for members of the opposite sex, with a choice of one of these for his mate.

Is it true that psychiatrists most often use the term homosexuality to designate a perfectly normal stage of growth and the simple friendly relations between pubertal boys (or girls) that have nothing to do with romantic feelings or sexual stimulation? If so, it would be difficult for such psychiatrists to make sense in expressing their opinions to others on this subject. Despite the sincerity of those who felt the public would benefit from such an opinion, I do not believe many psychiatrists fail to recognize a profound difference between the sexual perversion investigated in the State Department by the F.B.I. and the normal status of pubertal boys who spend most of their time together, still so socially immature, so lacking in poise and confidence, that they are afraid to mingle freely with the girls they nonetheless vividly recognize as the natural objects of sexual desire.[54]

If the word *sexual* is redefined in accordance with Freud's libido theory to include all affection, respect, and social interest, we may, and indeed must, diagnose all human beings at all ages as homosexuals, and most as also afflicted with bestiality and perhaps even more spectacular vices.[54] With such a change of definition I need only pat my dog on the head to "prove" unconscious but real and persistent inclinations to attempt sexual intercourse with him. So, too, if a father and son enjoy fishing trips together their enjoyment must be assumed to arise from a (homosexual) "instinct inhibited in its aim," that is to say, from an unrecognized but quite genuine drive toward fellatio or pederasty with each other. So far as I know, the only evidence for such assumptions lies in changing the definition of the word sexual, not in any psychiatric discoveries. Though these changes may be found helpful and ardently welcomed by those who feel need of faith in the libido theory as a metaphysical or quasi-religious article of belief, they can scarcely be said to promote accuracy in psychiatric investigation.[54]

For the sake of clarity, let us in this discussion take the term homosexuality in its ordinary and undoctored definition. Hinsie and Campbell say that up to the early part of this century homosexuality generally meant a form of sexual perversion. This will indicate to the reader with reasonable accuracy my subject in this chapter.

It would seem remarkable if any physician of experience could not call to mind many distinct and overt homosexuals who continue to lead peaceful, productive, and socially useful lives and who cannot be identified with the psychopath as he is here presented. It could hardly be said that characteristically these deviated people are incapable of kindness and consideration for the rights of others, that they are lacking in gratitude, affection, or compassion. Only confusion is promoted by efforts to identify them as a group with the obvious pattern of failure and profound, generalized incompetency of the other life pattern.

These successful and, generally speaking, reliable inverts do not, however, achieve in their sexual relations an approximation of happy, normal mating between man and woman. Despite the special pleading so popular at present in advanced literary and intellectual circles for homosexuality as a more or less natural alternative to heterosexual life,[58,102,307,312] unhappiness, disillusionment, and eventual cynicism regularly resulting from such attempts at amorous union plainly demonstrate the profound biologic contrariness, the essential pathology of this deviation.[20] However admirable some homosexuals may be in other phases of their lives, in civic work, art, business, etc., none seem to achieve in their attempts at sexual love anything more than a travesty or pathetic caricature of biologically natural mating between man and woman.[54]

The simplest facts of anatomy demonstrate that an actual genital union, a full and literal sexual relation, is for these people obviously impossible. Impelled by powerful urges but tragically misguided by their deviation, directed only toward biologic absurdity, their repeated quests for fulfillment result in confusion and disappointment. Unsatisfied with each partner, homosexuals are driven toward chaotic promiscuity. Sensuously attracted toward those of his own gender, some profound concomitant dissatisfaction impels him to dress the other male in woman's clothes or to call him by a woman's name. Or he may choose this sad caricaturing of the female as his own role. He may on the other hand try to assume that his anomaly is really an excess of masculinity instead of an effeminacy and, in a claim that suggests whistling in the dark, tell himself and his fellows:

> Among homosexuals there is found the *most* remarkable class of men, namely, those whom I call supervirile. These men stand, by the special variation of their soul-material just as much above Man, as the normal sex man does above Woman. Such an individual is able to bewitch men by his soul aroma, as they—though passively—bewitch him.*

Whether in his biologic disorientation he is driven into various travesties of woman's status, some of which include the demand for his own castration,[118] or toward misconceptions of a virility enhanced by incongruously putting another male into some burlesque of woman's natural role in sexual acts, his ventures end in frustration and he is likely to conclude that "love" is a bitter illusion.[54]

The erotic lives of celebrated champions of homosexuality show precisely those negative features so familiar to the psychiatrist in patients clinically studied. Oscar Wilde's eloquence in extolling the "love that dare not speak its name" as a pure, superbly beautiful, outrageously misunderstood, but supreme experience of honor and fidelity contrasts inexpressibly with his supercilious practice of sodomy among stable boys, immature valets, blackmailers, and other precocious specimens of London's riffraff.[147] The young nobleman, Lord Alfred Douglas, for whom Wilde admitted in court such an exalted infatuation but with whom he denied unnatural physical relations, apparently shared with Wilde the pleasure of such company as that mentioned previously.[147]

André Gide, an admirer of Wilde and perhaps the most frank protagonist of homosexuality in our century, has recorded an enlightening incident. Meeting the great literary figure with his favorite Douglas in Algiers, the three go to a restaurant. Noticing that Gide is attracted by an Arab boy musician, Wilde graciously acts as a procurer, then follows Gide uttering hoots of derision as he goes off with the young Arab to carry out sexual acts. Later Douglas, having acquired a 16-year-old Arab boy, writes enthusiastically to Gide and insists on bringing the boy some distance for the French writer's sexual appraisal.[204]

---

*From Carpenter, Edward: The intermediate sex, London, 1908, George Allen & Unwin, Ltd.

Almost incredibly confused and paradoxical attitudes toward sex and concepts of love are reflected in these and numerous other incidents recorded in the lives of Wilde and Gide. There is a strong impression that, for homosexuals, relations considered most pure and exalted are quite consistent with the mates' acting as pimps for each other.

In *De Profundis*,[304] Wilde's incessant whining at Douglas, his arrogant carping and bickering reiterations of accusation, reveal the same bitter ambivalence, the sense of betrayal and outrage and the pettiness in this relation that is familiar in the relations of homosexual patients with those they choose as partners.

It is highly improbable that the homosexual can ever find any sort of erotic relation that affords genuine and durable satisfaction. Despite wide variations of aim, attitude, and technique, despite all the attractions and repulsions and the diverse anatomic and emotional relations between themselves, every invert seems to be seeking what does not exist. Launched by deviation on a course contrary to nature, he continues to seize one unrewarding substitute after another, always avoiding the natural or the real. It is not uncommon for him to esteem the artificial above the actual, to acquire distinct preferences for almost anything erotic that reverses or denies the general postulates of life.

With many deviates the very inappropriateness or unsuitability of the object appears to constitute specific attraction. Thomas Mann's scholarly and aging Aschenbach in *Death in Venice* develops at first sight a startlingly morbid lust for a frail pubertal boy whose very unhealthiness and bad teeth augment the perverse charm, while the foul pestilence devastating the city is apparently welcomed as a romantically fitting background.[202] Confused poets have uttered this profound contrariness of choice in hopeless but fervid sensuous cravings for that impossible freak, the actual hermaphrodite of Greco-Roman mythology.[250] Stimulated repeatedly but always misled upon missions that end unhappily, the invert often confuses erotic feelings with their opposites, the natural fruits of passion with sad compounds of disenchantment, ennui, and spite.

Failing so often to find any lasting satisfaction in efforts to mate with other homosexuals, many apparently are, in a final and cruel term of paradox, attracted specifically toward a *normal* person of their own sex, conceiving somehow of him as the ideal love object. This quest for the axiomatically impossible brings not only inevitable frustration and repeated disillusionment, but, as can easily be seen, makes for cynical attitudes, bitter life rejection, and basic despair. The impossibility of the true invert's ever finding sexual love that is really love seems to be poorly understood by the average

308

victim of the disorder, although it is repeatedly demonstrated in his behavior. This point has been well emphasized by Bergler,[20] and evidence of it is usually not difficult to obtain from patients (despite their own confusion) without prolonged or profound exploratory techniques.

An athletic and successful young man who had fought with bravery and distinction as an infantry officer during the Battle of the Bulge expressed what is often the homosexual's inmost goal and the core of his tragedy. With frankness and dignity this patient had already discussed numerous and diverse experiences (all deviated) and shown evidence of a rather para- doxical distaste for other homosexuals as love objects, despite the super- ficial relief they afforded him. He could not, despite his own freely admitted homosexuality, identify himself with the group, for instance, in the way ordi- nary men accept each other in a nonsexual but fraternal fellowship. In addi- tion, then, to his rejections of "queers" as a substitute for what women are to ordinary men, he also found it impossible to accept them as a substitute for what men mean to each other. Totally blocked from woman as a sexual partner, and his deeper relations with the general body of heterosexual men seriously distorted by his anomaly, he found himself also alien and re- bellious among those most like himself.

During numerous interviews he struggled in bewilderment to express his feelings toward the one love object who had appealed to him as truly ac- ceptable. Not merely in his words, but more significantly in other evidences of emotion, this man showed a yearning, an idealization, almost a worship that strongly suggested the attitude of a genuine lover toward the adored sweetheart he seeks as a bride. This was in sharp contrast to the impulses of profound personal rejection which regularly accompanied such physical urges as made him carry out deviated acts with available "queers." There seemed to be, perhaps, an even sharper contrast than that between the heterosexual male's evaluation of a cheap whore and his evaluation of the supremely honored and beloved lady whom he humbly asks to share his name.

This patient recalled scores of small incidents, brief glimpses, personal mannerisms, characteristic expressions, and other details in which his memory cherished an image of the beloved. Joyous yearning that was almost tragically lyrical illuminated his account. Although his words had no special originality and he even seized upon phrases long worn into banality, the fresh reality of his feelings was no less convincing.

"He was just a typical, clean-cut American boy," the patient repeated, his face aglow not only with desire but with grief and reverence. "He was a perfectly typical young American."

The patient had apparently been able to conceal his real attitude from this acquaintance, who was, according to all the evidence, a thoroughly heterosexual fellow. Thoughts of what the patient desired would be to him in every respect repellent. Even granting the impossible and assuming that the love object could have responded in the desired manner, our patient would hardly have been less bitterly frustrated. The unattainable but uniquely necessary goal would, *ipso facto,* become the reverse of fulfillment. Even in imagination his quest was hopeless. What it seemed imperative to grasp would necessarily dissolve at the touch of his hand. His conflict appeared to be no less maddening (though much less clear to him) than what an impassioned lover would face in an existence in which any physical consummation of erotic aims would simultaneously transform the bride into the spiritual approximation of a despised trollop.

The paradox of erotic feelings and aims, the intrinsic conflict and contradiction of values prevalent among homosexuals, is subtle and profound. Rejecting in disgust real women as love objects, they nevertheless delight in having another man dress as a woman. This imitation of what they find abhorrent specifically arouses many. While calling upon society to respect their sexual life as a benign variant of ordinary erotic patterns, they often mock in each other the very qualities they attempt to glorify.

Mutual repulsion, a peculiarly deep ambivalence, inane bickering, ridicule, and infidelity seem to be integral parts of what passes for love between inverts. In Cory's book, *The Homosexual in America,*[58] these unhappy reactions are well illustrated, unintentionally perhaps, since the author, himself a homosexual, is attempting to make a favorable presentation. Let us quote briefly from his account of a scene in a *gay* bar:

> . . . We will look up with the others as a new face appears in the doorway, and we will hear a murmur:
>
> "Look what's coming!"
>
> "Isn't it gorgeous?"
>
> This last comment is not in whispered tone. The inflection denotes desire, the tone defiance.
>
> At one end of the bar, having beers, are three young queens; their eyebrows are plucked, their hair quite obviously bleached, and of course very wavy. Seldom seen in these bars, their presence is discouraged not only by the proprietors, but by the gay clientele. They gesticulate with graceful movements that are not so much feminine as caricatures and exaggerations of the feminine. They talk quickly, and their lips move in a manner not quite like the movements of either men or women. They can more aptly be compared to actors, seeking to imitate, yet not at all believing that they are play-acting.

"So, I told Margie [a man, of course!] that she'd just have to find herself a new apartment, because I wasn't going to put up with her carrying-on with my friends that way, and she got insulted and left in a huff."

"She said you raised a stink when she brought a friend home one night."

"She did? So you believed her?"

"I didn't say I believed anyone."

"Well you can't believe a word she says."

The onlooker or eavesdropper is puzzled but the initiate is accustomed to the curious change in gender found in conversation of a few of the homosexual circles. Perhaps no other aspect of their lives is so amusing and, even to some inverts, so revolting.

. . .

And yet after a few hours with groups of this sort, there is hardly a homosexual unable to say Joan for Joe, Roberta for Robert, although with trepidation and self-consciousness, perhaps even mocking himself: 'She's nice,' referring to a male entertainer.

A few gay young men, standing near the gesticulating group, listen to the conversation with amusement and contempt.

"My how those faggots camp!" one remarks in a loud voice.

A bleached blonde turns and the retort is quickly forth-coming, "Are you jealous, dearie, because nobody wants your trade?"*

However wise and successful the invert's behavior may be in other respects, his sexual activities seem distorted by an innate conflict that regularly turns these relations into farce or tragedy, and sometimes into both. Let us consider two men who do not appear to be at all congenial but often sit together in a fine apartment furnished luxuriously but with distinguished taste. The host, precociously successful in his work (commercial art), is even better known for the talent and scholarship he has demonstrated in avocations and occasionally in helping with civic movements of an intellectual or esthetic nature. He is, in fact, recognized throughout his state as an authority on early American furniture and the eighteenth century novel. Sophisticated and rather elegant, his general appearance might be regarded as suggestive of the deviate but not as obviously indicative. His companion, an employee of a filling station, seems, on the contrary, quite incongruous with all ordinary concepts of effeminacy. Powerful and stocky, outspoken and easily gregarious, he impresses most observers as an alert, practically oriented, commonplace fellow, no more prone to anything unmanly than a top sergeant in a Class B movie.

---

*From Cory, D. W.: The homosexual in America, New York, 1951, Greenberg.

These two have no overt erotic interest in each other and, despite a twisted and bitter bond of fellowship, there are considerable elements of shared repulsion. Together they await, sometimes until past midnight, the possibility that one or more of some younger men (whom the host often entertains at mixed cocktail parties and dinners) may drop in after their dates. A modicum of heterosexual impulse apparently remains in some of these acquaintances, for they not only go out with girls but also claim to have intercourse with them. The majority of these young men perhaps go with women chiefly in order to appear normal or to impress more complete inverts as being "bisexual." Such a status seems to make them far more desirable to their male admirers. The two older men who sit up together wait in the hope that, after leaving their dates, these somewhat epicene young friends may then come by the apartment for a nightcap and, influenced by chagrin and/or unrelieved tension, submit to fellatio as a substitute for what they missed or avoided earlier in the evening.

The successful and scholarly one of this pair seems to experience indignity in the thought of being, even when successful, a second choice to the girls. The very thought of carnal intimacies between man and woman is to him both distasteful and emotionally incomprehensible. He feels himself in a position to offer esthetically superior and far more genuine experiences to these undiscriminating beneficiaries who, misled by commonplace standards, put vulgar and trivial pursuits above what is choice, uniquely beautiful, but evaluated properly only by the elect. But, as he has explained to his companion ruefully, he is prepared to suffer this or any other personal humiliation if necessary for the attainment of his aims.

Although these younger men could scarcely be rated as normally heterosexual or as approaching this very closely, the relatively small degree of this approximation to the normal and unattainable male seems to constitute their charm.

Although fictional material cannot be relied upon for evidence in questions of this sort, it is useful sometimes to illustrate in detail patients' reactions which are difficult to present convincingly in brief summaries. In a recent novel, *The City and the Pillar*,[296] we find that the chief character (Jim Willard) is presented in a way that brings out very adequately the point now under consideration. His attitudes as he is shown in relation to a surrounding world of other homosexuals reflect accurately what we very often encounter clinically. An inescapable contempt, sometimes admitted, sometimes apparently less clear but no less real, prevails in Willard's feelings toward this entire company of male inverts, most, if not all, of whom he derogatorily regards as "queers," referring to some even as "queens." He is pictured as entering into promiscuous sexual activities with a wide variety of male partners, often very casually with those picked up "bar-hunting" and sometimes less casually with successful or intellectual figures. Although with the latter some faint, positive, interpersonal feelings seem to emerge, these are trivial and at best pathologically ambivalent. The love object really sought by Willard, despite his having once engaged in an unspecified youthful intimacy with the hero, is not pictured as a true invert. The mistaken hope that this man offers him the possibility of something romantic, permanent, beautiful, and life-fulfilling is well brought out in Willard and is a useful illustration of what emerges time after time from patients of this sort.

It is well to avoid sweeping generalizations on the basis of one's necessarily limited observations. Although I cannot say that this specific need or desire for such a love object is universal, I am particularly impressed with the evidence of it in cases I have had good opportunity to study. Such evidence has been more regular and more impressive in the male than in the female homosexual, but in the latter also the discriminatory need for a normal (unattainable) mate of her own sex often seems to play an important part.

Were it not for this inability to be satisfied with each other, efforts to adjust in "bohemian" groups where it would be thought congeniality could prevail might be more successful, and congenial mates might be found with whom some enduring happiness could result. Such arrangements seem, however, to be at best a poor compromise for the participants and usually a temporary one. The female homosexual, according to my own impressions, more often works out a better compromise than the male, sometimes, apparently, by discovering a partner who is a better facsimile of the normal woman than is possible among men.[54]

It is not surprising to find that people encountering such major difficulties in life show distortions or maladaptations or other special personality features aside from the circumscribed deviation. I do not, however, believe that the clinical picture of the psychopath coincides with what is typical of homosexuals as a group. This pattern of general behavior occurs but I believe that other patterns are more common.

Greenspan and Campbell[108] have briefly outlined personality features that impress me as much more characteristic of the invert. The retreat, as described by these observers, into a "cultural aloofness" where the ordinary proprieties and amenities are exaggerated and where a special sort of "intellectualism" and "estheticism" prevail, is far more common than the sharply contrasting heedlessness of the psychopath.

Keeping in mind the strong probability that a majority of this group never seek treatment or become available for psychiatric study, it is plain that our clinical observations should be applied only tentatively in all generalizing hypotheses. It is natural to think that those whose maladaptation includes antisocial behavior or other gross general failure would predominate in our clinical material. This must occur with the regularity of cream rising to the top of the milk bottle or the larger fragments of gravel remaining in the seive. Such an opinion is also supported by the attitude common among homosexuals that their erotic status, far from being a malady, is, on the contrary, something to cherish.[102]

When we consider sexual deviates in relation to society, two points particularly emerge: first, the direct effect upon others which the deviate has in his search for sexual gratification and, second, the indirect effect of accessory deviate reactions as manifested in literature, art, education, and other ideologic spheres.

I. If the typical invert were not repeatedly disillusioned in his sexual activity with other clear-cut inverts and continually seeking as an ideal partner someone different from other inverts he has known and therefore less available, fewer serious problems would arise. If the rather common specific attraction toward normal members of his own sex makes him display to them his inclinations, he is rebuffed and perhaps avoided even as an acquaintance. Often he is inclined to seek in the apparently normal or in the immature some approximation or facsimile of the biologic impossibility his deviation seems to demand. The pubertal boy whose sexual orientation is still normal often seems to offer him a unique opportunity of achieving the impossible ideal. In his basic frustration he may, particularly if he is intellectual, devise rationalizations whereby he convinces himself his disorder is a superiority. Quoting from the *Phaedrus* and the *Symposium,* he may seek to elevate adolescents above the commonplace and to save them from the vulgarities of the philistine majority by what he offers as a more esthetic and spiritual relationship. The very young may be confused and traumatized by contact with him, and sometimes the older person who is insecurely adjusted and already disturbed by other psychiatric problems. If he does not succeed in drawing others into abnormal physical practices, he may promote peculiar interpersonal relations and abnormal and unhappy basic attitudes. Evidence of this is abundant in the histories of patients who are not homosexual. Stronger than ordinary ethical impulses and superior ethical judgment are necessary in the deviate if he is to avoid direct antisocial acts. Those who avoid seriously confusing or harming others deserve special respect and admiration. With offenders, their unusual difficulties should be kept in mind, but precau-

314

tions should be taken to avoid the psychiatric damage that may be done to others through them.

II. The secondary reaction of cultural aloofness mentioned by Greenspan and Campbell[108] is in general a harmless and valuable protective measure for people who sorely need defense. Some inverts, probably a small minority, react not only with cultural aloofness but also with what might be called cultural contempt and destructiveness. Although a minority, it is a conspicuous minority, and conspicuous through the manifestations of more than ordinary talent.

The familiar exaggerations of critical taste in literature, art, music, etc., snobbish fears of being caught in some esthetic appraisal short of current "highbrow" standards, disdainful withdrawals from the commonplace, etc., so often prominent in the invert, are compensatory measures undeserving of mockery by others. Despite examples to the contrary, an understandable but definitely pathologic cynicism is common, particularly among the more forceful and talented. Those who can live peaceably in the shallows and content themselves with the trivia of social relations and lackadaisical ventures into the fringes of erudition and the arts (or perhaps a prolonged but a largely Platonic liaison with one or more of the Muses) seem to avoid the aggressive cynicism characteristic of some among the strong and the brilliant in this group.

In literature, music, and philosophy, the achievements of a few homosexuals stand among those most highly valued by man, and perhaps among the most healthful and undistorted. Here, too, stand the achievements of persons with other serious psychiatric disorders. Despite these immortal successes by some, it is no less true that others bring into what they create, largely or chiefly, the reflection of a very deep disorder. Though such productions afford informative material for psychiatric study, it is difficult to estimate all their influences and sociologic effects.

In faddist movements featuring an essential nihilism, in advanced groups who wax almost enthusiastic about futility and boredom, in charmed circles where a taste for decadence becomes dogma, it is not difficult for the psychiatrist (however poor a judge of art he may be!) to recognize something astonishingly similar to the secondary cynicism and defeatism of the intellectually aggressive homosexual patient. It is highly probable that some talented inverts, through the projection of their own bias, communicate in novels, in teaching, in poetry, etc., data which, if mistaken by the impressionable for valid data, make for confusion, misinterpretation, and regression.

Brilliant and talented people of this sort find that for themselves sexual love, wherever or however it may be sought, turns inevitably into a mocking chimera, into what leaves them outraged in their deepest yearnings and deepest needs. It is understandable that in the bitterness and loneliness of this fate they rationalize an anodyne in the conviction that only a grossness of taste or some spiritual shallowness or simple gullibility in the majority enables these benighted creatures to continue to believe that man and woman can really fulfill each other and find in ordinary experience something that, despite adversity and mortality, makes it magically worth while. Since in basic matters existence has proved itself so different to the invert, it is often difficult for him to avoid assuming that reports to the contrary are based on illusion or stupid pretense.[54]

This sincere but definitely pathologic cynicism, focused primarily on meaningful relations between man and woman but often spreading into a generalized life rejection, no doubt plays a significant part in ideologies that color the milieu. The more subtle the creative writing, the art, the criticism, the teaching, the philosophizing, etc., of talented people thus distorted, the more effective is this negative influence.

The projected distortion and the biologically inaccurate data are more likely to be encountered in implication than in direct argument and represent not a vicious, or even a voluntary, effort to falsify but a genuine communication of experience unrecognized as pathologic.

Alfred Towne, in his article entitled "Sexual Gentleman's Agreement,"[293] has discussed what he regards as insidious and pervasive manifestations of deviate influence in our current literature and art, occasionally even in our movies and relatively popular magazines that are sold at the newsstands. Let us consider a few of the points made by Towne:

> The first thing we see is that the intelligent, average American who, thirty years ago, frowned on nothing so much as "sissiness" and "the fairy," has been, in the last five years or so, exposed (if he reads) to a fairly large dose of the he's-more-to-be-pitied-than-censured approach to the homosexual problem. The list of novels alone that deals with this aspect is too long to bear reproduction. Add to this the growing amount of popular and clinical nonfiction on the subject and you have a small mountain of material.
>
> .   .   .
>
> It is safe to conclude that there has been a change in attitude. The recent wave of excitement and interest among intellectuals over the writings of the young French homosexual, Jean Genet, is a good, if extreme, example of this change. Genet is a flashy, mystical writer who might be called a homosexual Henry Miller. His one translated novel, "Our Lady of the Flowers," sells for $35.00 under the counter, but its buyers and praisers are not confined to homosexuals. The first serious

treatment of Genet was in *Partisan Review* in April, 1949, in an article entitled "The World of Jean Genet," written by Eleanor Clarke. In this seven-page piece, which concretized what had been heretofore only isolated interest in Genet and called him "one of the most gifted prose writers of this generation," there is little mention of the total, recurrent homosexual content of Genet's work. For a woman to seriously eulogize Genet in print might be some nadir of the ludicrous if it did not grotesquely illustrate the alarming degree to which a subtle traduction of sexual and critical values has proceeded. Is it somehow indiscreet for the non-homosexual to mention that three-hundred and fifty pages of minute descriptions of homosexual love (in the most unabashed language) may be interesting or well-written, but is also extremely distasteful to him? Judging from Miss Clarke's article, and others assessing similar work, it would seem to be so.

But it is not only with such overt examples of homosexuality as a theme for popular or highbrow art that we must deal. People buying these books, for instance, know what they are getting and, presumably, buy them for that very reason. Where the phenomena of homosexuality are brought right out in the open, the non-homosexual at least has the chance to orient himself before exposure. The problem raised by Belvedere* is that most people who watch his antics don't know what he is. His character and his incidental predilections are left intact; it is only the fact of his specific sexual anomaly that has been excised. Thus it is those books, movies, magazines etc. where it is not clearly labelled for all to see that raise the delicate and difficult question: what pervasive influence, subconscious or otherwise, does a steady diet of homosexually-motivated art have upon the non-homosexual?

One is treading on dangerous ground. Because a fashionable, eagerly-awaited ballet is written by one recognized homosexual, scored by another, choreographed by a third, and designed by still a fourth, can be conclude that it will be a "homosexual ballet"? (By which I mean a work reflecting, consicously or otherwise, images, ideas or situations that could be said to be either homosexually characteristic or motivated by those specific maladjustments which cause homosexuality.) Freud says quite clearly that homosexuality is psychogenic; and, in another context, that art and neurosis are intimately connected. Relying on this, it might be safe to assume that at least some of the content of this ballet would reflect the sexual attitudes of its creators. In other words, symbolic or actual love between men would be idealized, women would probably come off badly as sexual objects, and the dominant visual images of decor and choreography would be of a homosexual nature. But is this bad?

Most intellectuals today would look askance if one chanced to say, "Yes, in one sense this is bad." Their look would imply that one was a kind of sexual anti-semite. The sexual proclivities of the artist

*In the series of movies featuring the fictional Lynn Belvedere as chief character.

have only casual bearing on his work, they would reply; and as this ballet has no specific reference to homosexuality, the fact that it was created by four homosexuals is really beside the point.

But this is no answer, and again we must repeat: is a ballet (or book or magazine or novel) whose content may be said to be homosexual, bad for that reason? If clearly labelled as such, the non-homosexual can have no objection to it, except that his own sexual preferences limit the interest the work can have for him. But the fact that more and more of the highly touted, new novels by 'bright young men,' and more and more movies and plays, mask the homosexual nature of their content under a mock, non-homosexual surface, simply depriving the content of a name, changes the implications of the question.

For example, a movie ("Once More, My Darling") whose heroine is paraded through five reels in shorts, a tee-shirt with "KILLER" written across the front, and hair grotesquely gathered into a baseball cap, and whose hero is an aspiring actor living with his dominant mother, who acts love scenes while dressed in kilts to a burly propman because the actress for whom his impassioned lines were meant did not make rehearsal, and who is finally captured by the predatory "killer" in the tee-shirt when she hits him over the head with a slot-machine: a movie of this sort is seen by millions of non-homosexuals who might have done one of two things if the picture had been clearly labeled a homosexual comedy: (a) stayed away from it entirely, or (b) written off the overt anti-feminism as mere special pleading. As it is, they have been exposed to a biased idea without knowing it. Like the German people between the wars, they have been propagandized by subtle juxtaposition of images or situations which might have little effect if seen separately, but which add up, when taken together, to a typical homosexual case against women.*

Note that Towne emphasizes not so much the frank presentation of homosexuality as a subject but the veiled distortion of basic human values and orientations reflected in the art of deviates. Is it reasonable to believe that such appraisals of life may confuse the immature and the naive? Sexually disordered writers have often expressed cynical disillusionment about love which is usually presumed by the ordinary reader to be an estimate of normal biologic relations, perhaps an estimate by some genius whose superior understanding of human life it would be foolish or impertinent to challenge.

> When a man has loved a woman he will do anything for her, except continue to love her. . . .
>
> The proper basis for marriage is a mutual misunderstanding. . . .
>
> A man can be happy with any woman as long as he does not love her. . . .

---

*From Towne, Alfred: Sexual gentlemen's agreement, Neurotica 6:23-28, 1950.

One should always be in love. That is the reason one should never marry. . . .

The difference between a caprice and a life-long passion is that the caprice lasts a little longer. . . .*

These and many similar epigrams express a harsh judgment on the relations between man and woman. A reader familiar with Oscar Wilde's personal life realizes that the opinions are those of a homosexual and reflect the disillusionment of homosexual affairs.[147] The adolescent may mistake them for profound evaluations of normal love by one whose rare intellect enables him to see beyond conventional superficialities. Often the brilliantly cynical comments of a literary homosexual are thus projected in disguise and accepted as a genius's revelations of normal life.

Marcel Proust, generally regarded as a "giant of literature," devotes hundreds of pages in *Remembrance of Things Past* to minute analysis of his relations with Albertine.[252] He not only dwells upon her continual infidelity, the agonies of jealousy, the inevitably illusory nature of love, but even rhapsodizes on the theme that desire can be kept alive only through the pain and humiliation of his knowing she is having sexual relations with others.[211] This pathologic and perverse expression of human reactions becomes more understandable when we learn that the Albertine of the novel was in actual life another man, probably Proust's chauffeur.[184]

It is not my belief that such literary influences can make homosexuals out of normal people, but I would estimate them as a significant factor among the negative social forces worthy of attention from preventive psychiatry. Understanding and explanation offer, of course, more promising remedies than any efforts along the intrinsically futile lines of censorship or suppression.

Although it is improbable that grave sociologic damage occurs through the fluctuating medium of milady's fashions, these fluctuations offer a subject for speculation. Multitudinous and very diverse forces no doubt integrate into what causes the elevation or the lowering of a skirt. Despite the complexity and abstruseness that make confident interpretation absurd, I am willing to risk a guess that secondary homosexual reactions exert at times a discernible effect here. Those too young to recall the early 1920's may find it hard to believe how little female contours or other attributes remained discernible or imaginable after the interior strappings down and the exterior levellings out had done their utmost to translate full female actuality into the caricature of a pubertal boy. Here was a means not only of making women

---

*From Pearson, Hesketh: Oscar Wilde, his life and wit, New York, 1946, Harper & Brothers.

look less like women and more like boys but also, and this perhaps more fundamental, of making women look very ridiculous.

Other types of pathologic sexuality are often designated by such terms as *erotomania, perversion,* and *sexual immaturity.* So far as erotomania is concerned, the following points may be made: Most psychopaths known to me have shown little compunction about seeking sexual gratification. They are so frequently found in brothels and with other professional vendors of erotic wares that one might at first glance conclude that they indeed suffer from erotomania.* A closer consideration of the circumstances, however, reveals that the psychopath is not pushed into these situations by an excessively vigorous eroticism but that even the feeblest and most transient impulse will cause him to seek gratification with partners and in environments shunned by a person with ordinary judgment and discretion and taste. It is indeed open to question whether the impulse is more than feeble in the sense of genitalized sexuality, to say nothing of mature sexuality. Sometimes the male psychopath, after carefully setting the stage for seduction, will instead of achieving intercourse, straightway drink himself into the purgatorial Nirvana of maudlin semiconsciousness, leaving his partner to nurse and pamper him. In my experience, the typical psychopath of either sex does not appear to have a sexual drive, normal or perverse, of sufficient vigor to account for the poor judgment shown in what seems rather to be a vague blundering along the roads of folly and frustration toward what is essentially life rejection. There are, of course, persons activated by strong libidinous drive who often commit extremely indiscreet deeds and who sometimes even bring disaster on themselves. These, however, do not impress me as fundamentally similar to the psychopath.

Sexual immaturity can be more aptly used, in my opinion, as a term to describe all psychopaths than to segregate any particular group of them.

Masochism, sadism, bestiality, fetichism, necrophilia, scoptophilia, and the terms for various other perversions would seem to imply people who consistently sought definite erotic satisfaction in one or more of these ways and in whom this quest was a major and persistent life aim. Taken in this sense, such characteristics are not particularly common in the psychopaths whom I have studied. Psychopaths, of course, show a carelessness about drifting with what might be called one or another of the partial impulses[94] which have been said to underlie these perversions, but they do not regularly give the impression that efforts to attain specific gratification of this sort

---

*Such a conclusion would, however, be as seriously wrong as to assume that the inveterate reader of sentimental rhymes gave evidence of a strong inclination for poetry or that the empty and aggressive braggart were really of stoic fiber.

play an important role in their conduct or could account for their generalized patterns of failure.

In a broader sense it might be said that the apparently willful persistence with which they bring humiliation and emotional suffering upon those who love them, as well as failure and unpleasant circumstances upon themselves, marks all psychopaths as both sadists and masochists. Only in this sense, however, are these impulses common or consistent, and the gratification is probably not the directly erotic sensation enjoyed by perverts who literally whip others or have themselves whipped. It has been already stated that true psychopaths with serious criminal tendencies do exist. The real psychopath who is a real (persistently organized) sadist, of course, ranks as an extremely dangerous person. Like all psychopaths, he is unlikely to be greatly altered by punishment or training or treatment, and he constitutes a grave problem. People of this type are often responsible for perverse and murderous attacks on children frequently noticed in the newspapers.

If true and full sadistic tendencies are combined with the psychopath's lack of compunction, a formidable menace to others is likely to emerge. Let us consider Neville G. C. Heath, who within a period of three weeks committed two of the most gruesome sexual murders and mutilations ever to be reported.

According to reliable evidence, some of which was brought out at his trial, this man followed an extremely irresponsible career for many years. On several occasions he was court-martialed and discharged from the military service. Forgeries, thefts, housebreaking, impersonation of an officer, fraud, and many elaborate episodes of swindling brought him repeatedly to the attention of the police. The history available about this handsome, intelligent, attractive rebel against society prior to his two sadistic murders strongly indicates the typical psychopath.[61]

His record as a charmer among the ladies is difficult to match. Many intelligent, lovely, and wealthy girls apparently succumbed to his quickly irresistible wooing and, with rapture and pride, considered themselves engaged to him until he disappeared after ingeniously borrowing or otherwise obtaining large sums of money from their families. He was regularly able to convince not only the girls but also their families that he was a man of great distinction and tremendous financial resources. One report indicates that while on a sea voyage he seduced a young Hungarian beauty and also her similarly enticing and voluptuous mother. After the mother and daughter discovered that he had been alternating his sexual attentions between them, with convincing vows of eternal fidelity to both, they maintained a fierce and idealistic loyalty to Heath and each sought diligently to obtain financial advantages for him through intercession with the husband (of the older) and father (of of the younger), who had not, because of urgent and important business responsibilities, been able to accompany them on the voyage. This is apparently a typical example of Heath's ability to impress others, including very learned and intelligent people, with his appearance of profound sincerity and of innumerable other virtues and remarkable abilities and achievements.[136]

The sexually perverse murders carried out by this handsome, athletic young man of idealistic and intensely virile appearance were acts of memorable brutality and horror. Each of the two young women tortured and killed by Heath within a period of three weeks was cruelly butchered. The sexually sadistic quality of Heath's behavior on these two occasions is made plain by the nature of the mutilations. A nipple was bitten entirely from one girl's breast. Much of the breast itself had been chewed and mangled to bloody pulp. With the other girl this had almost been accomplished. At the autopsy both showed that some instrument, perhaps a poker, had been thrust with violence into the vagina, rupturing it and damaging the abdominal viscera. In one of the victims the poker had apparently been driven far up into the abdominal cavity and twisted about with great violence. One body had been lashed severely by a heavy, metal-tipped whip. The nude bodies were found covered with clotted blood. The abdomen of one women had been ripped open so extensively that the intestines emerged and spread sickeningly over the area about her body. One deep gash started below the genital organs and extended up into the breast. Heath is described as being extremely calm and poised after these deeds and entirely free of remorse. After the first murder he spoke with great interest about accounts of it in the newspapers, expressed opinions about how the gruesome wounds might have been inflicted, and even communicated with the police, offering to help them discover the murderer.

The victims were tightly bound and gagged. Points brought out at the autopsies indicate that Heath wanted the women to remain alive as long as possible to experience the agony resulting from his vicious torture and that he seemed to relish this particularly while the victims still remained conscious and capable of feeling it. Apparently he also found perverse sexual satisfaction in continuing after death the gruesome and protracted mutilation of the bodies.[61,136]

Those who devoutly believe that the psychopath carries out crimes because of an inner, unconscious sense of guilt and a need (also unconscious) to seek punishment in persistent efforts to gain expiation might say that Heath's getting in touch with the police and offering them advice after the first butchery and murder, and his making himself conspicuous at the scene of the first crime, afford proof of their assumptions. It appears to me, however, that such an argument ignores the peculiar and astonishing callousness of psychopaths and also ignores the fact that they appear to take a positive and boastful delight in showing off in the midst of their uninviting, destructive, and antisocial achievements. They often seem to relish this as an exhibition of their prowess. I think it much more likely that such a man as Heath would want to savor the afterglow of his perverse and sadistic crime, to exult in his success, and to flaunt his ability to hoodwink the police than that he would be unconsciously seeking punishment in order to ease a conscience which was causing him great remorse of which he remained unaware.

The argument advanced by some psychiatrists that such people as Heath are aching with (unconscious) guilt inside and seeking the redemption of adequate punishment through their repeated crimes has sometimes suggested to me other possible interpretations of natural events, similarly logical and, I think, similarly implausible. One of these is the assumption (available for anyone who may choose to make it) that gravity does not really cause the Niagara River to plunge over the celebrated falls and roar in stupendous violence down the course of the rapids. We can, if we choose, assume that gravity is actually working to pull the millions of tons of water upstream. We can then assume that, in reaction to this (as the psychopath is said to react to a postulated or inferred but never demonstrated unconscious guilt), the river rushes downstream in a dynamic defiance of gravity through some inner law of physics also not yet demonstrable. In both of these instances much depends on the definitions that are employed for *gravity* or for *guilt* and on assumptions that are made about the supposedly purposive but unconscious efforts to atone for guilt, or about hypothetical forces that might counteract gravity.

36

The erratic man of genius

Rather curiously, one might at first think, many persons widely recognized as geniuses have been placed by various writers in the classification of psychopathic (sociopathic) personality.[129,132,162] The vagueness and plasticity of the term as it has been officially used indeed allow it to be stretched in practice to cover nearly any type of abnormal behavior imaginable, and the literal or etymologic connotation is, of course, no less all-embracing.

It is true that a number of celebrities presented in school books as ornaments of our civilization are credited with isolated acts that would do justice to the cases discussed in this book. Some of the great figures in history, literature, philosophy, and art are said even to have behaved continually in abnormal patterns.

The concept of genius as a type of madness is particularly associated with Lombroso, who, in 1888, with *The Man of Genius,* advanced his familiar hypothesis that genius is a degenerative psychosis, a sort of "moral insanity" which may at times take the form of other mental disorders but which preserves certain distinguishing characteristics.[191]

Grasset,[106] following a similar line of thought, gives some striking examples. Tolstoi is said to have lashed himself with ropes and to have fallen a considerable distance while attempting to fly before wondering seriously whether to abandon civilization for a primitive life in the desert. Jean Jacques Rousseau's many false starts as medical student, clockmaker, theologian, painter, servant, musician, and botanist are noted, as well as his curious letter addressed to God Almighty which he placed under the altar of Notre Dame.

Rousseau's expressed repugnance toward the normal sex act is hardly less significant. Schopenhauer's peculiarities, long famous, are reviewed by Grasset. His abnormal attitude of esthetic distaste toward women, his morbid suspiciousness which led him to write even trivial notes in dead languages, and his occasional assaults on unsuspecting bystanders who he fancied were talking about him all suggest a deep-seated maladjustment.

Unusual and apparently irrational behavior has indeed been so commonly reported in the lives of those acclaimed as great artists and thinkers that there is a popular tendency to regard it as the rule rather than the exception. Vincent Van Gogh's career is a familiar example. His justly celebrated exploit in cutting off his own ear and sending it to a prostitute of Arles is one of many.[238]

Richard Wagner, according to some of his biographers[143] at any rate, manifested an utter disregard for the feelings and the rights of others, a petty vanity, and an emotional hollowness almost worthy of the psychopath. Nordau[234] has indeed said that Wagner is accused of having a greater degree of degeneracy than all the other degenerates heretofore seen put together!

Jonathan Swift, in his poem *The Lady's Dressing Room* and in other writings, manifests an attitude so basically distorted that it is difficult not to believe he was a very ill man psychiatrically. In an interesting discussion of life-rejecting attitudes and their relation to obsessive disorder, Straus[280] makes clear something that is probably not only pertinent to that syndrome but also to other psychiatric conditions. The basic emotional judgment expressed by Swift might, if it were an unconscious stratum in the psychopath, play an important part in his clinical manifestations. The life of this learned and brilliant man does not show consistent behavioral features that would justify his being classed in our group.

Is it not pertinent here to ask ourselves again: What is a genius? In the dictionary, among other definitions, we find, "a man endowed with transcendent ability." Shall we conclude that the authentic genius will demonstrate more than ordinary wisdom in the conduct of his life? Or should we consider his books or his music or his statuary apart from his personal acts? Shall we say that his creative productions furnish the evidence of superior wisdom or of essential greatness that he may have failed to display in his role as a husband, father, friend, or citizen?

From his unhappy career of drunkenness, irresponsibility, and failure, did Edgar Allan Poe distill into his stories and poems sufficient wisdom and beauty to establish him as vastly superior to the ordinary happy citizen of our nation?

Throughout Europe and America, Paul Verlaine is acclaimed as an important figure in world literature. In our colleges and universities young people are encouraged to admire his works and to recognize him as a rare and wonderful spirit, towering above the level of common humanity. The sordid folly, the senseless and distasteful misconduct, parasitism, indolence, depravity, and irresponsible squandering reported as habitual of Verlaine might make it difficult for some, despite his established reputation as a poet, to believe he was a man of superior qualities and sensibilities.[250,295,309] Others may assume that this man's unprovoked and truly murderous assaults on a close friend and also on Arthur Rimbaud, his favorite homosexual intimate, and on his mother arose from the turbulent passions of a great creative artist. Could such acts and the general conduct of his life be related to callousness, perversity, and a deficiency of basic human reactions? It has been said that "probably the greatest misfortune ever to befall Paul Verlaine in his tragedy-riddled career was the fact that he was sentenced to only two years in jail—instead of life imprisonment—for the attempted murder of Arthur Rimbaud."* These apparently were the least miserable and humiliating, the most nearly normal years of his adult life.

For centuries moralists have sometimes condemned the artist's life as licentious, as given over to sensual delights, to violent and exquisite but unconventional erotic pursuits and consummations. Others have argued, often indignantly, that the creative genius is exempt from our ordinary standards of behavior, that his mightly passions justly sweep aside ethical barriers suitable for lesser men, and that his vast spiritual fulfillments and accomplishments not only excuse but even sanctify conduct that in others might be classed as irresponsible or even criminal.[147,203] The immature and the naive often picture those who choose the bohemian life as virile standard-bearers of youth, gallant rebels against puritanical restrictions, strong men who claim a rich and lusty fulfillment of what Eros demands.

It is popularly believed also that the genius is neglected or, through outrageous injustice, even condemned by his contemporaries because they are too stupid to understand him and to recognize his superior wisdom and spiritual values. According to legend, subsequent generations at last catch on or wake up and come to see that the creative artist was right and the surrounding social group stupidly wrong. Those who do not in retrospect justify and romantically glorify the poet's or musician's actual conduct often conclude that his productions show that he understood or felt more profoundly than ordinary men the issues of human life and that his lofty and magnificent being reveals itself to us through his cantos, his odes, or his symphonies.

---

*From Wolf, M. L.: Introduction to Verlaine, Paul: Confessions of a poet, New York, 1950, Philosophical Library.

We find in Thomas Mann's appraisal of Dostoevsky viewpoints not entirely the same as those just mentioned.[203] It is plain that he regards the venerated Russian novelist as profoundly disordered, as perhaps chief among "the great sinners and the damned, the sufferers of holy disease." ". . . I am," Mann says, "filled with awe, with a profound, mystic, silence-enjoining awe, in the presence of the religious greatness of the damned, in the presence of genius of disease and the disease of genius, of the type of the afflicted and the possessed, in whom saint and criminal are one."* Mann feels that Dostoevsky was personally preoccupied with fantasies of bestial brutality such as the rape of a girl child he described in *Stavrogin's Confession*.[77] "Apparently this infamous crime constantly occupied the author's moral imagination."*

Mann apparently does not regard Dostoevsky as great despite his disease or as redeemed by art from what he finds in "the criminal depths of the author's own conscience." To the contrary he identifies disease and genius, saying:

> . . . the disease bears fruits that are more important and more beneficial to life and its development than any medically approved normality. The truth is that life has never been able to do without the morbid, and probably no adage is more inane than the one which says that "only disease can come from the diseased." Life is not prudish and it is probably safe to say that life prefers creative, genius-bestowing disease a thousand times over to prosaic health; prefers disease, surmounting obstacles proudly on horseback, boldly leaping from peak to peak, to lounging, pedestrian healthfulness. Life is not finical and never thinks of making a moral distinction between health and infirmity. It seizes the bold product of disease, consumes and digests it, and as soon as it is assimilated, it is health. An entire horde, a generation of open-minded, healthy lads pounces upon the work of diseased genius, genialized by disease, admires and praises it, raises it to the skies, perpetuates it, transmutes it, and bequeathes it to civilization, which does not live on the home-baked bread of health alone. They all swear by the name of the great invalid, thanks to whose madness they no longer need to be mad. Their healthfulness feeds upon his madness and in them he will become healthy.
>
> In other words, certain attainments of the soul and the intellect are impossible without disease, without insanity, without spiritual crime, and the great invalids are crucified victims, sacrificed to humanity and its advancement, to the broadening of its feeling and knowledge—in short, to its more sublime health. . . . They force us to re-evaluate the concepts of "disease" and "health," the relation of sickness and life; they teach us to be cautious in our approach to

---

*From Mann, Thomas: Introduction to Dostoevsky, Fedor: The short novels, New York, 1951, Dial Press.

the idea of "disease," for we are too prone always to give it a biological minus sign.*

Mario Praz, in his well-known work *The Romantic Agony*,[250] makes this comment about the French decadents:

> . . . [they] found or thought they found in the novels of Dostoevski a sadism which had become more mystical and more subtle, no longer limited to the grossness of physical torture but penetrating like a worm-hole into all moral phenomena. . . . they found also a thirst for the impossible, and impotence elevated to the height of a mystical ecstasy. . . . In Sade and in the sadists of the "frenetique" type of Romanticism it is the integrity of the body which is assaulted and destroyed, whereas in Dostoevski one has the feeling . . . of the "intimacy of the soul brutally and insolently violated."†

Unlike Thomas Mann, Praz does not express a belief in any mystical value superior to that of health in such reactions or claim that they save subsequent generations from madness. He does, however, present much evidence to support his argument that in the work of many important literary figures generally regarded as geniuses it is the pathology itself that has won admiration and been acclaimed as beauty or wisdom. He offers many examples of the influence of the Marquis de Sade, and of his tastes, in the writings of Baudelaire, Verlaine, Swinburne, Flaubert, Gautier, Huysmans, and others too numerous to mention here.

The rapt attention which Praz demonstrates in the literary productions of this large group for literal algolagnia is complicated by many nuances of perversion. Truly corrupt and appalling depravities of taste and impulse are expressed, some passing beyond the antisocial or the unnatural and well deserving to be called antibiologic. Sexual inversion sometimes overreaches itself into rapturous praise and lustful yearning for such tragic monstrosities as those exemplified by the literal hermaphrodite. Pain, disfigurement, torture, putrefaction, disgrace, ennui, death, profanation, and nearly all things detestable to sane men are esthetically invoked, equivocally identified as love or glory, and treated with perverse veneration. Through the sensibilities of these famous decadents, woman is enthusiastically perceived as an overpowering, murderous vampire, man as a furtive and gelded weakling. Necrophilia and coprophilia apparently have attractions for at least a few of the group presented by Praz. In some of their writings delight is expressed not merely in things naturally disgusting, but in disgust itself.[250]

---

*From Mann, Thomas: Introduction to Dostoevsky, Fedor: The short novels, New York, 1951, Dial Press.
†From Praz, Mario: The romantic agony, London, 1951, Oxford University Press.

The pathology and perversion of axiomatic human values demonstrated by Praz in the literary productions he discusses are indeeed profound. If these productions represent the life experience of the authors, accurately reflect their taste and judgment, it is difficult to refrain from asking why they should be accepted as intellectual or spiritual superiors qualified to enlighten or inspire ordinary men and women.

If Baudelaire or Swinburne achieves a genuine excellence of art in poetry, need we concern ourselves with its substance, with what human values it proclaims or implies, or with what kind of personal experience it embodies or reflects? Can we appraise the worth of this poetry as art entirely apart from its content? If the viewpoints and emotional reactions that produced it are psychotic or obviously perverse, must we say that this is irrelevant, that it has nothing to do with the greatness of the poet?

Perhaps this can be done by the critic of art who in his role ceases to react as a human being. To the ordinary man, and certainly to the physician, esoteric attempts to isolate art from biologic experience, to consider it without reference to the personal emotion it reflects or evokes, are likely to appear speciously mystical and unenticing.

Baudelaire's actual life is reported as that of a feeble and affected eccentric, a wastrel apparently without normal passions or friendships. Dyeing his hair green and sometimes leading a live lobster through the streets on a pale blue ribbon, he lived, at times, in an atmosphere chiefly of vexation and disgust, with an ignorant mulatto girl for whom his attachment is said to have been "cerebral rather than sensuous."[21] Some of his biographers concluded that he may have been sexually impotent. His reported disdain for ordinary morality was apparently surpassed by his repulsion at prospects of physical relations with beautiful and intelligent[21] women.[250]

Can it be said, despite his unenviable personal career, that Baudelaire's art establishes him as a very great man, a lofty spirit resplendent above the ordinary and deserving our reverent admiration? Before trying to answer such a question is it not reasonable to inquire into what sorts of judgment and feeling, what evaluations of experience—ethical, esthetic, or otherwise—are reflected in this work? If we find in it wisdom and beauty, something to sustain or enrich lesser men, it might be argued that we should ignore the conduct of his life and bow our heads in acknowledgment of his message.

Praz credits Baudelaire's poetry with having given "a psychological turn to the refinements of perversity"[250] and from it demonstrates a vividly persistent taste for joy in damnation, an insistence on achieving religious beliefs in order to enhance the shame and horror of desecrating them. Here the sexual mate emerges scarcely at all except in terms of derisive obscenity or hideous monstrosity. Not occasionally but pervasively we see that "inversion of values which is the basis of sadism, vice [representing] the positive active element, virtue the negative and passive. Virtue exists only as a restraint to be broken."[250] Actual voluptuousness is travestied, achieving little or no recognition except in perverted forms of physical brutality or moral abuse. Praz not only speaks of but amply illustrates Baudelaire's "inexhaustible need to be occupied with macabre and obscene subjects . . ."[250] His works are shown to abound in enthusiastic references to nearly all those defilements, reversals, butcheries, and abortions of basic human feeling embodied in the Black Mass and apparently relished there so avidly by J. K. Huysmans.[146,226] The fraudulent or counterfeit is regularly accorded superiority over the actual. Baudelaire states that it is his purpose to "extract beauty out of evil." It is doubtful if such an extract can be made beautiful or valuable through being renamed, however melodiously, or through being welcomed, however lyrically. Ignominy is rapturously embraced and pronounced sublime. Ennui is accepted as an esthetic triumph. Perhaps nothing is more typical of how this genius reacted to life than his famous statement: "Woman is natural, that is to say abominable."[250]

A recent biographer speaks of Baudelaire as "a soul of such profound spirituality and a mind of such heightened sensibility."[21] We are also told that, "through his own sufferings he came to understand the sufferings of mankind."[21] Do his works really reveal this spirituality and understanding? Have the courts who during his life condemned *Les Fleurs du Mal* as "an outrage upon morals and decency" been proved stupidly wrong?

"I have loved overmuch . . . ," Swinburne says.[286] The youthful and the naive often believe him. The surging rhythms of his verse, the sumptuous imagery, the cumulative efflorescence of his alliteration readily stir the uninitiated. Many who encounter Swinburne during high school or college assume he speaks for the hot desire of youth, that the fervor of his poetry is a quintessential fervor of Eros. He is often pictured by the unsophisticated as a gallant, vital figure, the sensuous and virile bard of passionate love and physical ardors. Even those who ordinarily reject poetry, having vaguely relegated it to the province of bookish pedants or to the effeminate, sometimes respond to lines from *Dolores* or *The Garden of Proserpine*.[286] During the imperious urges, the inarticulateness, and the confusion of a first love, they may find in Swinburne an intensity that seems to match their wildest aspirations. His brilliantly ringing lines must, they believe, represent a noble pagan vigor, a spirit so strong and vital that it sweeps through ordinary restraints and conventional artificialities. His voice is often taken to be the mighty voice of a lover calling on life to flood and fecundate parched deserts of asceticism and negation, on nature to flower in ultimate fulfillment.

In the vivid urgency to consummate amorous desires which society insists they defer and only dream about for so long, the normal boy and girl may read:

> By the ravenous teeth that have smitten
> Through the kisses that blossom and bud,
> By the lips intertwisted and bitten
> Till the foam has a savour of blood.
> By the pulse as it rises and falters,
> By the hands as they slacken and strain,
> I adjure thee respond from thine altars,
> Our Lady of Pain.*

They often find reflected in this something of the vigor of their natural impulses. Anticipating sexual fulfillments that must be delayed, they normally picture these fulfillments as hot-blooded, wholehearted, and breathtaking. Perhaps such a term as our Lady of Pain is surprising, but, after all, sorrow is often mentioned in connection with love. The heart aches and in separation there is suffering.

They find Swinburne thus speaking of a female figure:

> As of old when the world's heart was lighter,
> Through thy garments the grace of thee glows,
> The white wealth of thy body made whiter
> By the blushes of amorous blows,
> And seamed with sharp lips and fierce fingers,
> And branded by kisses that bruise;
> When all shall be gone that now lingers,
> Oh, what shall we lose?*

Normally oriented young people will probably assume that the poet is referring to sexual ardor. What matters an accidental bruise or abrasion from embraces and caresses exchanged in the joy and vigor of amorous consummation? Ordinary readers may be puzzled when the female is referred to thus:

> Fruits fail and love dies and time ranges;
> Thou art fed with perpetual breath,
> And alive after infinite changes,
> And fresh from the kisses of death;
> Of languors rekindled and rallied,
> Of barren delights and unclean,
> Things monstrous and fruitless, a pallid
> And poisonous queen.*

---

*From Swinburne, A. C.: Dolores. In Selected poems of Algernon Charles Swinburne, New York, 1928, Dodd, Mead & Co., Inc.

Perhaps they are puzzled. But after all, poetry, they remember, is not necessarily literal like a blueprint or like a pamphlet giving instructions about how to repair radios. Their uncertainties are dissolved in the stimulation of

> Thou wert fair in the fearless old fashion,
> And thy limbs are as melodies yet,
> And move to the music of passion
> With lithe and lascivious regret.*

They will probably continue to feel that Swinburne is dealing with the passions they feel even after he says

> I could hurt thee—but pain would delight thee;
> Or caress thee—but love would repel;
> And the lovers whose lips would excite thee
> Are serpents in hell.*

After all, the real speech between lovers is seldom exact. Literally inappropriate words are often risked to convey opposite meanings, perhaps through efforts to register intensity about what cannot be adequately defined or soberly conveyed as a matter of fact.

From what is known of Swinburne's life, it seems unlikely that he could have "loved overmuch." He apparently had little or no interest in normal relations with women. This was so conspicuous that his close friend Rossetti is said to have bribed a particularly enterprising and alluring lady with ten pounds to evoke in him some amorous response. After her best efforts she confessed her failure and returned the money.[250] After repeatedly showing himself unable to avoid disastrous drinking or to handle his ordinary affairs with minimum competency, the poet spent nearly all his adult life living with his bachelor friend and protector Watts-Dunton, who apparently acted as an informal guardian or voluntary lay attendant.[21,250]

The evidence strongly indicates that Swinburne habitually sought bizarre satisfactions and shames in "queer houses" where flagellation was practiced as a substitute for, or a mockery of, biologically oriented sexual relations. Since early in life he pored over the writings of the Marquis de Sade, for whom he is said to have maintained not only a strong affinity but, indeed, hero worship. The poet's writing copiously illustrate his concept of sensual pleasure and of "love" as painful brutality and foul humiliation. It is difficult to find in them, or from what is reported of his life, anything to indicate that

---

*From Swinburne, A. C.: Dolores. In Selected poems of Algernon Charles Swinburne, New York, 1928, Dodd, Mead & Co., Inc.

he enjoyed an appreciable awareness of what women mean to ordinary men, or of human love.[250]

Praz presents strong evidence that in Swinburne's poetry recurrent reflections of a most malignant sadism become at times frankly cannibalistic and that he projects perversion and morbid derogation into the surrounding universe. When Swinburne writes of "the mute melancholy lust of heaven," according to Praz, "heaven merely reflects the mute melancholy lust of the poet himself."*

Depicting what he apparently means to be taken for sexual love, Swinburne is sometimes explicit:

> I would my love could kill thee; I am satiated
> With seeing thee live, and fain would have thee dead.
> I would earth had thy body as fruit to eat,
> And no mouth but some serpent's found thee sweet.
> I would find grievous ways to have thee slain,
> Intense device, and superflux of pain;
> Vex thee with amorous agonies, and shake
> Life at thy lips, and leave it there to ache;
> Strain out thy soul with pangs too soft to kill,
> Intolerable interludes, and infinite ill;
> Relapse and reluctation of the breath,
> Dumb tunes and shuddering semitones of death.†

. . .

> Ah that my lips were tuneless lips, but pressed
> To the bruised blossom of thy scourged white breast!
> Ah that my mouth for Muses' milk were fed
> On the sweet blood thy sweet small wounds had bled!
> That with my tongue I felt them, and could taste
> The faint flakes from thy bosom to the waist!
> That I could drink thy veins as wine, and eat
> Thy breast like honey! that from face to feet
> Thy body were abolished and consumed,
> And in my flesh thy very flesh entombed!†

. . .

> . . . Oh that I
> Durst crush thee out of life with love, and die,
> Die of thy pain and my delight, and be
> Mixed with thy blood and molten into thee!

---

*From Praz, Mario: The romantic agony, London, 1951, Oxford University Press.
†From Swinburne, A. C.: Anactoria. In Selected poems of Algernon Charles Swinburne, New York, 1928, Dodd, Mead & Co., Inc.

Would I not plague thee dying overmuch?
Would I not hurt thee perfectly? not touch
Thy pores of sense with torture, and make bright
Thine eyes with bloodlike tears and grievous light?
Strike pang from pang as note is struck from note,
Catch the sob's middle music in thy throat,
Take thy limbs living, and new-mould with these
A lyre of many faultless agonies?*

It may be that Baudelaire, or that Swinburne, shows sufficient mastery over the rhythms, and the other technicalities of poetry to be correctly classified as a genius. Is it, however, even sane to argue that the basic tastes and judgments expressed or implied on human life should be accepted as superior to those of the ordinary man? Regularly reversing the most axiomatic human orientations, do these not stand as expressions in art of what has been unforgettably illustrated in conduct by such figures as Jack the Ripper, Gilles de Rais, and Neville George Clevely Heath?[17,61,226] Can these tastes and judgments be regarded as anything but obvious manifestations of disease, of disease that is uninviting and malignant?

Praz, in his detailed and serious study, offers impressive evidence of the influence exerted by earlier exponents of the pathologic and perverse on subsequent artists and literary figures of similar inclination. The Marquis de Sade apparently is accepted as a true prophet or seer by Baudelaire and Gautier: these in turn profoundly influence Swinburne, Oscar Wilde, Walter Pater, d'Annunzio, Octave Mirbeau, J. K. Huysmans, Barbey d'Aurevilly, and scores of others.[250]

If we conclude that some men accepted as superior to the common stature of humanity prove, on closer acquaintance with their artistic works, no less than with their lives, to be not great and admirable figures in the ordinary meaning of such terms, how shall we try to explain their continuing recognition as remarkably inspired or enlightened personages? An attempt to answer this question adequately would lead us far afield. One point, however, may be briefly noted.

If there are among those commonly accepted as geniuses some who could be accurately classified as apostles of disease and negation, it is scarcely surprising that they continue to gain disciples. The malignant perversions of the Marquis de Sade are accepted by Baudelaire and Swinburne as a rich gospel of estheticism. The schizoid misogyny of August Strindberg, listed in encyclopedias as Sweden's foremost literary figure, prompts him to hail pub-

---

*From Swinburne, A. C.: Anactoria. In Selected poems of Algernon Charles Swinburne, New York, 1928, Dodd, Mead & Co., Inc.

licly and reverently as a genius the pathetic Viennese youth, Otto Weininger, who expressed a similar schizoid misogyny in fantastic terms shortly before taking his own life.[4] Pathologic reactions expressed in art apparently appeal to persons similarly disordered. Finding the normal premises of human life unacceptable, the ordinary biologic goals invisible or illusory, they seem to welcome the viewpoint of those who in poetry or philosophy reflect a life rejection they share. It is not difficult to see how such viewpoints may appear as manifestations of superior esthetic sensibility, as a special wisdom, to new cults of intellectual defeatists and deviates who gather in succeeding generations.

In a magazine article, "The Cool Cat Era," Helen Lawrenson vividly portrays among certain avant-garde Greenwich Village groups an effeteness and emotional vitiation peculiarly malignant.[182] The "young futility set" she describes apparently regard themselves as advanced intellectually and esthetically by virtue of their extraordinary capacities for achieving boredom.

> They don't dance; they don't flirt; their laughter is a mechanized device infrequently used; and their conversation is of a genre that is utterly forgettable. . . .
> . . . For the great, outstanding quality about this cool-cat generation is its overpowering inertia. Everything is simply too much effort and what's the use, anyway? Down through the ages, the one never-changing mark of youth has been its enthusiasm. This is probably the first generation in history that hasn't got any. That is what strikes you most forcibly when you see its members in the slightly dank bars where they cluster like fungi. You look at them and listen to them— all young and bright enough, with handsome men and pretty girls— and suddenly you realize the incredible, the shocking, the obvious fact. they aren't having any fun! Sex, liquor, dope, perversion they try it all, and it's all so much spinach. This is not youth on a spree, or the classic wild oats of the younger generation. . . .
>
> • • •
>
> . . . Their attitude toward sex is possibly the strangest in the history of youth. By and large, they think it's a lot of bother. In the bars they inhabit, you almost never see a young man panting over a pretty girl, oblivious to all else, straining every nerve to convince her that she's the most beautiful creature he ever saw and that he's madly, rapturously in love with her. That is for squares. What you may see is an attitude of: "Well, sex is a bore. Life is a bore. I don't really feel anything, but you're here and I'm here and we can't think of anything else to do, so let's give it a try."
> Most of the time, they don't even make that much of an effort at courtship. When you hear an apparently healthy young man in his

early twenties say, with a faintly nauseated look, "I had sex last Thursday," in exactly the same tone as if he had said, "I ate some cottage cheese and it didn't agree with me," you begin to realize that something has certainly gone haywire. . . .

. . .

. . . Things have come to a pretty pass when young girls are so bored with men that they prefer dope. But even the please-pass-the-heroin set finds its own routine anything but sheer pleasure. They spend a lot of time screaming, or retching endlessly, until they manage to kill themselves one way or another, and they're cool forever. . . .

. . . These are the archetypes of the "cool cats," the new cult of youngsters whose attitude toward life, toward love, toward themselves is one of frantic apathy. There are probably more of them in the Village than anywhere else, because the Village has always been the unofficial headquarters for rebellious youth. What makes this group different from all its predecessors is that the chief thing it seems to be rebelling against is life itself. . . .

. . .

. . . "It's ugly, Carter, it's all so terrible and useless."
"What is?"
"Everything, Life!"*

Among such groups languidly withdrawn in the name of art or bohemian self-expression from ordinary affairs, it is scarcely remarkable that the bards of pathology and life perversion find disciples in each new generation.

If it is true that some creative artists of great renown show both in their conduct and their work indications of serious personality disorder, how shall we class them? Are some of those established by tradition as high priests of truth, beauty, and inspiration really members of the clinical group we call psychopaths? Although some of their works convey reactions and evaluations as inadequate as those of the typical psychopath and as incompatible with even minimum standards of human feeling and behavior, we should not necessarily identify their disorder with that of the patients presented in this book. Sexual deviation with its inevitable frustrations and reversals of response and masked but profound schizoid disorder formulated in disdainful misanthropy and life perversion seem more likely to account for the tastes and viewpoints revealed by these talented people.

In contrast with them, the typical psychopath does not labor consistently to express in art pathologic reactions or distorted appraisals of life. In words

---

*From Lawrenson, Helen: The cool cat era, Park East, Jan., 1953.

the typical psychopath characteristically gives normal evaluations, defines excellent moral standards, enthusiastically claims the accepted goals and aims of civilized man as his own. He is often an articulate spokesman for the good life. If the sort of patient described here should have sufficient talent and industry to produce works accepted as valuable literature or art, I do not think it likely he would in them try to express nihilistic or perverse attitudes. Whatever he might express would probably be as spurious, as little representative of authentic human experience, as his convincing but empty promises, his eloquent protestations of a love he does not feel. His production, however brilliant technically, would be a valid rendering of neither health nor disease but a counterfeit.

It is possible that behind the psychopath's disorder there once lay extraordinary potentialities. I have seen patients who in critical periods of development seemed to face problems that arose largely from their own precocity, their own distinctly superior qualities. Such patients sometimes seem, it might be said, to have advanced intellectually and in some respects emotionally so far ahead of what is average that they encounter problems and pressures which demand greater general maturity than it has been possible for them to acquire, although their general maturity may well excel the average. Patients in such situations have been observed who, it seemed, were being pushed into various patterns of psychiatric illness, pushed toward clinical psychoneurosis or even toward schizophrenia, by factors brought into play more through the indirect effects of their superiority than by any specific personality deficits.

Although excellent capacity is of value in efforts to work through problems, to avoid dangerous pathologic reactive patterns, it is also, I believe, likely that high magnitudes of emotional and other functional potentiality have something to do with the degree of destructiveness when regressive withdrawals and disintegrative forces set the course. A man of unusual integrity and loyalty is likely to be more severely damaged than a man mediocre in these respects if complicated and confusing situations cause him to make grave errors in his business (or in his decision as an officer during combat) that result in disaster for which he holds himself responsible. Abandonment or betrayal by a fiancé or mate is likely to put stress upon persons in direct proportion to the depth of genuineness with which the other is loved. Persons of great dignity and pride may find it necessary to destroy their own lives under circumstances in which those with a shallower scope of feeling can adjust with only moderate emotional damage.

The possibility that a once great capacity for positive living may have played some part in the development of the psychopath's negative (destructive) patterns is, I believe, worthy of careful consideration. Certainly these patterns are thorough and uncompromising (no halfway measure) and if they do represent something purposive, though consciously involuntary, their effectiveness suggests an invisible purpose of uncommon force. If the psychopath's disorder does arise in some such fashion, it is so subtle and so monumentally effective a job that it is easy to imagine that the potentialities represented here in reverse might deserve the estimate of genius. No real evidence, however, has been presented to support this purely speculative hypothesis.

37

The injudicious hedonist and some other drinkers

Those who devote their lives unduly to sensual pleasure are popularly regarded by more sober and restrained members of society as wicked or depraved. By his fellows who are especially austere the ways of the careless bon vivant are often attacked with thunderous vigor and even, by certain extremists, held as largely responsible for the ills of mankind.

It is well known, of course, that a large number of human beings, during their development, pass through a stage of recklessness in which strong drink and casual lovemaking are snatched at injudiciously. These jejune efforts to drink life to the lees sometimes bring embarrassment or misfortune to young people. Having tried out his wings of independence or of revolt and usually having received a fair number of bumps, jolts, or bruises, the average fledgling learns his way about and ceases to lay aside altogether his judgment and common sense when in pursuit of pleasure.

Ordinary people, young or old, if they contract gonorrhea, become illegitimately pregnant, lose their jobs because of excessive drinking, or suffer some other sharp reverse, observe the sequence of cause and effect and try to adapt themselves so as not to suffer in the same way again. Indeed, even a severe headache or other unpleasant features prominent in the aftermath of late hours and excessive drinking will cause the normal person to avoid waking in the same condition the next day. Sometimes, of course, indiscretion is piled on indiscretion and the bout of dissipation causes prolonged discomfort. The general rule, however, is to learn, even if slowly, by experience.

A significant difference then between the man popularly regarded as a dissipated person and the psychopath is that the former, even though he breaks over into indiscretion from time to time on occasions of excitement, tends to be guided by painful consequences.[298] More important still, the ordinary hard drinker or high liver appears plainly to be motivated by pleasure principles which we can all understand.

What difference will one more drink make? What spoilsport insists on leaving? Words and ideas come to him. The occasion grows more festive and he more sparkling. Perhaps he is putting his best foot forward before some attainable or unattainable lady or merely embracing in good fellowship and understanding some group which he finds, in the general merriment, better able to know and value him. Someone breaks into song, snatches of poetry are quoted, each man gives tongue to his special enthusiasm or his special dislike. There is laughter, merriment, play, the dance. The general effort is toward life, toward a more full and active living.

Sometimes these activities in the relatively make-believe world of synthetic freedom, these pursuits of joy that is often not quite joy itself, make real living, or one's ordinary capacity to live, seem drab or feeble by comparison. Sometimes it seems desirable to shirk the harder, soberer transactions of the day and exist chiefly for the escape into another world which is not quite one's own. In varying degree, depending on how sound is one's integration and how obdurate one's insight, persons profit by experience and limit these indulgences in accordance with the hard and inescapable facts of self and of the objective world.

In the wide range of the accepted normal, various degrees of responsibility, various ethical and esthetic standards, various demands of ambition, and various exigencies of the next day or of the next decade must be reckoned with before one even comes to the question of whether drinking and conduct under the influence of alcoholic drink constitute a psychiatric illness. Even when a person arrives at the point where a definite illness or maladjustment unquestionably exists, many psychopathologic pictures must be considered and discarded before segregating the particular picture which we will, lacking a better name, call the psychopath.

For the Methodist pastor in Paris, Ala., to drink at all would indicate some maladaptation of the man to his way of life. Yet the Anglican vicar in Stoke Poges or the priest in Amalfi may take his port or his Vino Orvieto Bianco Secco without arousing our suspicion. The middle-aged bachelor whose only tasks are to clip coupons and squire admiring dowagers about his gardens may regularly sip whiskey and soda for hours past midnight without invoking the significant consequences which such doings would bring to a surgeon called on for major emergencies several nights a week or to a young and ambitious businessman who must face a hard day's work each morning at 8 o'clock.

Several young doctors of philosophy might gather on Saturday night and hurl loud argumentative words about until dawn, consuming no mean quantities of whiskey while the structure of the hypothalamus, the prose of James Joyce, the sexuality of Sappho, and the ideas of Norbert Wiener or of Arnold Toynbee are discussed, challenged, and defended. A couple of friendly mill workers whose wives are out of town might settle down some evening before a holiday in a barroom and drink through stages of shouting conviviality, loud song, blustering amorousness with prostitutes, to snoring stupefaction. Such activities might be defended as human by some critics, assailed as wicked by others, and interpreted, perhaps, as efforts to escape the routine of the classroom or of home and factory by still others.

Two lovers who cannot for economic or legal reasons have each other freely under the same roof may on every available occasion lie in each other's arms until 3 A.M. in a parked automobile, having sexual intercourse as frequently as their abilities will permit. They may drink enough whiskey to blur recognition of the inevitable morrow, pouring out their feeling and fantasy to each other in a transient delirium of bliss. Each may suffer definite impairment of effectiveness at work, fatigue, headache, nausea, and many other discomforts day after day from deficient sleep and superfluous alcohol. They may be condemned as unconventional, sinful, or foolish by other people of various viewpoints. But their conduct has little in common with that of the psychopath. They feel that the game is worth the candle and they mean to play it.

A man whose desire for his wife has palled may at every party he attends drink too much, sway a little as he goes from group to group, try to make minor overtures to every woman he encounters, and, with the slightest encouragement, attempt seduction. Such a man, most people would perhaps agree, is maladjusted in the sense that he is far from happy in his life situation. His efforts to gain happiness may incur social disapproval of varying degree, be they adroit or ludicrous. Whatever of his other life plans or his ideologies he is ignoring, he is still moved by a fundamentally normal drive, that is, to accomplish sexual relations with a woman who appeals to him.

Another man may successfully avoid drinking to excess but also seek every opportunity to seduce female acquaintances, whether or not they are wives or sisters or sweethearts or daughters of his friends. He may try to induce the lady he seeks to drink to excess and so facilitate his purpose. This man might be called a sorry fellow by some, a fiend by others, or a latent homosexual by still others. Again he might be explained as one whose unconscious sense of inferiority or whose unrecognized sexual immaturity demands compensation for his inadequacy or his regular failure to achieve mature fulfillment with each love object. Still another observer might regard him as a shrewd, cynical person who merely knows how to get what he wants and is above ordinary compunction. In some patients represented by the last example I have observed attitudes, personality mechanisms, and efforts at adjustment which have considerable resemblance to those of the psychopath. In the latter, however, is found a far greater regression, a failure to follow out consistently any aim that could be understood by the normal man, and a general disorganization of the whole life plan. The spite reaction may be fundamental in the complete psychopath, but it is directed less consistently toward bringing about an actual sexual union than in untranslatable activities. It is also less obvious and more deeply concealed, not only from the patient but also from the observer. He may start on his spree with such an objective consciously before him, but he will occasionally pour into himself not stimulating but emetic or soporific doses of alcohol and end by vomiting in the bed or falling limp on the floor long before any other aim is achieved.

There are scores of patterns in which superficially hedonistic behavior can be seen to represent an escape from or a compensatory reaction to some emotional problem that the person has not solved. The man so attached to his mother that his mature sex aims are distorted may over years maintain a reputation for heavy and boisterous drinking, for being a great man about town with the women.

Deep marital unhappiness may lead one or both of a married couple to dull the edge of frustration by drinking regularly to excess or by whooping it up at parties in a relatively vain pursuit of excitement and fulfillment. I have known successful businessmen and professional men who, over the years, have each day consumed astonishing amounts of alcohol. Among these are persons who, sober or under considerable influence, remain reliable, pleasantly sociable, and quite themselves. In such cases it must be granted that the excessive drinking, whatever its value as an anodyne, usually constitutes a problem in itself. It is not uncommon to find persons who continue to make a successful adjustment in general, despite the fact that they drink considerably more than many psychopaths. The distinguishing point is that gross changes from a normal attitude and from normal behavior do not occur and a whole life plan is not demolished.

There are people who may drink regularly to excess to enliven a career that has fallen into boredom or relative idleness but who find a level of intake at which they make an adjustment. Here the drinking is perhaps hit upon to kill time or as a substitute for the diversity and activity lacking in their daily routine. Although persons of this sort may lose control of the situation and become alcoholics in the clinical sense, many continue to maintain themselves without help. Drinking in such cases may be thought of as a handicapping factor but, since there are few responsibilities or vivid interests to demand full activity, the subject remains able to carry on his attenuated career.

Specifically disturbed emotional and social relations may result not only in alcoholism as a distinct illness but also in excessive indulgence over years or decades without progressive loss of control. Persons with varying components of latent homosexuality often find a partial and disguised outlet for their impulses in frequent and injudicious alcoholic sessions with stag groups. Mildly schizoid personalities shut off from close personal contacts and lacking in occupations or preoccupations may solitarily consume alcohol in excess but avoid any spectacular behavior attributable to drink.

Other types who use alcohol as a partial anesthetic include such figures as O'Malley in Donn Byrne's story,[36] who closes his career as a broken man, wandering from tavern to tavern drinking steadily to excess. A brilliant, able, and charming person in his ordinary life, he submits to this transformation when life holds nothing more for him. His love object, whom he lost because of her being driven to an Anglican nunnery by religious or pseudoreligious manifestations, had come to play so important a part in his life that she could not be replaced. Without her it was a relief for him to avoid full awareness, which he did by drink. He is pictured as a man old before his time, shabby, aimless, slightly intoxicated nearly always, and looking forward to nothing particularly except perhaps death. This, too, is drinking unlike drinking to be happy. It is, however, far from the bellowing, vociferous episodes of the lyings-out of the psychopath. In O'Malley's case the cause of his drinking is readily visible, and his choice of a means to an end is not without logic and purpose. There is no effort on O'Malley's part to make himself objectionable to others or to create shocking and fantastic situations. He quietly becomes a drunkard to dull his sorrow and only seeks to be let alone.

The psychopath, then, in my opinion, is something very much more than the ordinarily dissipated or profligate person, even though the latter happens to be extremely injudicious. An important mark of distinction is that the profligate is after what everyone can see is a kind of pleasure or is seeking simple relief from pain we can conceive, whereas the psychopath seldom drives at anything that looks very much like pleasure or necessary analgesia.

Another type of behavior sometimes confused with the psychopath's life pattern might be represented by the fairly common case of the married man, well established in business and fond of his children, who throws away his security and his respectable position to seek love with some trivial woman who cares nothing for him and on whom he soon throws away what he has. It might be said that such a man is rash or even foolish and some may call him depraved. But the appeal which drives him to his folly is one that most normal people have no difficulty in understanding. Love is well known for its power to make even sages give all, and some commitments between man and woman are all but impossible to explain. Such a man gives up all the fruits of his life to fulfill a definite erotic impulse. But the psychopath's impulse is not the result of fatal infatuation, nor is it so well formulated and comprehensible as the desire of a man for a woman's body.

The wrecked career of the psychopath is sometimes used by reformers and prohibitionists who crusade against alcohol and vice in general as an example of what dissipation will do to those who essay the primrose path. Well-meant though such warnings may be, they are based on a premise of doubtful validity. What drives the psychopath on in his career is not in any ordinary sense the love of wine or song or women. Whiskey is sometimes one of his means to an end, and certainly it aids him in his spectacular exploits, but it is not a primary cause in his life scheme. Though many may come to grief in such pursuits, they are scarcely more likely to become psychopaths than they are to become schizophrenics.

> To drift with every passion till my soul
> Is a stringed lute on which all winds can play,
> Is it for this that I have given away
> Mine ancient wisdom and austere control?
>
> . . .
>
> Surely there was a time I might have trod
> The sunlit heights, and from life's dissonance
> Struck one clear chord to reach the ear of God:
> Is that time dead? . . .*

Such drifting with passions may indeed prevent the development of greatness and cheat the drifter of achievement and of deep happiness. There are many ways in which a man can waste his energy, cheapen his emotional

---

*From Wilde, Oscar: Helas. From The ballad of Reading gaol and other poems, New York, Little Leather Library Corp.

powers, and bring about his maladjustment. There are many ways, indeed, by which a man can fall into mental disorders and many types of disorder into which he can fall.[128] Flowers of evil, whether splendid, redolent and darkly glittering, or mediocre, may choke out the blossoms ordinarily considered desirable. But the psychopaths whose stories are offered here do not seem driven wildly and at random by such winds of passion as those referred to in Oscar Wilde's familiar verse, nor is it likely that their souls are played upon like stringed lutes. One may listen indefinitely for the tragico-romantical notes of such a vibration, but he will listen in vain. The winds of passion are blowing almost imperceptibly, if at all, and no strings are in the lute. No vivid *fleurs du mal* will be culled from this garden, for the garden is barren.

38

The clinical alcoholic

The term clinical alcoholic is chosen for convenience to signify the large group of pathologic drinkers who are still making some genuine effort to adjust in normal life but are using drink to escape reality which they cannot quite face and, by a vicious cycle, making themselves steadily more inadequate to face this reality. Such types of maladjustment have been well described by Strecker and Chambers, to whose book the reader is referred.[283]

Such drinkers may, in several respects, be contrasted with the psychopath (sociopath) just as the nonalcoholic neurotic contrasts with the psychotic patient.

Like the psychopath, their drinking is not primarily for pleasure or has at least ceased to afford much pleasure. They often give a strong impression of drinking to avoid sober self-appraisal or some other aspect of reality. With alcohol they can remain a little more comfortably and longer in the false world of fantasy or in analgesia. They are often introverted people, often tender-minded and shy. Alcohol enables them to be less self-conscious and to make their way with greater ease into the social group. They become more and more disabled for real life, and reverses due directly or indirectly to their alcoholism accumulate, making it ever more urgent for them to escape into the numbness of drink.

To a certain point this picture is not unlike that of the psychopath. Perhaps the psychopath sometimes arrives at his life scheme by way of phases almost identical with those of some neurotic drinkers, and perhaps the neurotic drinker may regress to levels at which he can be plainly recognized as a sociopath. Some of the patients described here as partial psychopaths might be placed by some observers in the class of neurotic drinkers.

For the purpose of drawing a useful distinction, however, the following points are offered:

Often the neurotic drinker wants to get well. This may not be obvious, but with proper psychiatric treatment it may be possible to obtain sincere cooperation. Although the neurotic drinker lacks insight and often cannot get well by his unaided efforts, he retains a capability of gaining insight, and good improvement is often possible under treatment. The psychopath's actual conduct when drinking, and sometimes when sober, is bizarre, often shameful and shocking, and actively damaging to himself. In the neurotic drinker such tendencies, if present, are much less pronounced.

The neurotic drinker on his spree is unintentionally destroying his chances for success and happiness, but this does not appear to be his fundamental aim; his fundamental aim apparently is to avoid facing his failures. Although this aim may be present in the established psychopath, it is not easily or regularly discernible. The latter appears to be driving primarily at evading, or ignoring, or destroying life itself, that is to say, life in the sense of social attainments and subjective integration.

Drinkers who can be classed as neurotic show better capacity for insight and may come voluntarily to seek treatment or may be persuaded by relatives to do so. The psychopath will not come voluntarily, except when he seeks hospitalization to avoid legal action, and he cannot be persuaded to carry out sincerely any therapeutic program.

To summarize, then, it may be said that the neurotic drinker is capable of insight and wants to get well. The psychopathologic picture is more readily comprehensible in terms of cause and effect and, under favorable conditions, is perhaps reversible. The psychopath, on the other hand, despite his superficial appearance of being a normal man, shows in his whole behavior pattern deviation and disorder that seem fundamental. His real drives, when one tries to surmise them from his reactions, strike the observer as foreign to ordinary human impulse. The process, if reversible at all, is not ordinarily found to be so. Apparently there is no latent insight that can be aroused or sincere desire to become well or, rather, to become like other men. I do not mean to state dogmatically that the psychopath's illness is irreversible but merely that in my own experience it has, in typical cases, proved to be so. It may be said that the process of schizophrenia as compared with hysteria is relatively less reversible, that it ordinarily brings about a greater and deeper disintegration of the personality. Despite this fact, schizophrenics often recover. Perhaps the psychopath, too, can recover.

Perhaps some generally satisfactory means of treating him can eventually be devised.

Taking the group of chronic alcoholics as a whole, we are likely to find here people in whom the excessive drinking is a common symptom of underlying disorders that vary widely in type and in degree somewhat as we might say that fever may arise from a bad cold, measles, pneumonia, tuberculosis, meningitis, and other differing illnesses too numerous to list.

Alcoholics Anonymous,[7] whose excellent work it is appropriate to mention here, has, in my experience with this group as a whole, appeared to be one of the most valuable therapeutic agencies available. Many gravely maladjusted patients in whom alcoholism was at the same time a disabling symptom and a secondary but major causal agent in disastrous life patterns have, through this agency and its program, made changes and progress that with no exaggeration can be called remarkable. Some patients whose behavior and emotional attitudes definitely suggested the psychopath's disorder have to my knowledge not only avoided for years the disabling effects of their former drunkenness but also other unrewarding and antisocial activities. Whether or not these were psychopaths in the full and deepest sense is not a question that can be answered confidently.

It is my belief that this type of disorder, like all other psychiatric disorders, may be seen in almost limitless variations of degree and severity. We see the utterly disorganized schizophrenic who has for twenty years been on the worst ward of a state hospital, and we also see schizoid reactions and limitations that persist for decades in people who continue to be self-supporting and to a considerable degree socially competent. I recall one patient who has expressed to me delusions typical of full-blown schizophrenia over some years and who is still an able worker with many pleasant social relations and recreational activities. Many more come to mind whose delusions are less extreme but who for decades have manifested autistic withdrawal, oddities, emotional distortions, and impairments consistent only with a schizoid reaction.

We also see manifestations identical with those of full-blown schizophrenia in every respect except their transiency. A 30-year-old man who, after taking a small dose of testosterone, experienced not only hallucinatory sexual and spiritual sensations within himself but also in others will serve as an excellent example. Vivid delusions were very prominent for approximately a week. These included an absolute conviction that all virtuous women at the mere sight of him caught the impact of magic, glowed with a fire both erotic and holy, and were visibly transformed. It was also his belief that this caused harlots who might sense his powers a block off to run up alleyways in shame. For several days, through false perceptions, he specifically "felt" men and women some miles away responding viscerally, intellectually, and spiritually, and in diverse ways, to what had miraculously become incarnate in his person. After being psychotic for a week and without specific treatment, he regained insight, lost his schizophrenic symptoms, and has for a number of years remained entirely free of them.

In the other disorder, that of the psychopath, I believe there also occur similar variations in chronicity, in severity, in completeness, in depth, and in every other respect. Although malignancy and irreversibility seem typical of the psychopathology as we meet it clinically in its advanced or long-fixed forms, outwardly similar behavioral and characterologic patterns sometimes prove reversible. Few, if any, features of the full psychopath are more impressive than his inability to respond with consistent acts or in other ways that would indicate deep or genuine desire to change his situation. In therapeutic programs it is characteristic of him not to make valid or persistent efforts to cooperate. In their relations with Alcoholics Anonymous, psychopaths sometimes show at first what seems extraordinary zeal, sincerity, and promise, only to reveal after varying intervals that the whole matter was only a sort of prank or lightly taken adventure in versatile careers of self-ruin.

Fundamental points in the Alcoholics Anonymous system of group therapy and self-reorganization are the following:

1. The need for a most profound intention (an authentic and major desire) to overcome one's disability
2. The necessity for extensive and basic changes in attitude and orientation at the core of the personality

At both of these points we find in the full psychopath an almost uniquely unfavorable situation. Although I know of nothing available today that can be counted on to succeed regularly, the evidence has suggested that Alcoholics Anonymous may in some cases affect favorably latent resources very difficult to reach by most methods in patients showing reactions that may have something in common with those of the typical psychopath.

39

The malingerer

The malingerer, so far as his relation to the psychopath is concerned, may be dismissed with a few words. Many psychopaths malinger at times. They seldom malinger consistently over long periods toward a constant aim. The malingerer pure and simple sticks to his purpose and, on gaining his objective, uses it in some fairly human way. Malingering is merely an incident in the psychopath's versatile career. Even if he should succeed in obtaining a large fortune by efforts at malingering, he will not be able to use it consistently or to keep out of subsequent difficulty. No life of ease and riches could tempt him from his well-known ways.

Perhaps the chief occasions for malingering by psychopaths arise when they fail to escape the consequences of antisocial deeds. Faced by the prospect of confinement in prison or other unwelcome measures, they feel it would be well to simulate some other mental disorder that will get them to a hospital instead. Any psychopath of much experience in this field is entirely aware of the fact that he will soon be recognized at the psychiatric institution, correctly diagnosed, and, under prevailing conditions, dismissed without much delay. If circumstances are unusual and the hospital, in recognition of the patient's thoroughly demonstrated disability, attempts a practical solution by keeping him under supervision and care, he can nearly always take legal steps to effect his release and return to the community and to his old disquieting activities.

Theoretically this should not occur, since it would seem logical and according to law for the psychopath, on being pronounced competent and free of mental disability, to fall again under ordinary legal restraints. In fact, this is not what usually occurs. Often the specific charges against the patient are relatively minor, and during the feint whereby he is hospitalized some adjustment is made so that he is brought back into the community entirely free from any restraining influence.[158]

40

Fictional characters of psychiatric interest

Characters from literature, it may be argued, not being real people, are therefore of no value in the discussion of a medical problem. It can scarcely be doubted, however, that genuinely creative writers have often presented personalities more fully and more truly than we can readily get to know them in life. And sometimes minor writers succeed in portraying personalities that seem to be reliably true. The characters of the novelist and the dramatist are, furthermore, accessible to all who care to read about them, unlike the patient who has been seen and studied but cannot be presented personally to the reader. For the purpose of this discussion I feel that several points can be made by citing fictional characters, some of whom I believe have been no less faithfully drawn than patients reported in psychiatric examinations. Whether real people exist like them or not is beside the point, since I do not mean to use them as evidence to establish any conceptions of psychopathology but to illustrate personality reactions, whether real or imaginary, which I shall attempt to relate to the reactions considered in this volume.

Those who spend their lives in serious effort to put down in various forms a reflection of their human experience must sometimes encounter the psychopath or at least fragments of such behavior, hints of such an attitude.

Abstruse and complex psychopathologic features of many types have for centuries emerged in literary creations and seem to emerge sometimes through an inexplicable insight of the poet, novelist, or dramatist, who, by his special talent, may successfully convey what he has accurately sensed in the life about him. What he senses may not be discernible to many and it may be most difficult to convey by the direct textbook methods. The possibility of help from this source in efforts to gain understanding of the by no means simple riddle of the sociopath is a possibility that should not be rejected.

Certain personalities have been described and perhaps exist in actual life, who, unlike the ordinary criminal, seem to live by hate and cherish destructiveness not so much to gain power or material benefits but because they grow to love hate and destructiveness. The character Heathcliffe as presented in *Wuthering Heights*[30] might be chosen as a puzzling example of misanthropy, ruthlessness, and maladjustment which has little in common with ordinary viciousness. Heathcliffe works to destroy others and to destroy what is generally regarded as happiness for himself as well. He unquestionably falls within the scope of psychopathology, a strange, terrible, and compelling figure. But he has little specific kinship with the personalities discussed here. He is strong, he is persistent, and his emotion, however distorted, appears greater by far than that of the average man. He never loses his imposing dignity, even though this dignity might be regarded as a dignity of evil. He remains integrated, not only superficially but profoundly. The personalities described in this book, in contrast, show no consistent pursuit of what might be called evil; their exploits are fitful, buffoonish, and unsustained by any obvious purpose. Consistent hatred of others is not a guiding line in their life scheme. And in Heathcliffe we find evidence of more than ordinary love for Kathy, of love that appears to be genuine and changeless despite the fact that it is a major factor behind his destructiveness.

It is not common to find in literature characters that could be grouped with the patients studied here. Creative artists have often presented the villain, the psychotic, the psychoneurotic, the erratic genius, the weak, the strong, the wise, and the stupid; but we seldom find in imaginative writing anyone who could fit the picture that emerges as we consider the histories in this book. Often, however, we find characters who in some aspect or in some phase of their activities suggest what we have seen in the psychopath, and we find others no less abnormal whose qualities may be used in contrast.

Iago,[25,78,264] perhaps the most interesting and ingenious creation of vindictiveness known to man, carries out his schemes of hate and treachery without adequate motivation in the ordinary sense. In *King Lear* the cruelty of Edmund,[265] bastard son of Gloucester, is plainly pathologic. Herr Naphta[201] in *The Magic Mountain,* although a professional Christian in holy orders, is addicted to destructiveness despite his great intellectual powers. All these characters are consistent, effective, and despite their interesting psychiatric aspects, remote from the psychopath.

Mr. Micawber[70] and Tolstoi's Stepan Arkadyevitch Oblonsky[291] are convincing examples of people who do not seem to learn by experience and who cannot, in important matters, be relied on by others. But neither shows the active pattern of self-defeat with which we are familiar. Both seem to represent ordinary human frailties that are much exaggerated. Falstaff indulges in outlandish excesses with sack, falls into humiliating situations repeatedly without evincing ordinary shame, and shows himself callous to the appeal of dignity and honor. Yet we sense in him a strong tide of normal, even if superficial, life, some Rabelaisian gusto, which makes his follies stand out in sharp contrast to the activities of the psychopath. He is bent on animal pleasure and coarse merriment whatever they may cost. We can understand him whether we should like to emulate him or not.[266]

Mr. Burlap in Aldous Huxley's *Point Counter Point*[144] is presented as a pious lecher, a literary windbag, and a hypocritical opportunist. He impresses the average reader as a most unpleasant personality, and he is portrayed as lacking many of the emotional capacities which the psychopath also lacks. His opportunism works to his material advantage, and he is steady in his aims and in his progress. However inconsistent or hypocritical his affect, it seems more real than what we see in the psychopath. In the same novel we find in Maurice Spandrell a man who seems to love cruelty and to love it best in its most unpleasant forms. Despite his inexcusable practices we feel in him extraordinary emotional richness and a peculiar but impressive latent integrity which are in contrast to the cold-bloodedness and viciousness appearing in his outer life. It is plain that a personality disorder exists, but it is not the type of disorder with which we are here concerned.

Dostoevsky's Prince Myshkin in *The Idiot,*[76] a person of great wisdom and spiritual insight, yet eccentric and in some ways inadequate, might be called a psychopath by writers who use this term for maladjusted or uneven geniuses. He is, however, a person who feels more profoundly than the ordinary man the very aspects of life to which our patients are numb.

In the figure of Zuleika Dobson, Max Beerbohm gives an impression not so much of indicating a personality, even in caricature, as of lightly embodying his fantasy. This wraithlike figment is used to suggest a carelessness about the fate of others, a preoccupation with trivialties, an absolute and mysterious incapacity for serious emotion that, in a way both outlandish and whimsical, echoes something of the psychopath. She nevertheless succeeds consistently in her aims.[18]

Peer Gynt,[148] although he, too, belongs perhaps in Elfland and very little in the ordinary world, shows a capacity for spiritual failure, an almost perverse unreliability, and an insouciance in self-frustration that suggests a translation of our problem, or some aspect of it, into poetry.

The children presented by Richard Hughes in *A High Wind In Jamaica*[140] and those very different children Henry James gives us in *The Turn of the Screw*[151] suggest an incapacity for normal feeling, an unalterable, subtle, and sinister resistance to human approach that might be compared to the callousness of the psychopath. Both authors seem to be more concerned with general aspects of life or of evil, however, than with a personality disorder.

Ferenc Molnar's Liliom,[229] an altogether astonishing character to the average reader or theater-goer, fails all who trust him and fails himself with the prodigious consistency of a real psychopath. His final manifestation of the old inadequacy, even after being brought back from the dead to earth, really suggests that the dramatist may have had in mind something like the psychopath as we know him. His power to arouse inalienable devotion in women is also as impressive as what we see in real patients. Liliom's suicide, his capacity to admit his misdeeds with what impresses one as a measure of sincerity, his warmth, and his depicted strength and fearlessness all stand out in contrast, however, to the personality patterns discussed in this book.

In Proust's *Remembrance of Things Past,* the Baron de Charlus,[252] a masterpiece of psychopathology no less than of literary creation, would of course be classed as a psychopath in the broad and orthodox meaning of the term. This most imposing and vivid character shows not only homosexuality but a taste for flagellation and other deviations of the sexual impulse, and he shows them as they can seldom be appreciated from the reading of textbooks. There is much about Charlus to suggest that he also shares in some measure the special disorder that we treat here. He seems to care little for the rights of others or for their suffering. He is found repeatedly in fantastic and shameful situations. Much of his abnormal behavior becomes more comprehensible, however, once we grant the authenticity of his abnormal sexual cravings. There are indications of a real learning and a more nearly sincere culture than in the personalities we describe here. A paradoxical and fragmentary but not totally false dignity in his living contrasts with the psychopath's great lack in this respect.

Charlus might justifiably be classed as a partial psychopath, at least. As in some psychopaths seen clinically, he has specific sex deviations which are basic (as contrasted with incidental careless acts of perversion) and which readily account for much of his folly. This figure is depicted as surpassingly haughty in cultural and social aloofness, as a superesthete who aggressively represents almost an apotheosis of the secondary defensive reactions pointed out as typical of the real homosexual by Greenspan and Campbell.[108]

Such a figure as Jondrette (or Thénardier) of *Les Miserables*[141] shows petty opportunism, little ability to profit by mistakes, an extreme degree of selfishness, and a talent for failure. Although these are superficially suggestive of the psychopath, I believe that Jondrette and others like him are conceived as rascals with a better organized antisocial revolt than what is seen in the psychopath. Svidrigailov in *Crime and Punishment*[73] is more strange than Jondrette and appears for a time entirely callous to such feelings as pity or pride. He finally shows a magnanimity that distinguishes him from our subject.[74]

Many female characters have been presented by novelists and dramatists as astonishingly faithless and astonishingly deficient in the stronger, richer emotions. In some of these the spiritual limitation appears to be absolute and unchangeable. Nina Leeds[236] of Eugene O'Neill's *Strange Interlude* was regarded by some critics as shameless, immoral, and self-seeking to an extreme degree. The still celebrated Scarlett O'Hara in *Gone With the Wind*,[228] in some contrast to Nina, fails regularly to respond to sincere emotion in her lovers and pursues above all else aims that are fundamentally egocentric and trivial. Nina Leeds, however, seems capable of real feeling toward her first lover, and her reactions after his death, all of which are based on strong emotional drives, can be understood without assuming the same type of disorder postulated in the psychopath. In fact, she shows very little in common with such a disorder.

Scarlett O'Hara, in my opinion, is a very convincing figure and really shows some of the emotional impoverishment described here in the patients presented as partial psychopaths. Her incapacity for a true commitment in love is apparently unmodifiable; her egocentricity is basic. She seems to be without means of understanding the strong emotions in those about her or of having adequate awareness of what makes them act when they act in accordance with principles they value. Unlike the complete psychopath, she successfully pursues ends that lead to her material well-being and she avoids putting herself in positions of obvious folly and shame. In her, however, we sense an inward hollowness and a serious lack of insight.

An interesting feature of *Gone With the Wind* and one that illuminates an important distinguishing characteristic of the psychopath can be found in a comparison between Scarlett O'Hara and Captain Rhett Butler. Although the captain's conduct is often at variance with most ethical standards, although he evades joining wholeheartedly in the war effort and even seeks to gain personal profit through complications of the war, he can hardly fail to give readers the impression of a man warmly and deeply human. If his objective misdemeanors and other bits of wrongdoing are added up and balanced against Scarlett's actions in the book, it is possible that his score would be technically worse and that he would be more liable to legal action and social censure.

Scarlett, as a matter of fact, is kind in the shallower ranges of feeling, rather consistently considerate about all matters except the most vital. The real contrast becomes clear when fundamental personal issues are at stake. Here Captain Butler's nuclear integrity and his valid reactions of love and compassion are communicated not so much by narration and exposition or by what he directly says as in small reflections of his essential personality that cumulatively reveal him.

It might be argued that of the two, Scarlett, as depicted in the novel, is on the whole a more conforming person, one who can better avoid conduct which will bring about social retaliation. Without attempting a judgment based on ethical absolutes, which is not the province of this book, a significant contrast can be shown between what appears to be the inmost core of each. As indicated already, the fictional Scarlett O'Hara would be a poor representative of the clinical psychopath, but limitations in her personality so effectively brought out in the novel seem closely related in quality to the more disabling deficit that I believe is fundamental in the enigmatic disorder.

Anyone concerned at all with psychiatry is likely to find in Jenny Hagar Poster Evered of *The Strange Woman* (Ben Ames Williams)[306] detail and concreteness familiar in the direct study of patients but hard to put into medical histories. In that she does not respect the rights of others and particularly in that she reacts in anything but a normal way in the deepest personal relations, Jenny might be proclaimed a psychopath whose deviation is extraordinarily complete. Sharply distinguishing points emerge when we consider the persistent purposiveness, the strong and sustained malice with which this woman works to destroy all happiness for children, husbands, and paramours. A conscious brutality prevails. Destructive impulses are directed by open hate.

In contrast with this picture of a well-organized paranoid life scheme we find the typical psychopath not consistently seeking to inflict major disaster on anyone. More characteristic is the psychopath's pettiness and transiency of affect (both positive and negative) and his failure to follow a long-range plan, either for good or for evil. The emotional damage he may (and often does) inflict on mate, parents, children, etc., is not, it seems, inflicted for any major voluntary purpose or from a well-focused motive but from what weighs in at little more than whim or caprice. He does not seem to intend much harm. In the disaster he brings about he cannot estimate the affective reactions of others which are the substance of the disaster. A race of men congenitally without pain sense would not find it easy to estimate the effects of physical torture on others. A man who had never understood visual experience would lack appreciation of what is sustained when the ordinary person loses his eyes.

In contrast to anything of this sort, Jenny shows a rather accurate awareness of how it is going to hurt as she skillfully, and in response to consistent impulse, pursues her plans. All this is very typical of severe paranoid reactions seen clinically. Jenny is also depicted as having components of overt sadomasochistic deviation. Elements of callousness (from incomplete comprehension) are probably necessary for such reactions. Followed far enough inside the surface of action and consciousness, such callousness might be found based on similar pathology to that which constitutes the psychopath's basic incompleteness. As clinical pictures, nevertheless, there is more to contrast than to identify the two life schemes.

To illustrate a feature of what I shall subsequently try to formulate as the psychopath's real underlying condition, the remarkable character of Adrian Harley in George Meredith's *The Ordeal of Richard Feveral*[218] offers an excellent example. This "wise young man" makes a very successful and comfortable adjustment to life in its exterior aspect. He is, of course, no psychopath in the full sense as this disorder is described here. He is a most shrewd, urbane, and learned person. His learning is, furthermore, in the humanities. Yet his incapacity to feel the actual living, the tragedy and joy that are so real to Richard and to Lucy Desborough, is absolute. He does not apparently intend to be cruel but, because of a particular blindness, his shrewdness is used consistently to bring about disaster. He is entirely without insight and remains unable to see that he has seriously damaged others. No schizophrenic could be less cognizant of what existence means to Richard and Lucy than Adrian Harley as he stands with them on a terrace in the Isle of Wight chanting Greek hexameters into the sunset.[219] If we consider such an emotional limitation as that seen in Scarlett O'Hara or in Adrian Harley as similar to what is seen in the psychopath, we must admit that many persons regarded as normal show less marked limitations of the same sort. This, I believe, is entirely true, just as many ordinary persons are slightly schizoid or slightly cyclothymic.

In literature of this century such characters as Jeeter Lester of *Tobacco Road* (Erskine Caldwell)[37] and Pop-Eye (*Sanctuary,* by William Faulkner)[87] deserve brief consideration. The first of these seems to learn little indeed by experience. He is callous to many situations involving himself and others that the ordinary man could scarcely bear. Jeeter Lester impresses me, however, as very little akin to the psychopath. His shiftlessness and resignation are entirely passive. He is to some extent a natural victim of his surroundings. He shows no active drive toward such folly and failure as lure the psychopath, but merely an aimless drifting. He is somehow warm with humanity.

The other figure, Pop-Eye, is depicted as a malign and vindictive man who pursues criminal aims successfully though somewhat peculiarly. His delight in watching the girl he has chosen for himself ravished by another man is extraordinary in the annals of orthodox criminal taste but is comprehensible in terms of voyeurism and masochism and especially in view of his own sexual impotence. An incompletely overt homosexuality is perhaps even more strongly contributory to this choice of role. Although there are features in common, he does not belong among the personalities discussed here.

In Don Birnam, hero of *The Lost Week-End* (Charles Jackson),[150] we find a psychiatric presentation of remarkable force. Beneath the surface of alcoholic addiction, very complicated and subtly distorted causal factors reveal themselves. Eventually a picture emerges in which important features of the psychopath are discernible. There are also contrasts. In Birnam awareness of major frustration is more clear, and anxiety and despair are not successfully avoided. What has happened and is still happening is bizarre and terrifying to the subject since he retains some important degree of insight. When measured against the typical psychopath, this rather remarkable fictional creation suggests another comparison.

Several times recently, patients in early, incomplete schizophrenic reactions have impressed me with varying degrees of ability to see or sense the strangeness and gravity of the processes operant within themselves. In sharp contrast to the ordinary patient with schizophrenia, in whom unawareness and indifference characterize the subject's attitude to all that is so obviously grotesque or tragic to the observer, these patients reacted to some degree as if with the fear, bewilderment, and horror that might be expected in one who recognizes such changes as occurring within himself. Many schizophrenics may show anxiety, alarm, and other strong affective reactions toward other matters, particularly toward delusional projections. This very different atypical residue of insight struck me not only as a remarkable feature but as one affording the observer an unusual viewpoint—the viewpoint of seeing, to some degree, this indescribable process through the eyes of the subject. Ordinarily the disintegration in schizophrenia is such, in specific quality whatever the degree, that the patient does not see the changes in himself with sufficient accuracy to react to them vividly or with anything like the emotional responses of an ordinary person.

In Don Birnam a good many things are revealed as within or near his own comprehension which suggest what may lie beneath the reactive patterns of the psychopath but, if there, are so far beneath that the typical psychopath is unaware of them and indifferent. The observer also has peculiar difficulty in gaining direct access to what may be beneath the surface. Although it may not be accurate to give the unqualified diagnosis to this marvelously interesting fictional patient, it is undeniable that he shows, very convincingly, important features of the sociopath.

A literary creation who impresses me as remarkably like a psychopath in the full sense is Dostoevsky's senior Karamazov,[75] father of the wonderful and puzzling brothers who themselves offer so much of interest to the psychiatrist. The elder Karamazov is not only free from major human feelings, but he also drives actively at folly. He shows a greedy relish for the very sort of buffoonery and high jinks that the psychopath seeks. He has no regard apparently for consequences and cannot be persuaded by reason or appealed to by sentiment. He appears superficially to be a man of strong passions, but in my opinion this is only an appearance. He does not pursue selfish or vicious ways consistently in the aim of self-interest. He immerses himself in indignity for its own sake. He does outrageous things, especially to his son Dimitri, yet he is not adequately motivated by consistently vindictive or cruel impulses.

The personality and behavior of Mildred as she appears in *Of Human Bondage* (Somerset Maugham)[209] also have features that are difficult to reconcile with anything except this disorder, and this disorder in a serious degree. To petty, affective promptings this girl responds appropriately as a rule. All the stimuli that in the normal person evoke serious and lasting responses she perceives little more than a blind man perceives the sunset. Her positive responses to the trivial, the cheap, and the vulgar are understandable in view of the affective limitations so memorably revealed. It is not through savage and violent impulses that she mangles or destroys, but because only mild affect is necessary for action when the larger emotional consequences are invisible. They are invisible not through lack of rational foresight but through specific and more profound defects of evaluation. It is not at all necessary to assume genuine cruelty of any magnitude in Mildred as she reviles the man who has so convincingly demonstrated love for her and whom she wounds as only he could be wounded by the final epithet—*cripple*. So far as she can tell, she is doing little more than what anybody might do if moderately irked.

Like the full psychopath, Mildred cannot continue to provide successfully for her material needs. Unlike what is typical, she does not appear to be especially clever or to have great superficial charm and promise. Nevertheless, she illustrates, perhaps even more accurately than Karamazov the father, what seems to be most fundamental in our subject.

I have seldom seen in fiction so complete and so faithful a portrayal of the psychopath as in the character Rags in *The Story of Mrs. Murphy* (Natalie Anderson Scott).[263] No attempt is made to explain why this man behaves as he does. But he is revealed, not by efforts at description and exposition, but with rare fidelity in the concrete rendering of his behavior. The author of this book understands something fundamental about the true psychopath that often is notably lacking in textbook accounts. This is communicated in a form singularly impressive and worthy of careful study.

One would not ordinarily expect to find among the comic cartoon strips of the daily newspapers enlightening information about psychiatric disorder. Nevertheless, in the widely published strip "Judge Parker," an excellent presentation of the psychopath has been made to the public in the unforgettable character Sandra Deare. It is remarkable that so accurate and informative a treatment of such a problem could be given in this medium. This can be better understood when it is known that the creator of "Judge Parker" is a psychiatrist, Dr. Nicolas Dallis,[297] who uses a pseudonym to indicate his authorship. I believe that this serious and wonderfully effective portrayal of the psychopath has served an important purpose in conveying to the public valuable knowledge about the psychopath's peculiar status and perplexing problems.

In many respects the most realistic and successful of all portrayals of the psychopath is that presented by Mary Astor[14] in *The Incredible Charlie Carewe*. The rendition is so effective that even those unfamiliar with the psychopath in actual experience are likely to sense the reality of what is disclosed. The subject is superbly dealt with, and the book constitutes a faithful and arresting study of a puzzling and infinitely complex subject. Charlie Carewe emerges as an exquisite example of the psychopath—the best, I believe, to be found in any work of fiction.

The Incredible Charlie Carewe should be read not only by every psychiatrist but also by every physician. It will hold the attention of all intelligent readers, and I believe it will be of great value in helping the families of psychopaths to gain insight into the nature of the tragic problem with which they are dealing, usually in blindness and confusion.

41

Synopsis and orientation

In an earlier chapter it was noted that an attempt would be made to follow the general methods of science. Let us stop for a moment to orient ourselves. In Section two some examples of the material were offered and certain observations recorded. In the preceding parts of this section an effort was made to consider traditional concepts of the problem and to differentiate broadly the subject of this study from certain other personality reactions. These may be regarded as preliminary steps in the process of sifting and arranging our observations into some sort of order for the purpose of giving them, as much as possible, distinct and comprehensible form. To take another step in this process, let us now attempt to put down in more concise statement the general facts of behavior and appearances of emotion and purpose which emerge from our recorded observations and which appear to be common qualities of the group in question.

Before going on to the perhaps still unanswerable questions of why the psychopath behaves as he does or of how he comes to follow such a life scheme, let us, as was just suggested, attempt to say what the psychopath is in terms of his actions and his apparent intentions, so that we may recognize him readily and distinguish him from others.

We shall list the characteristic points that have emerged and then discuss them in order:

1. Superficial charm and good "intelligence"
2. Absence of delusions and other signs of irrational thinking

3. Absence of "nervousness" or psychoneurotic manifestations
4. Unreliability
5. Untruthfulness and insincerity
6. Lack of remorse or shame
7. Inadequately motivated antisocial behavior
8. Poor judgment and failure to learn by experience
9. Pathologic egocentricity and incapacity for love
10. General poverty in major affective reactions
11. Specific loss of insight
12. Unresponsiveness in general interpersonal relations
13. Fantastic and uninviting behavior with drink and sometimes without
14. Suicide rarely carried out
15. Sex life impersonal, trivial, and poorly integrated
16. Failure to follow any life plan

42

Superficial charm and good "intelligence"

More often than not, the typical psychopath will seem particularly agreeable and make a distinctly positive impression when he is first encountered. Alert and friendly in his attitude, he is easy to talk with and seems to have a good many genuine interests. There is nothing at all odd or queer about him, and in every respect he tends to embody the concept of a well-adjusted, happy person. Nor does he, on the other hand, seem to be artificially exerting himself like one who is covering up or who wants to sell you a bill of goods. He would seldom be confused with the professional backslapper or someone who is trying to ingratiate himself for a concealed purpose. Signs of affectation or excessive affability are not characteristic. He looks like the real thing.

Very often indications of good sense and sound reasoning will emerge and one is likely to feel soon after meeting him that this normal and pleasant person is also one with high abilities. Psychometric tests also very frequently show him of superior intelligence. More than the average person, he is likely to seem free from social or emotional impediments, from the minor distortions, peculiarities, and awkwardnesses so common even among the successful. Such superficial characteristics are not universal in this group but they are very common.

Here the typical psychopath contrasts sharply with the schizoid personality or the patient with masked or latent schizophrenia. No matter how free from delusions and other overt signs of psychosis the schizoid person may be, he is likely to show specific peculiarities in his outer aspect. Usually there are signs of tension, withdrawal, and subtle oddities of manner and reaction. These may appear to be indications of unrevealed brilliance, perhaps even eccentricities of genius, but they are likely to complicate and cool easy social relations and to promote restraint. Although the psychopath's inner emotional deviations and deficiencies may be comparable with the inner status of the masked schizophrenic, he outwardly shows nothing brittle or strange. Everything about him is likely to suggest desirable and superior human qualities, a robust mental health.

43

Absence of delusions and other signs of irrational thinking

The so-called psychopath is ordinarily free from signs or symptoms traditionally regarded as evidence of a psychosis. He does not hear voices. Genuine delusions cannot be demonstrated. There is no valid depression, consistent pathologic elevation of mood, or irresistible pressure of activity. Outer perceptual reality is accurately recognized; social values and generally accredited personal standards are accepted verbally. Excellent logical reasoning is maintained and, in theory, the patient can forsee the consequences of injudicious or antisocial acts, outline acceptable or admirable plans of life, and ably criticize in words his former mistakes. The results of direct psychiatric examination disclose nothing pathologic—nothing that would indicate incompetency or that would arouse suspicion that such a man could not lead a successful and happy life.

Not only is the psychopath rational and his thinking free of delusions, but he also appears to react with normal emotions. His ambitions are discussed with what appears to be healthy enthusiasm. His convictions impress even the skeptical observer as firm and binding. He seems to respond with adequate feelings to another's interest in him and, as he discusses his wife, his children, or his parents, he is likely to be judged a man of warm human responses, capable of full devotion and loyalty.

44

Absence of "nervousness" or psychoneurotic manifestations

There are usually no symptoms to suggest a psychoneurosis in the clinical sense. In fact, the psychopath is nearly always free from minor reactions popularly regarded as "neurotic" or as constituting "nervousness." The chief criteria whereby a diagnosis of hysteria, obsessive-compulsive disorder, anxiety state, "neurasthenia," etc., might be made do not apply to him. It is highly typical for him not only to escape the abnormal anxiety and tension fundamentally characteristic of this whole diagnostic group but also to show a relative immunity from such anxiety and worry as might be judged normal or appropriate in disturbing situations. Regularly we find in him extraordinary poise rather than jitteriness or worry, a smooth sense of physical well-being instead of uneasy preoccupation with bodily functions. Even under concrete circumstances that would for the ordinary person cause embarrassment, confusion, acute insecurity, or visible agitation, his relative serenity is likely to be noteworthy.

It is true he may become vexed and restless when held in jails or psychiatric hospitals. This impatience seems related to his inability to realize the need or justification for his being restrained. What tension or uneasiness of this sort he may show seems provoked entirely by external circumstances, never by feelings of guilt, remorse, or intrapersonal insecurity. Within himself he appears almost as incapable of anxiety as of profound remorse.

45

Unreliability

Although the psychopath is likely to give an early impression of being a thoroughly reliable person, it will soon be found that on many occasions he shows no sense of responsibility whatsoever. No matter how binding the obligation, how urgent the circumstances, or how important the matter, this holds true. Furthermore, the question of whether or not he is to be confronted with his failure or his disloyalty and called to account for it appears to have little effect on his attitude.

If such failures occurred uniformly and immediately, others would soon learn not to rely upon psychopaths or to be surprised at their conduct. It is, however, characteristic for them during some periods to show up regularly at work, to meet their financial obligations, to ignore an opportunity to steal. They may apply their excellent abilities in business or in study for a week, for months, or even for a year or more and thereby gain potential security, win a scholarship, be acclaimed top salesman or elected president of a social club or perhaps of a school honor society. Not all checks given by psychopaths bounce; not all promises are uniformly ignored. They do not necessarily land in jail every day (or every month) or seek to cheat someone else during every transaction. If so, it would be much simpler to deal with them. This transiently (but often convincingly) demonstrated ability to succeed in business and in all objective affairs makes failures more disturbing to those about them.

Furthermore, it cannot be predicted how long effective and socially acceptable conduct will prevail or precisely when (or in what manner) dishonest, outlandish, or disastrously irresponsible acts or failures to act will occur. These seem to have little or no relation to objective stress, to cyclic periods, or to major alterations of mood or outlook. What is at stake for the patient, for his family, or for anybody else is not a regularly determining factor. At the crest of success in his work he may forge a small check, indulge in petty thievery, or simply not come to the office. After a period of gracious and apparently happy relations with his family he may pick a quarrel with his wife, cuff her up a bit, drive her from the house, and then throw a glass of iced tea in the face of his 3-year-old son. For the initiation of such outbursts he does not, it seems, need any great anger. Moderate vexation usually suffices.

The psychopath's unreliability and his disregard for obligations and for consequences are manifested in both trivial and serious matters, are masked by demonstrations of conforming behavior, and cannot be accounted for by ordinary motives or incentives. Although it can be confidently predicted that his failures and disloyalties will continue, it is impossible to time them and to take satisfactory precautions against their effect. Here, it might be said, is not even a consistency in inconsistency but an inconsistency in inconsistency.

46

Untruthfulness and insincerity

The psychopath shows a remarkable disregard for truth and is to be trusted no more in his accounts of the past than in his promises for the future or his statement of present intentions. He gives the impression that he is incapable of ever attaining realistic comprehension of an attitude in other people which causes them to value truth and cherish truthfulness in themselves.

Typically he is at ease and unpretentious in making a serious promise or in (falsely) exculpating himself from accusations, whether grave or trivial. His simplest statement in such matters carries special powers of conviction. Overemphasis, obvious glibness, and other traditional signs of the clever liar do not show in his words or in his manner. Whether there is reasonable chance for him to get away with the fraud or whether certain and easily foreseen detection is at hand, he is apparently unperturbed and does the same impressive job. Candor and trustworthiness seem implicit in him at such times. During the most solemn perjuries he has no difficulty at all in looking anyone tranquilly in the eyes. Although he will lie about any matter, under any circumstances, and often for no good reason, he may, on the contrary, sometimes own up to his errors (usually when detection is certain) and appear to be facing the consequences with singular honesty, fortitude, and manliness.

It is indeed difficult to express how thoroughly straightforward some typical psychopaths can appear. They are disarming not only to those unfamiliar with such patients but often to people who know well from experience their convincing outer aspect of honesty. A saying current among psychiatric residents, secretaries, medical associates, and others familiar with what goes on in my office may illustrate this point. The saying is in substance that excellent evidence for the diagnosis of psychopathic personality can be found in my own response to newcomers who seek to borrow money or cash checks. It is rather generally believed that only psychopaths are successful and that in typical cases success is inevitable. Although I argue that some exaggeration has perhaps colored this story and overemphasized the infallibility of my reaction as a test, I must admit there is much truth in the matter. Even after so many years of special interest in the subject, I am forced to confess that fairly often observers have had the opportunity to make a snap diagnosis from my response to this sort of appeal and see it gain full confirmation in subsequent events. I might add that no such loan has ever been repaid and that all such checks have bounced.

After being caught in shameful and gross falsehoods, after repeatedly violating his most earnest pledges, he finds it easy, when another occasion arises, to speak of his *word of honor,* his *honor as a gentleman,* and he shows surprise and vexation when commitments on such a basis do not immediately settle the issue.

The conception of living up to his word seems, in fact, to be regarded as little more than a phrase sometimes useful to avoid unpleasantness or to gain other ends. How inadequate such ends may be to account for the psychopath's neglect of truth can be shown in a brief example:

In a letter to his wife, at last seeking divorce and in another city, one patient set down dignified, fair appraisals of the situation and referred to sensible plans he had outlined for her security. He then added that specified insurance policies and annuities providing for the three children (including their tuition at college, etc.) had been mailed under separate cover and would, if she had not already received them, soon be in her hands. He had not taken a step to obtain insurance or to make any other provision, and, once he had made these statements in his letter, he apparently gave the matter no further thought.

47

Lack of remorse or shame

The psychopath apparently cannot accept substantial blame for the various misfortunes which befall him and which he brings down upon others. Usually he denies emphatically all responsibility and directly accuses others as responsible, but often he will go through an idle ritual of saying that much of his trouble is his own fault. When the latter course is adopted, subsequent events indicate that it is empty of sincerity—a hollow and casual form as little felt as the literal implications of "your humble and obedient servant" are actually felt by a person who closes a letter with such a phrase. Although his behavior shows reactions of this sort to be perfunctory, this is seldom apparent in his manner. This is exceedingly deceptive and is very likely to promote confidence and deep trust. More detailed questioning about just what he blames himself for and why may show that a serious attitude is not only absent but altogether inconceivable to him. If this fails, his own actions will soon clarify the issue.

Whether judged in the light of his conduct, of his attitude, or of material elicited in psychiatric examination, he shows almost no sense of shame. His career is always full of exploits, any one of which would wither even a rather callous specimen of the ordinary man. Yet he does not, despite his able protestations, show the slightest evidence of major humiliation or regret. This is true of matters pertaining to his personal and selfish pride and to esthetic standards that he avows as well as to moral or humanitarian matters. If Santayana is correct in saying that "perhaps the true dignity of man is his ability to despise himself," the psychopath is without a means to acquire true dignity.

48

Inadequately motivated antisocial behavior

Not only is the psychopath undependable, but also in more active ways he cheats, deserts, annoys, brawls, fails, and lies without any apparent compunction. He will commit theft, forgery, adultery, fraud, and other deeds for astonishingly small stakes and under much greater risks of being discovered than will the ordinary scoundrel. He will, in fact, commit such deeds in the absence of any apparent goal at all.

Yet we do not find the regularity and specificity in his behavior that is apparent in what is often called compulsive stealing or other socially destructive actions carried out under extraordinary pressures which the subject, in varying degrees, struggles against. Such activities, and all disorder distinguished by some as impulse neurosis,[09] as we have mentioned, probably have important features in common with the psychopath's disorder. In contrast, his antisocial and self-defeating deeds are not circumscribed (as in pyromania, kleptomania, etc.), and he shows little or no evidence of the conscious conflict or the subsequent regret that are not regularly absent in these other manifestations. Again the comparison of a circumscribed dissociation typical of hysteria with the general ego disintegration of schizophrenia may be usefully cited.

Objective stimuli (value of the object, specific conscious need, etc.) are, as in compulsive (or impulsive) stealing, inadequate to account for the psychopath's acts. Evidence of any vividly felt urge symbolizing a disguised but specifically channelized, instinctive drive is not readily available in the psychopath's wide range of inappropriate and self-defeating behavior.

Two incidents in typical cases are offered:

1. An 18-year-old boy often stole objects for which he had some use, but stealing was not a dominant feature in his almost universally manifested maladjustment. Drifting one day into church, he chose to remain after services and speak personally with the clergyman. As might be expected, he made a profound impression and, spontaneously professing conversion, brought justifiable pride to the latter. Although disappointed because this new religious attitude did not curtail the boy in his flagrant truancy, his desultory cheating in examinations, lying, etc., the clergyman worked hopefully and assiduously with him. On one occasion, after hanging around juke joints and street corners until 3 A.M., he explained his tardiness to his parents in a vivid account of having been injured while wrestling at the school gymnasium. He had, he explained to them, spit up blood and so was taken in an ambulance to the hospital emergency room, where he was treated by the family physician. He gave realistic detail about difficulties in locating the physician, the spirit of emergency prevailing, techniques of treatment, etc. This story was elaborated despite his knowledge that the next day he was, in the company of his father, going to visit this very physician (for a previously made appointment) and that all he said would be proved untrue.

Despite repeated and versatile acts inconsistent with the boy's profession of religion, the patient clergyman, naturally impressed with one who seemed so sincere and whose stated attitudes were so admirable, did not lose hope and at times even became quite optimistic. This optimism was particularly shaken after the discovery that his convert had, during communion, succeeded in stealing one of the small glass goblets used in the ceremony.

2. Stealing was a very minor feature of this lady's career, a few details of which have already been cited.* While on parole for the afternoon from a private psychiatric institution, she accepted the hospitality of an old friend who had planned tea and sandwiches for several rather demure women whose common interest centered on Sunday school activities. While accompanying her hostess on a preparatory visit to a large grocery store, the patient, as if by whim, slipped into her ample handbag a bottle of vitamin tablets, a package of cream cheese, a tin of anchovy paste, etc. On arriving at the house (prior to the gathering), she presented all but the vitamin tablets to her hostess as a contribution to the party. She was a woman of considerable wealth and had funds with her. She apparently realized that her theft might be detected and would almost surely be suspected. In carrying out the act she behaved with

---

*Pp. 125 to 144.

what can perhaps best be called moderate caution. Apparently she was not strongly influenced by fears of being caught. Nor, on the other hand, did she seem to be seeking purposively but unconsciously any specific thrill, masochistic or otherwise, that might arise in this event. Nothing about her reactions to this and scores of similar acts ever suggested an irresistible force compelling her on against her judgment and will.

49

Poor judgment and failure to learn by experience

Despite his excellent rational powers, the psychopath continues to show the most execrable judgment about attaining what one might presume to be his ends. He throws away excellent opportunities to make money, to achieve a *rapprochement* with his wife, to be dismissed from the hospital, or to gain other ends that he has sometimes spent considerable effort toward gaining. It might be said that he cares little about financial success and little about regaining his wife, but it is difficult indeed to say that he is not extremely fain to get out of the psychiatric hospital where he has been locked up for months with other patients whom he regards as "lunatics" and who are, indeed, not desirable associates for the average man or for him. Be it noted again that the psychopath appears as unwilling to remain in a psychiatric hospital and as impatient to regain his freedom as would be the normal man. I have not in these patients ever found reliable evidence that unconsciously they seek and enjoy as punishment such confinement.

This exercise of execrable judgment is not particularly modified by experience, however chastening his experiences may be. Few more impressive examples of this could be offered from the records of humanity than the familiar one of the psychopath who, in full possession of his rational faculties, has gone through the almost indescribably distasteful confinement of many months with delusional and disturbed psychotic patients and, after fretting and counting the days until the time of his release, proceeds at once to get drunk and create disorder which he thoroughly understands will cause him to be returned without delay to the detested wards. It is my opinion that no punishment is likely to make the psychopath change his ways. Punishment is not, of course, regarded as an appropriate measure in medical treatment. It is, however, often considered and administered by legal authorities. And it must be remembered that at present the law deals with these patients more frequently than physicians deal with them.

Despite the extraordinarily poor judgment demonstrated in behavior, in the actual living of his life, the psychopath characteristically demonstrates unimpaired (sometimes excellent) judgment in appraising theoretical situations. In complex matters of judgment involving ethical, emotional, and other evaluational factors, in contrast with matters requiring only (or chiefly) intellectual reasoning ability, he also shows no evidence of a defect. So long as the test is verbal or otherwise abstract, so long as he is not a direct participant, he shows that he knows his way about. He can offer wise decisions not only for others in life situations but also for himself so long as he is asked what he would do (or should do, or is going to do). When the test of action comes to him we soon find ample evidence of his deficiency.

50

Pathologic egocentricity and incapacity for love

The psychopath is always distinguished by egocentricity. This is usually of a degree not seen in ordinary people and often is little short of astonishing. How obviously this quality will be expressed in vanity or self-esteem will vary with the shrewdness of the subject and with his other complexities. Deeper probing will always reveal a self-centeredness that is apparently unmodifiable and all but complete. This can perhaps be best expressed by stating that it is an incapacity for object love and that this incapacity (in my experience with well-marked psychopaths) appears to be absolute.

Terms in use for what we experience as "emotion" contain much ambiguity, and their referential accuracy is limited. This contributes to confusion and paradox which are difficult to avoid in attempts to convey concepts about such a matter.

In a sense, it is absurd to maintain that the psychopath's incapacity for object love is absolute, that is, to say he is capable of affection for another in literally no degree. He is plainly capable of casual fondness, of likes and dislikes, and of reactions that, one might say, cause others to matter to him. These affective reactions are, however, always strictly limited in degree. In durability they also vary greatly from what is normal in mankind. The term absolute is, I believe, appropriate if we apply it to any affective attitude strong and meaningful enough to be called love, that is, anything that prevails in sufficient degree and over sufficient periods to exert a major influence on behavior.

True enough, psychopaths are sometimes skillful in pretending a love for women or simulating parental devotion to their children. What part of this is not pure (and perhaps in an important sense unconscious) simulation has always impressed this observer as that other type of pseudolove sometimes seen in very self-centered people who are not psychopaths, which consists in concern for the other person only (or primarily) insofar as he enhances or seems to enhance the self. Even this latter imitation of adult affectivity has been seldom seen in the full-blown psychopath, although it is seen frequently in those called here partial psychopaths. In nonpsychopaths a familiar example is that of the parent who lavishes money and attention on a child chiefly to bask in the child's success and consciously or unconsciously to feel what an important person he is because of the child's triumphs. Although it is true that with ordinary people such motives are seldom, if ever, unmixed, and usually some object love and some self-love are integrated into such attitudes, in even the partial psychopath anything that could honestly be called object love approaches the imperceptible.

What positive feelings appear during the psychopath's interpersonal relations give a strong impression of being self-love. Many psychologists and philosophers have, of course, challenged the existence of any love which is not on final analysis selfish, saying that the mother who gives up her own life for her child really does so because it would be more painful to her to see the child perish. Without attempting to take up the cudgels in this interesting dispute, it will suffice to say that whatever normal and highly developed and sincere object love may actually be, it is, whether judged behaviorally or intuitively, something that impresses the ordinary observer as definitely unlike anything found in the psychopath.

The psychopath seldom shows anything that, if the chief facts were known, would pass even in the eyes of lay observers as object love. His absolute indifference to the financial, social, emotional, physical, and other hardships which he brings upon those for whom he professes love confirms the appraisal during psychiatric studies of his true attitude. We must, let it never be forgotten, judge a man by his actions rather than by his words. This old saying is especially significant when it is the man's motivations and real feelings that we are to judge. This lack in the psychopath makes it all but impossible for an adequate transference or rapport to arise in his treatment and may be an important factor in the therapeutic failure that, in my experience, has been universal.

51

General poverty in major
affective reactions

In addition to his incapacity for object love, the psychopath always shows general poverty of affect. Although it is true that he sometimes becomes excited and shouts as if in rage or seems to exult in enthusiasm and again weeps in what appear to be bitter tears or speaks eloquent and mournful words about his misfortunes or his follies, the conviction dawns on those who observe him carefully that here we deal with a readiness of expression rather than a strength of feeling.

Vexation, spite, quick and labile flashes of quasi-affection, peevish resentment, shallow moods of self-pity, puerile attitudes of vanity, and absurd and showy poses of indignation are all within his emotional scale and are freely sounded as the circumstances of life play upon him. But mature, wholehearted anger, true or consistent indignation, honest, solid grief, sustaining pride, deep joy, and genuine despair are reactions not likely to be found within this scale.

Craig[60] has said that patients who suffer from hysteria do not react with awe, reverence, wonder, or pity. They do not, it might be said, appear capable of achieving in sincerity the major emotions, although their protestations of such emotions are prominent and their show of feeling is sometimes so vigorous that the observer is often misled to believe that they are in tragic grief or remorse. Although such a diminution of emotional range, especially along the deeper notes, is often seen in the patient with hysteria, in the psychopath it is very much more far-reaching, profound, and final. Even in the situations of squalor and misery into which he repeatedly works himself, when confined in jails and what he regards as lunatic asylums, after throwing away fortunes or catching and transferring gonorrhea to his bride— even under these circumstances he does not show anything that could be called woe or despair or serious sorrow. He becomes vexed and rebellious and frets in lively and constant impatience when confined, but he does not grieve as others grieve.

Psychopaths are often witty and sometimes give a superficial impression of that far different and very serious thing, humor. Humor, however, in what may be its full, true sense,* they never have.[42] I have thought that I caught glimpses of it in psychopaths and, despite a typical history, was inclined to question the diagnosis. Further observation of these patients gave convincing evidence that the apparent humor, like the apparent insight, was really an artifact.

One might feel a superficial inclination to credit with humor the patient described under "The Psychopath as Scientist" who, after his lamentable marriage to the very unprepossessing streetwalker, laughed and admitted that the joke was on himself. At first glance such a reply might appear to be the valiant humor of a man who can smile in any adversity. And, indeed, it might be correctly judged as this if the speaker showed any evidence of feeling his adversity or accepting his responsibility. But in this instance the only convincing appraisal is that "he jests at scars who never felt a wound." When the normal man makes a gay or ironic quip on the subject of his own adversity, we may justifiably applaud it as humor. If the quip concerns an adversity which scarcely touches the maker, it is as empty of humor as the empty boldness of a daredevil who wagers his fortune in a dice game where no one is playing for keeps.

In such a discussion only personal opinions of what is real humor and what is not real humor can be expressed. Everyone's capacity to appreciate or appraise such a quality varies, no doubt, as widely as one's sense of what is beautiful.

The emotional poverty, the complete lack of strong or tragic feeling universally found in all the psychopaths personally observed, has caused me con-

---

*Carlyle said, "True humour springs not more from the head than from the heart; it is not contempt, its essence is love; it issues not in laughter, but in still smiles which lie far deeper. It is a sort of inverse sublimity, exalting, as it were, into our affections what is below us." Cited in Parkhurst, Helen Huss: Beauty, New York, 1930, Harcourt, Brace & Co., Inc.

siderable bewilderment in connection with frequent references in the literature to the powerful instinctual drives and passions said to be manifested in such people.[88,129,162] Although weak and even infantile drives displaying themselves theatrically in the absence of ordinary inhibitions may impress the layman as mighty forces, it is hardly to be concluded that wise and deeply experienced psychiatrists would be similarly deceived. Perhaps such descriptions apply to other types of personality than that discussed here. And since, as has already been stressed, the present aim is to present a type of personality disorder well known and believed to be a clinical entity rather than to argue about names, efforts will be limited to describing and trying to interpret the material at hand.

In considering the general shallowness of affect common to all members of this series in connection with their incapacity for object love, there is temptation to wonder about the possible interdependence of these faculties. Is it possible for tragic or transforming emotion to arise in any person without that peculiar and indescribable personal commitment to another? Or, if not to another personality, at least to some abstraction well outside the self?

52

Specific loss of insight

In a special sense the psychopath lacks insight to a degree seldom, if ever, found in any but the most seriously disturbed psychotic patients. In a superficial sense, in that he can say he is in a psychiatric hospital because of his unacceptable and strange conduct, and by all other such criteria, his insight is intact. His insight is of course not affected at all with the type of impairment seen in the schizophrenic patient, who may not recognize the fact that others regard him as mentally ill but may insist that he is the Grand Lama and now in Tibet. Yet in a very important sense, in the sense of realistic evaluation, the psychopath lacks insight more consistently than some schizophrenic patients. He has absolutely no capacity to see himself as others see him. It is perhaps more accurate to say that he has no ability to know how others feel when they see him or to experience subjectively anything comparable about the situation. All of the values, all of the major affect concerning his status, are unappreciated by him.

This is almost astonishing in view of the psychopath's perfect orientation, his ability and willingness to reason or to go through the forms of reasoning, and his perfect freedom from delusions and other signs of an ordinary psychosis.

Usually, instead of facing facts that would ordinarily lead to insight, he projects, blaming his troubles on others with the flimsiest of pretext but with elaborate and subtle rationalization. Occasionally, however, he will perfunctorily admit himself to blame for everything and analyze his case from what seems to be almost a psychiatric viewpoint, but we can see that his conclusions have little actual significance for him. Some of these patients mentioned spoke fluently of the psychopathic personality, quoted the literature, and suggested this diagnosis for themselves. Soon this apparent insight was seen to be not merely imperfect but a consistent and thorough artifact. Perhaps it was less a voluntary deception than a simulation in which the simulator himself fails to realize his lack of emotional grasp or that he is simulating or *what* he is simulating. The patient seems to have little or no ability to feel the significance of his situation, to experience the real emotions of regret or shame or determination to improve, or to realize that this is lacking. His clever statements have been hardly more than verbal reflexes; even his facial expressions are without the underlying content they imply. This is not insight but an excellent mimicry of insight. No sincere intention can spring from his conclusions because no affective conviction is there to move him.

Such a deficiency of insight is harder to comprehend than the schizophrenic's deficiency, for it exists in the full presence of what are often assumed to be the qualities by which insight is gained. Yet the psychopath shows not only a deficiency but apparently a total absence of self-appraisal as a real and moving experience. Here is the spectacle of a person who uses all the words that would be used by someone who understands, and who could define all the words but who still is blind to the meaning. Such a clinical picture is more baffling to me than any of the symptoms of schizophrenia, on which some light at least is thrown by psychopathologic theories.[88,98,130,279] Here we have a patient who fulfills all the ordinary theoretical criteria of a "sound mind" and yet with this apparently sound mind is more incomprehensible than the psychotic patient.

Some observers believe that what the psychopath expresses about himself and his situation constitutes insight and merits such a term. I cannot agree with this opinion. The chief and most valid connotations of the word disappear in such an application. Other patients whose gross lack of insight would be admitted by all sometimes express opinions which, if fully meant and appreciated, would indicate what is plainly not there. A few brief examples may help:

A young man with a very active manic psychosis was interviewed some years ago. He whistled, shouted, winked, expressed the belief that he controlled the movements of the sun by his glance, sang snatches of bawdy songs, announced himself as a "sort of Messiah," and laid claim to the sexual vigor of seven bulls. Leaping about in a hospital shirt he had torn almost to shreds, he found exposed wires at a place on the wall from which he had torn the electric fixtures.

Seizing and releasing them and seizing them again, he got good jolts of the city current, which he relished, apparently interpreting the sensation as a manifestation of his own vitality. When asked if he felt anything was wrong with him mentally, he shouted in glee, "Sure, Doc, I'm crazy as a coot! I'm nuts I tell you. Crazier than anybody you ever saw!"

Another patient on a closed ward, a patient badly disabled for years by obvious schizophrenia, often shouts out to the passerby, "Simple case of dementia praecox, Doc, simple case of dementia praecox," pointing to himself several times. Despite the chance diagnostic accuracy of what he says, this patient, like the one just mentioned, has little grasp of his situation and almost no real appreciation of his disorder and its meaning. Another manic patient not only spoke words that correctly indicated a good deal about his situation but even hammered out with a metal object he had obtained these letters in deep gashes in the wood door:

Bug house nutty

Indications of serious impairment of insight abound in the psychopath's reactions after his failures have been undeniably demonstrated or his anti-social acts detected. The persistent tendency to ask for recommendations from those they have every reason to know cannot furnish anything but a negative report fatal to their plans has been illustrated. Such decisions in highly intelligent people can hardly mean less than that something crucial is absent from the realization of their status.

The calm assurance with which they report a successful rehabilitation in the midst of egregious and immediate maladjustment often does not seem so much a real effort to deceive as an indication that the patient himself is greatly deceived. Despite his awareness of major facts, the pivotal significance of these facts seems not to be in his evaluations.

After a peculiarly overt and spectacular succession of failures, thefts, truancies, falsehoods, expulsion from school, etc., a young man had to be sent home to a distant state by his aunt and uncle with whom he had been staying. They had taken him in the hope that he might do better in another environment. His parents, after years of struggle, had found no solution.

All the details of his recent failure and disaster were factually known to him and had been discussed with his aunt and uncle. They made no effort to deceive him about why he had to be sent home. The physician to whom he wrote the letter which follows had also been frank with him. The letter was mailed a couple of days after he returned in what to another person could not have seemed less than total failure and disgrace.

Dear Doctor:

Arrived home safe and sound. I really was astonished at the great change in this small, typical, mid-western town when I pulled into it on Sunday. . . . I'm getting

on fine here with Mother and Father. I feel like a different fellow. Dr. ⸻
I don't know how I'll ever thank you for what you did for me down there. It was
my chance to straighten out and I took it. I believe I can say I did a good job of it.
I don't know whether I could have done it alone. But the main thing is it's done and
I want you to know I appreciate your help.

Well, I have to go now . . . .

He also mentioned in other correspondence that he was helping his
brother, who had shown some delinquency, to see the light, explaining that if
he himself had been able to do such a thorough job the brother might profit
and direct himself by the example, pull himself together, and "be a real
man too." While writing to this effect, he continued the typical behavior
without modification.

Let us consider a man whose wife, after many years of struggle equal
to that of others discussed in some detail here, had left him and was seriously considering divorce. It is difficult to imagine a situation in which the
necessity of permanent separation could be more clear or imperative. Nor
is it likely that any patient described here has given a marital partner more
reason to feel this need or has more fully demonstrated that, no matter what
he said, he would continue to behave, toward her and in general, just as he
had since their marriage. A few excerpts from his letters to the wife are
illuminating:

. . . You will never be happy either by yourself or with some other man . . .
we have too much in common. . . . I have no reason to lie or to misrepresent things
to you now, even though I did try to explain it to you before. . . . There'll be another
day, so I'm told and believe, and even though I don't expect to get proper judgment here on earth from you and yours I will up there and if I'm wrong I'm willing
to suffer for eternity. . . .

I do love you. I've never loved anyone else since childhood. . . . If I kill myself
my blood will be on your hands . . . it will be heavy on your heart and soul. . . .
All wrongs will be righted on Judgment Day. . . . You should have stuck by me—
should never have left me. . . . I've suffered now really more than I can stand. . . .
You think it will bring you happiness to be rid of me. . . . I sincerely hope and pray
that it does if you do such a thing. I wish I could feel likewise . . . and believe
everyone is at fault but me.

There is more in all this than simply false promises and fraudulent efforts
to persuade the wife not to get a divorce. There is also indication of inability
in his fundamental reactions to size up normally what he has done, what he is,
and what he has been.

386

53

Unresponsiveness in general interpersonal relations

The psychopath cannot be depended upon to show the ordinary responsiveness to special consideration or kindness or trust. No matter how well he is treated, no matter how long-suffering his family, his friends, the police, hospital attendants, and others may be, he shows no consistent reaction of appreciation except superficial and transparent protestations. Such gestures are exhibited most frequently when he feels they will facilitate some personal aim. The ordinary axiom of human existence that one good turn deserves another, a principle sometimes honored by cannibals and uncommonly callous assassins, has only superficial validity for him although he can cite it with eloquent casuistry when trying to obtain parole, discharge from the hospital, or some other end.

As in attempting to delineate other aspects of the sociopath, we find ourselves again confronting paradox. Although he can be counted on not to be appreciably swayed in major issues by these basic rules, we often find him attentive in small courtesies and favors, perhaps even habitually generous or quasi-generous when the cost is not decisive. Occasionally his actions may suggest profound generosity in that large sums are involved or something presumably of real value is sacrificed. Usually, however, these appearances are deceiving.

The psychopath who squanders $1,000 on a lady of the night usually seems not to share very actively in the distressing worry and deprivation that his wife and children (or his parents) may experience quite substantially. The motives of a boy at boarding school who casually sells his new clothes to buy candy bars and Coca-Colas (for the whole dormitory) seem to lack an important dimension of magnanimity. This dimension could be presumed if after his extravagance the boy set to work assiduously in efforts to carry the burden he had created.

In relatively small matters psychopaths sometimes behave so as to appear very considerate, responsive, and obliging. Acquaintances who meet them on grounds where minor issues prevail may find it difficult to believe that they are not highly endowed with gratitude and eager to serve others. Such reactions and intentions, although sometimes ready or even spectacularly facile, do not ever accumulate sufficient force to play a determining part in any important issues. The sociopath who causes his parents hardship and humiliation by repeatedly forging checks and causes his wife anguish by sordid (and perhaps halfhearted) relations with the housemaid, may gain a considerable reputation in the community by so often volunteering to cut the grass for the frail old lady across the street, by bringing a bottle of sherry over now and then to bedridden Mr. Blank, or by leaving his work to take a neighbor's injured cat to the veterinarian.

Outward social graces come easy to most psychopaths, and many continue, throughout careers disastrous to themselves and for others, to conduct themselves in superficial relations, in handling the trivia of existence, so as to gain admiration and gratitude. In these surface aspects of functioning, the typical psychopath (unlike the classic hypocrite) often seems to act with undesigning spontaneity and to be prompted by motives of excellent quality though of marvelously attenuated substance.

54

Fantastic and uninviting behavior with drink and sometimes without

Although some psychopaths do not drink at all and others drink rarely, considerable overindulgence in alcohol is very often prominent in the life story. Delirium tremens and other temporary psychoses directly due to alcohol were not commonly found in the hundreds of patients observed by me. The view of professional moralists to the effect that demon rum is the fundamental cause of disaster such as that of the sociopath appears to have little claim to validity. It has been pointed out already that an irreconcilable difference in primary aim appears to exist between the ordinary person who drinks too much and the psychopath. This may be restated briefly as follows: The ordinary drinker gets into trouble by drifting with enthusiasm into the opinion that if two or six or eight drinks have made him feel so good, another (or two more or perhaps five more) will make him feel just so much better. Such rationalizations may assist the normal drinker, especially if he has serious fundamental conflicts, in a progress toward becoming a neurotic drinker or toward an alcoholic breakdown.

It may be possible in certain persons for a state of mental disorder identical with that described here as psychopathic personality to be reached eventually in this way. Often, however, these neurotic drinkers, in sharp contrast with the psychopath, worry about their state when sober, are capable of making an earnest effort to get well under psychiatric treatment, and lack most of the deeper personality features of the psychopath. Even in the neurotic drinker it is more often an independent and preexisting personality maladjustment rather than the alcohol which is primarily causal. Many psychiatric observers make this vividly clear and no less convincing. An interesting interpretation of alcoholism from a psychoanalytic viewpoint has been offered by Knight.[174,175] These formulations may also apply to the psychopath, although it must be admitted that the factors of parental inconsistency and lack of unanimity in parental discipline has not been demonstrated regularly in our cases.

A major point about the psychopath and his relation to alcohol can be found in the shocking, fantastic, uninviting, or relatively inexplicable behavior which emerges when he drinks—sometimes when he drinks only a little. It is very likely that the effects of alcohol facilitate such acts and other manifestations of the disorder. This does not mean, however, that alcohol is fundamentally causal. Good criteria for differentiation between psychopaths and others who drink, moderately or excessively, can be found in what tendencies emerge after similar amounts have been consumed.

A peculiar sort of vulgarity, domineering rudeness, petty bickering or buffoonish quasi-maulings of wife, mistress, or children, and quick shifts between maudlin and vainglorious moods, although sometimes found in ordinary alcoholics with other serious patterns of disorder, are pathognomonic of the psychopath and in him alone reach full and precocious flower. Even in the first stages of a spree, perhaps after taking only two or three highballs, he may show signs of petty truculence or sullenness but seldom of real gaiety or conviviality. He frequently drinks alone and, if he is a heavy drinker, may take with particular relish to the special practice of lying out.* Evidence of any pleasurable reaction is characteristically minimal, as are indications that he is seeking relief from anxiety, despair, worry, responsibility, or tension.

Alcohol, as a sort of catalyst, perhaps contributes a good deal to the long and varied series of outlandish pranks and inanely coarse scenes with which nearly every psychopath's story is starred. Free from alcohol, such a patient would scarcely sit under a house all night idly striking matches or, concealing himself behind book stacks, urinate from the window of a public library on passersby in the street below. Nor would he, like the psychopathic son of a prominent family, suddenly, as a prank, decide to climb into a tree at a busy street corner, where he deliberately undressed, shouting wildly

---

*Pp. 146 to 147.

and puerilely to draw public attention. This man could not be persuaded to withdraw until the local fire department was called to remove him. The alcohol probably does not of itself create such behavior. Alcohol is not likely to bring out any impulse that is not already potential in a personality, nor is it likely to cast behavior into patterns for which there is not already significant subsurface predilection. The alcohol merely facilitates expression by narcotizing inhibitory processes.[137] In cases of this sort very little narcotizing may be needed. The oil which lubricates the engine of an automobile neither furnishes the energy for its progress nor directs it.

Sociopaths often indulge in these strange performances after drinking relatively little. They know perfectly well what they have done before when drinking and, with these facts squarely before their altogether clear and rational awareness, decide to drink again. It is difficult indeed for me to see any substantial grounds for placing the responsibility for the psychopath's deeds primarily on alcohol instead of on the disorder which, in ways no less serious even if less spectacular, he shows also when entirely sober.

Although his most theatrical exploits in public are usually carried on when drinking, the psychopath, even after he has been free from all alcohol for months, as for instance, when he is in a psychiatric hospital, retains all the essential personality features which have been mentioned. These show little or no tendency to diminish when he cannot drink. These words translated from Aeschylus, "Bronze is the mirror of the form; wine of the heart," express something pertinent about alcohol and man, whether the man be ill or well.

All the curious conduct recorded in the cases presented here occurred in the absence of delirium tremens, alcoholic hallucinosis, or any other of the well-known psychoses due directly to intoxication. Of course, such psychotic conditions may occur in psychopaths and in neurotic drinkers. It is important to keep such symptoms separate, since they are clearly due to another type of mental disorder and based on cerebral toxemia, edema, avitaminosis, etc.

Most of this asocial, unacceptable, and self-defeating behavior associated with the psychopath's drinking seems to occur without the benefit of extreme inebriation. If actual confusion from alcohol prevailed or states of genuine amnesia were induced before the grotesque shenanigans began, intoxication could more plausibly be suspected of playing a larger causal role. The psychopath often reacts in his typical way while in perfect orientation, with unclouded awareness and in anything but the deeply drugged state thought by some to be a prerequisite.

For whatever reason the sociopath may drink, it is true that, in contrast with others who use alcohol to excess, he hits upon conduct and creates situations so bizarre, so untimely, and so preposterous that their motivation appears inscrutable. Many of his exploits seem directly calculated to place him in a disgraceful or ignominious position. He often chooses pranks and seeks out situations that would have no appeal for the ordinary person, whether the latter be drunk or sober. The observer sometimes wonders if a truly astonishing ingenuity, or an actively perverse inventiveness is directing him, so consistently does he bring off scenes not only uncongenial but even unimaginable to the average man.

Furthermore, these exploits seem to such little purpose, almost as hard to understand on the assumption that they are for amusement or play as on the grounds of utility. One patient with numerous other outstanding incidents in his career, while sitting at a formal dinner party given by friends in honor of his birthday, turned cooly and spat with deliberation on the cake as it was brought to his side for him to cut.

One patient who developed typical symptoms early in life showed, long before he had ever touched anything alcoholic, prankish tendencies worth noting here. When taken into a store by his parents to be fitted with new clothes, he often allowed intestinal gas to pass quietly but with vivid olfactory manifestations. Considerable embarrassment and vexation were experienced by the clerks and by his parents, but he was never ruffled and apparently took mild or moderate pleasure in the situation. He occasionally resorted to these tactics while riding with his parents and dignified company in a car when the windows were tightly closed because of cold weather. A few times he discomfited his family considerably by the same means in church. At first the parents accepted his apologies after reprimands and they were inclined to believe his innocent-faced explanation that an involuntary lapse of control had occurred. The timing of events and the predilection for close places and special surroundings, as well as the emergence of other behavior, convinced them in time that these acts were deliberate.

Another young psychopath who had never encountered liquor of any sort did many things that would not attract the ordinary mischievous teen-ager. Finding time a little heavy on his hands (and his parents out of the house for a few hours), he took tools from the cellar and, working with no little skill and dispatch, got the connections of the bathroom toilet apart, put into the outlet pipe a small electric motor, and then carefully reconnected the fixture. The subsequent flooding, mess, trouble, and expense did not seem to give him hilarious mirth or vindictive satisfaction. Certainly he showed no evidence of such feeling in a degree to warrant his risking the punishment he received.

The pranks or buffoonery of the sober adult psychopath naturally differ somewhat from those typical of adolescence or earlier. With a few drinks the similarity of the adult's behavior often increases.

55

Suicide rarely carried out

Despite the deep behavioral pattern of throwing away or destroying the opportunities of life that underlies the sociopath's superficial self-content. ease, charm, and often brilliance, we do not find him prone to take a final determining step of this sort in literal suicide. Suicidal tendencies have been stressed by some observers as prevalent. This opinion, in all likelihood, must have come from the observation of patients fundamentally different from our group, but who, as we have mentioned, are traditionally classified under the same terms. It was only after a good many years of experience with actual psychopaths that I encountered my first authentic instance of suicide in a patient who could be called typical.

Instead of a predilection for ending their own lives, psychopaths, on the contrary, show much more evidence of a specific and characteristic immunity from such an act. This immunity, it must be granted, is, like most other immunities, relative.

Although suicide, then, cannot be named an impossibility among this group, its unlikelihood still merits strong emphasis. Since most psychopaths do not remain hospitalized or under other protective supervision, the rarity of this act becomes more significant. Also worth noting is the fact that most real psychopaths, not once or a few times but habitually, work themselves into situations that would strongly prompt the normal man to end his own life. Since suicidal threats, like promises and well-formulated plans to adopt a new course, are so frequently offered by these patients, there is good reason to keep in mind the fact that they are nearly always empty. Many bogus attempts are made, sometimes with remarkable cleverness, premeditation, and histrionics.

56

Sex life impersonal, trivial, and poorly integrated

The psychopath's sex life invariably shows peculiarities. The opinion has already been expressed that homosexuality and the other specific deviations, though of course occurring in psychopaths, are not sufficiently common to be regarded as characteristic. Evidence of consistent, well-formulated deviation was extremely rare in a large group of male psychopaths personally observed in a closed psychiatric institution. Among male and female subjects seen as outpatients and in general hospitals, such complications, though more frequent, do not seem to be a distinguishing feature. If we take another viewpoint and consider the group who come or are sent to the physician primarily for sexual deviation, we find again some patients with behavior patterns resembling in various degrees that of the real psychopath. These patients are probably not typical of the deviate group as a whole, whose members much more frequently show different fundamental patterns of adjustment and maladjustment.

Unmistakable psychopaths who do not show evidence of strong or consistent deviated impulses but who nevertheless occasionally carry out abnormal sexual acts have been seen much more often than those in whom the two fundamental patterns seem to overlap. This is not surprising in view of the psychopath's notable tendencies to hit upon unsatisfactory conduct in all fields and his apparent inability to take seriously what would to others be repugnant and regrettable. The real homosexual seeking an outlet for his own impulses often finds it possible to engage the psychopath in deviated activities, sometimes for petty rewards, sometimes for what might best be called just the hell of it.

It has been said that some people whose sexual activities are normal under ordinary circumstances may, in the absence of normal opportunities, resort to immature or abnormal practices as a substitutive measure. It is not hard to believe that a man of orthodox sexuality, if stranded and alone for years on an uninhabited island, might develop impulses toward masturbation. Some studies of prisoners give the impression that mutual masturbation and far more abnormal relations occur in persons who, when not confined, sought only heterosexual intercourse.[189,308] Surely every psychiatrist has seen people whose sexual aims are usually directed toward the other sex but whose orientation is so confused, and whose evaluation of sexual experience is so trivial, that they sometimes also engage in homosexual and other types of abnormal relations.

In psychopaths and in many other people who cannot be correctly grouped with the well-defined homosexual, there are varying degrees of susceptibility or inclination to immature or deviated sex practices. In contrast with others, the psychopath requires impulses of scarcely more than whimlike intensity to bring about unacceptable behavior in the sexual field or in any other. Even the faintest or most fleeting notion or inclination to forge a check, to steal his uncle's watch, to see if he can seduce his best friend's wife, or to have a little fling at fellatio is by no means unlikely to emerge as the deed. The sort of repugnance or other inhibiting force that would prevent any or all such impulses from being followed (or perhaps from even becoming conscious impulses) in another person is not a factor that can be counted on to play much part in the sociopath's decisions.

The activities of a typical patient of this sort whom I once studied are highly illustrative. This 27-year-old man, honor graduate of a college despite great irregularity in his studies, had for a number of years followed a career so similar to those of the other patients cited that there is no point in going into detail. He showed no indications of ordinary homosexuality in manner, dress, physique, or in personality features. He had been rather active in heterosexual relations since about fifteen, his partners being professionals, girls of respectable family, married women, etc.

All of these relations had apparently been to him more or less equivalent and entirely without personal significance. He admitted having once or twice, and more or less experimentally, submitted to the wishes of a homosexual and also to a couple of blundering ventures into deviated activity while drinking with others apparently more like himself. These did not seem to give him any particular satisfaction and there is reason to believe that he distinctly preferred what he did with women. To the patient, any idea that he might be a homosexual seemed absurd.

In the absence of any persistent or powerful urge in this specific direction, the patient, apparently without much previous thought, hit upon the notion of picking up four Negro men who worked in the fields not far from his residence. In a locality where the Ku Klux Klan (and its well-known attitudes) enjoyed a good deal of popularity, this intelligent and in some respects distinguished young man showed no compunction about taking from the field these unwashed laborers, whom he concealed in the back of a pickup truck, with him into a well-known place of amorous rendezvous. At the place he chose, "tourists' cabins" were discreetly set up in such a way that women brought by men to them for familiar purposes could enter without the possible embarrassment of being identified by the management. Despite these facilities suspicion arose and the patient was surprised by the man in charge of the resort while in the process of carrying out fellatio on his four companions. He had chosen to take the oral role.

When seen not long after this event, the young man was courteous but a trifle impatient about how long he might have to be hospitalized. He showed some concern with what use psychiatric examination might be in helping him avoid the term of imprisonment that would, according to the law, befall him if he should be convicted of the charges made by the proprietor and which he did not deny. This possibility did not, however, greatly alarm him.

He had often evaded penalties for antisocial acts in the past, and he had a good deal of easy confidence. Although he expressed regret and said his prank was quite a mistake, he seemed totally devoid of deep embarrassment. On the whole, his attitude might be suggested by such phrases as "Well, boys will be boys," or "Now wasn't that a foolish damn thing for me to do." These were not his literal words, but they are congruent with his behavior. By some legal step, his family, whose members were wealthy, succeeded in having him avoid trial. Finding himself free, he left against medical advice within a few days.

As might be expected, in view of the forementioned incapacity for object love, the sexual aims of psychopaths do not include any important personality relations or any recognizable desire or ability to explore or possess or significantly ravish the partner in a shared experience. Their positive activities are consistently and parsimoniously limited to literal physical contact and relatively free of the enormous emotional concomitants and the complex potentialities that make adult love relations an experience so thrilling and indescribable. Consequently they regard sexual activity very casually, sometimes apparently finding it less shocking and enthralling than a sensitive normal man would find even the glance of his beloved.

None of the psychopaths personally observed have impressed me as having particularly strong sex cravings even in this uncomplicated and poverty-stricken sense. Indeed, they have nearly all seemed definitely less moved to obtain genital pleasure than the ordinary run of people. The impression one gets is that their amativeness is little more than a simple itch and that even the itch is seldom, if ever, particularly intense.

The male psychopath, despite his usual ability to complete the physical act successfully with a woman, never seems to find anything meaningful or personal in his relations or to enjoy significant pleasure beyond the localized and temporary sensations. The female, whether or not she has physiologic orgasm, behaves in such a way as to indicate similar evaluations of the experience. Even these sensations seem to wither precociously and leave the subject a somewhat desiccated response to local stimuli. Sensations so isolated are, no doubt, peculiarly vulnerable to routine and to its justly celebrated antidotes for excitement.

What is felt for prostitute, sweetheart, casual pickup, mistress, or wife is not anything that can bring out loyalty or influence activities into a remedial or constructive plan. Nor do sexual desires always seem to compete successfully against such trivial impulses as wanting to hang about street corners or idle in juke joints where the sociopath may, by tampering with slot machines or cheating at dice or cards, pick up a little change and demonstrate his cleverness to the other fellows. So little is apparently found in heterosexual experience that deviate impulses (even when weak) are sometimes accepted and acted upon largely because of reasons like the reason why all cats look gray at night.

For the person who has ever known even one mature and normal erotic fulfillment, it is impossible to imagine turning by choice to a biologically inappropriate partner or placing partial or deviated aims above what has been so obviously well designed for the purpose. What the human organism shows anatomically is scarcely more clear than the emotional evidence, at physiologic as well as at broader interpersonal levels of reactivity. Even from more remote and less tangible sociologic aspects, nature has left no room here for doubt. It is difficult, without postulating an extremely dulled or otherwise inhibited sensual response in heterosexual experience, to account for the psychopath who can drift into deviate pranks as approximations or acceptable novelties in the same field. It has been said that "the thalamus outdid itself in devising pleasures to go with the conjugating act itself."* Without support from ethics or convention, it seems these would suffice for normal choice in the intact personality.

The familiar record of sexual promiscuity found in both male and female psychopaths seems much more closely related to their almost total lack of self-imposed restraint than to any particularly strong passions or drives. Psychopaths often seem by preference to seek sexual relations in sordid surroundings with persons of low intellectual or social status. Sometimes, however, the convenience by which what is little more than a whim can be gratified may play a greater part in this than specific preference. Another and more serious kind of sordidness also seems to constitute real inducement.

Entanglements which go out of their way to mock ordinary human sensibility or what might be called basic decency are prevalent in their sexual careers. To casually "make" or "lay" the best friend's wife and to involve a husband's uncle and/or one of his business associates in a particularly messy triangular or quadrilateral situation are typical acts. Such opportunities, when available, seem not to repel but specifically to attract the psychopath. Neither distinct appeal of the sex object nor any formulated serious malignity toward those cuckolded or otherwise outraged seems to be a major factor in such choices. There is more to suggest a mildly prankish impulse such as might lead the ordinary man to violate small pedantic technicalities or dead and preposterous bits of formality as a demonstration of their triviality.

Sexual exploits often seem chosen almost purposively to put the subject himself, as well as others, in positions of sharp indignity and distastefulness. The male psychopath who goes through legal matrimony with the whore he has picked up for the evening furnishes a clear example. And so does the well-born woman who submits to several men in succession, none of whom takes the least trouble to conceal his contempt for her. I have seen sociopaths who seriously attempted to seduce sisters, mothers-in-law, and even their actual mothers. One boasted to his wife in glowing detail of his erotic feats with her mother and with his own. His excellent talents at lying lead me to doubt the truth of his claims. I have little doubt, however, that he would have hesitated to carry out all that he boasted of if the ladies had allowed him to proceed.

Beneath his outwardly gracious manner toward women and his general suavity and social charms, the male psychopath (or part psychopath) nearly

*From Woods, Andrew J.: Courtship and marriage. In Sladen, Frank J., editor: Psychiatry and the war. Springfield, Ill., 1943, Charles C Thomas, Publisher.

always shows an underlying predilection for obscenity, an astonishingly ambivalent attitude in which the amorous and excretory functions seem to be confused. He sometimes gives the impression that an impulse to smear his partner symbolically, and even to wallow in sordidness himself, is more fundamental than a directly erotic aim, itself hardly more to him than a sort of concomitant and slightly glorified backscratching.

57

Failure to follow any life plan

The psychopath shows a striking inability to follow any sort of life plan consistently, whether it be one regarded as good or evil. He does not maintain an effort toward any far goal at all.[46,52] This is entirely applicable to the full psychopath. On the contrary, he seems to go out of his way to make a failure of life. By some incomprehensible and untempting piece of folly or buffoonery, he eventually cuts short any activity in which he is succeeding, no matter whether it is crime or honest endeavor. At the behest of trivial impulses he repeatedly addresses himself directly to folly. In well-marked cases, it is impossible for wealthy, influential, and devoted relatives to place the sociopath in any position, however ingeniously it may be chosen, where he will not succeed eventually in failing with spectacular and bizarre splendor. Considering a longitudinal section of his life, his behavior gives such an impression of gratuitous folly and nonsensical activity in such massive accumulation that it is hard to avoid the conclusion that here is true madness—madness in a sense quite as vivid as that conveyed to the imaginative layman by the terrible word *lunatic*. With the further consideration that all this skein of apparent madness has been woven by a person of (technically) unimpaired and superior intellectual powers and universally regarded as sane, the surmise intrudes that we are confronted by a serious and unusual type of genuine disorder. Not merely a surmise but a strong conviction arises that this apparent sanity is a sanity in name only. When we consider his actual performance, evidence of mental competency is sorely lacking. We find instead a spectacle that suggests madness in excelsis.

Some questions still without adequate answers

58

A basic hypothesis

Now that we have proceeded with our task through the stages of (1) presenting observations of the gross material and (2) sifting and tabulating as conveniently and intelligibly as we were able the pertinent residue of our data, let us attempt the next step. This will consist in searching for some concept or formulating some theory that might satisfactorily account for the facts observed. Much of the material appears contradictory, not only in the ordinary world of average or normal living but even in the world of mental disorder commonly granted to be less readily comprehensible in terms of ordinary reason. Even the accepted postulates which help us come to some understanding of the patient with hysteria or the delusional schizophrenic seem at first to fail when applied to the psychopathic (sociopathic) personality.

A patient whose fragmented personality prevents him from becoming aware of significant facts and puts him at the mercy of phantasies indistinguishable from what is real may conduct himself in a fashion that strikes us as altogether absurd and irrational if we fail to take into consideration this fragmentation. A man who is sane by the standards of psychiatry, aware of all the facts which we ourselves recognize, and free from delusions but who conducts himself in a way quite as absurd as many of the psychotic becomes another problem altogether. The observer is confronted with a paradox within the already baffling domain of mental disorder.

In the attempt to arrive at an applicable conception, one consistent with the facts of our observation, I find it necessary first of all to postulate that the psychopath has a genuine and very serious disability, or disorder, or deviation. To say that he is merely queer or perverse or in some borderline state between health and illness does little or nothing to account for the sort of behavior he demonstrates objectively and obviously. The practice, quite popular until recent years, of classifying the disorder of these patients, no matter how plain their incapacity to lead normal lives, as (1) no nervous or mental disease and (2) psychopathic personality, whatever the sanctions afforded by tradition, emerges not only as an error but also as an absurdity when we honestly examine the material to which such terms are applied.

Let us for a moment consider the essential evidence brought out in staff meetings on which experienced psychiatrists establish in an obvious case the diagnosis of schizophrenia and on which legal action is taken to declare the patient psychotic and incompetent (insane) and commit him for treatment. In the brief summarizing statement to support such opinions we often find such words as these:

> The history shows that he has failed repeatedly to make a satisfactory adjustment in the social group. His actions indicate serious impairment of judgment and show that he cannot be relied upon to conduct himself with ordinary regard for the safety of himself or of others. His irrational and unacceptable behavior has, furthermore, occurred without normal or adequate motivation. He shows no real insight into his conditon and tends often to project the sources of his troubles to the environment. His emotional reactions are grossly impaired and he has repeatedly shown inappropriate or inadequate affect. We may say, then, that he is psychotic, incompetent, incapable of carrying on the usual activities of life, and in need of close supervision.

Such facts have often constituted more convincing evidence for the diagnosis of schizophrenia than the delusions and hallucinations also frequently present but sometimes not demonstrable in that psychosis. All of these statements just recorded (excepting only the one word "psychotic") may be applied with full validity to the psychopath. This, of course, does not make him a patient with schizophrenia but it does, I maintain, afford grounds for saying he has a grave psychiatric disorder, and grounds that cannot be dismissed lightly. Although I insist on the gravity of his disorder, I frankly admit that it is a different kind of disorder from all those now recognized as seriously impairing competency. It is a disorder that differs more widely in its general features from any of those than they differ from one another.*

The first and most striking difference is this: In all the orthodox psychoses, in addition to the criteria just mentioned, or to some of these criteria, there is a more or less obvious alteration of reasoning processes or of some other demonstrable personality feature. In the psychopath this is not seen. The observer is confronted with a convincing mask of sanity. All the outward features of this mask are intact; it cannot be displaced or penetrated by questions directed toward deeper personality levels. The examiner never hits upon the chaos sometimes found on searching beneath the outer surface of a paranoid schizophrenic. The thought processes retain their normal aspect under psychiatric investigation and in technical tests designed to bring out obscure evidence of derangement. Examination reveals not merely an ordinary two-dimensional mask but what seems to be a solid and substantial structural image of the sane and rational personality. He is then, in the full literal sense, an example of Trélat's expressive term, *la folie lucide*. Furthermore, this personality structure in all theoretical situations functions in a manner appar-

---

*After some years of experience with them, I was forced to conclude that, theoretical technicalities notwithstanding, severe psychopaths showed a disorder more like the disorder of those classed as psychotic than the mild or questionable deviation presumed by official psychiatric standards. It was therefore interesting in 1938 to encounter an opinion expressed by Karl Menninger about patients of this type.

After stating that in his earlier psychiatric experience he regarded alcohol addiction as a bad habit and a little later as a neurotic manifestation, Menninger adds, "Now I regard it as near a psychosis." He also states, "I would be inclined, if one of my young relatives had to have either schizophrenia or addiction to alcohol, to believe that his chances for getting back into normal life would be greater if he had schizophrenia." (Discussion of Knight, Robert: The psychoanalytic treatment in a sanitorium of chronic addiction to alcohol, Journal of the American Medical Association 111:1443-1448, 1938.)

Although the term psychopathic personality was not used to designate the patients of whom Menninger speaks, it is plain that he is referring to the underlying personality disorder and not to the direct effects of drinking. I feel that this personality disorder is the one discussed here. This term is, in fact, used by the author of the paper Menninger is discussing, and there seems no reason to doubt that it is the psychopath to whom these statements apply and not reactive or neurotic drinkers.[175]

In view of our current practice of calling persons diagnosed as sociopathic personality legally sane and, in many institutions, of judging them ineligible for treatment, an opinion of such disorders expressed in 1804 by John Cox is significant. Dr. Cox wrote, "Persons of this description might appear actuated by a bad heart, but the experienced physician knows that it is the head and not the heart which is defective." (Cited in Henderson, D. K.: Psychopathic states, New York, 1939, W. W. Norton & Co., Inc.)

ently identical with that of normal, sane functioning. Logical thought processes may be seen in perfect operation no matter how they are stimulated or treated under experimental conditions. Furthermore, the observer finds verbal and facial expressions, tones of voice, and all the other signs we have come to regard as implying conviction and emotion and the normal experiencing of life as we know it ourselves and as we assume it to be in others. All judgments of value and emotional appraisals are sane and appropriate when the psychopath is tested in verbal examinations.

Only very slowly and by a complex estimation or judgment based on multitudinous small impressions does the conviction come upon us that, despite these intact rational processes, these normal emotional affirmations, and their consistent application in all directions, we are dealing here not with a complete man at all but with something that suggests a subtly constructed reflex machine which can mimic the human personality perfectly. This smoothly operating psychic apparatus reproduces consistently not only specimens of good human reasoning but also appropriate simulations of normal human emotion in response to nearly all the varied stimuli of life. So perfect is this reproduction of a whole and normal man that no one who examines him in a clinical setting can point out in scientific or objective terms why, or how, he is not real. And yet we know or feel we know that reality, in the sense of full, healthy experiencing of life, is not here.

Fortunately for the purpose of this discussion, but unfortunately indeed in any other light, an objective demonstration is available which coincides perfectly with our slowly emerging impression. The psychopath, however perfectly he mimics man theoretically, that is to say, when he speaks for himself in words, fails altogether when he is put into the practice of actual living. His failure is so complete and so dramatic that it is difficult to see how such a failure could be achieved by anything less than a downright *madman** or by a person totally or almost totally unable to grasp emotionally the major components of meaning or feeling implicit in the thoughts that he expresses or the experiences he appears to go through. In the actions of his living, then, he confirms our subjective impression, or it might be said that our surmise coincides with the objective and demonstrable facts.

Let us then assume, as a hypothesis, that the psychopath's disorder or his difference from the whole or normal or integrated personality consists of an unawareness and a persistent lack of ability to become aware of what the

*This violent and unfortunate term I use with apology but cannot spare here because of its clear-cut emphasis.

most important experiences of life mean to others. By this is not meant an acceptance of the arbitrarily postulated values of any particular theology, ethics, esthetics, or philosophic system, or any special set of mores or ideologies, but rather the common substance of emotion or purpose, or whatever else one chooses to call it, from which the various loyalties, goals, fidelities, commitments, and concepts of honor and responsibility of various groups and various people are formed.* Let us assume that this dimension of experience which gives to all experience its substance or reality is one into which the psychopath does not enter. Or, to be more accurate, let us say that he enters, but only so superficially that his reality is thin or unsubstantial to the point of being insignificant. Let us say that, despite his otherwise perfect functioning, the major emotional accompaniments are absent or so attenuated as to count for little. Of course he is unaware of this, just as everyone is bound, except theoretically, to be unaware of that which is out of his scale or order or mode of experience. If we grant the existence of a far-reaching and persistent blocking, absence, deficit, or dissociation of this sort, we have all that is needed, at the present level of our inquiry, to account for the psychopath.

The effort to express what is meant by experiencing life in a full sense, or by awareness of a solid emotional contact, runs through the psychoanalytic literature, which so often stresses the difference between an actual, or emotionally participating, understanding of some important situation and a mere verbal or academic understanding, however complete in that dimension.[11,193] This point is also implicit in the concepts of psychobiology, which, by its very definition of terms, shows that it is striving to emphasize the wholeness of experience or the full meaning of reactions.[22,71,230] Among lay observers of human problems and human values is sometimes found a sharp awareness of the very point we mean to stress in trying to describe the so-called psychopath.

A poet of our century, Donald Parson, chilled by the dead perfection of the celebrated glass flowers at Harvard, seems to see and translate into metaphor and allegory something closely related to the problem of

---

*A vast difference exists, of course, between what various persons regard as good or beautiful or desirable. John Locke observed that "those who are canonized as saints among the Turks lead lives that we cannot with modesty here relate." "An apple by Paul Cézanne is of more consequence artistically than the head of a Madonna by Raphael," is the initial sentence in a work on painting.[33] In contrast with all the various diversities of viewpoint and degrees of conviction found among ordinary people, the so-called psychopath holds no real viewpoint at all and is free of any sincere conviction in what might be called either good or evil.[48]

the personalities we here discuss and whose outer state we describe as
a mask of sanity:

I stand in wonder. What amazing art!
No counterfeit is this, but counterpart
Itself, carved with the infinite detail
That makes the plodding step of patience fail.
From life's authentic prompt-book is this leaf,

. . .

And here are flowers, petaled every one
To cup the rain and captivate the sun:

. . .

The poignant lilac whose sharp sword of scent
Can make the memory bleed—that sacrament
We call a rose—a thousand other blooms,
Forever mummied in their crystal tombs.

. . .

And yet . . . somehow . . . as I behold
These mimic plants, they leave the fancy cold;

. . .

Then, frigid patterns, sleep inviolate
Within your glassy cells. Unkindly fate
Denied you death and so denied you life.
I want my plants to feel the tonic strife
Of all the testing elements; to know
The flagellation of the rain, the snow,
The scathing sun, the shrapnel of the hail;
To bear the hundred lashes of the gale
And all that soul of man or flower needs
For flowering—the rivalry of weeds,

. . .

Not clipped or clamped in time's unyielding vise—
Eternal molds of sempiternal ice—

. . .

Farewell, stark forms. No more can you beguile,
You wear the sleety artificial smile
That freezes as it falls. My earthly flowers
Can hear the wing-beat of the flying hours
And, blushing for your deep immortal lie,

Are unafraid—nay, eager—proud—to die.
So shall they burgeon with a sweeter breath
Because, like us, they wait the frost of death.*

Although to the casual reader these words may suggest more readily the obvious artificiality familiar in the schizophrenic and the schizophrenic's withdrawal from the pain and pleasure of objective life, a point may be made that the full implication of the poem more properly bears on the state of these personalities we now discuss.

Such outward perfection as that seen in the glass flowers at Harvard and such complete lack of participation in the essence of life and mortality suggest wonderfully the situation which we mean to portray in the personalities described in this volume. The schizophrenic does not preserve the intact outer form and function of a complete personality, but the psychopath (or sociopath) does.

Without suffering or enjoying in significant degree the integrated emotional consequences of experience, the psychopath will not learn from it to modify and direct his activities as other men whom we call sane modify and direct theirs. He will lack the real driving impulses which sustain and impel others toward their various widely differing but at least subjectively important goals. He will naturally lack insight into how he differs from other men, for of course he does not differ from other men as he sees them. It is entirely impossible for him to see another person from the aspect of major affective experience, since he is blind to this order of things or blind in this mode of awareness.

It must be granted of course that the psychopath has some affect. Affect is, perhaps, a component in the sum of life reactions even in the unicellular protoplasmic entity. Certainly in all mammals it is obvious. The relatively petty states of pleasure, vexation, animosity, etc., experienced by the psychopath have been mentioned. The opinion here maintained is that he fails to know all those more serious and deeply moving affective states which make up the tragedy and triumph of ordinary life, of life at the level of important human experience. Such capacities vary widely, of course, among normal people and are perhaps proportionate to the general personality development, or, in a far-reaching sense, to true cultural level. The scope or the substantiality of such reactions, if they could be accurately and objectively estimated, would, perhaps more than any other criteria, make it possible to judge how successful and how complete an experiment in nature[223] a par-

*From Parson, Donald: Glass flowers, Boston, 1936, John W. Luce & Co.

ticular person has proved to be. A Beethoven, a Dante, or an Aeschylus, if his real inner life is faithfully represented in his works, would probably present no less a contrast in this aspect with the illiterate peasant or the successful criminal than in objective accomplishments. Nevertheless, no normal person is so unevolved and no ordinary criminal so generally unresponsive and distorted, that he does not seem to experience satisfaction, love, hate, grief, and a general participation in life at human personality levels much more intense and more substantial than the affective reactions of the psychopath. Our concept of the psychopath's functioning postulates a selective defect or elimination which prevents important components of normal experience from being integrated into the whole human reaction, particularly an elimination or attenuation of those strong affective components that ordinarily arise in major personal and social issues.

However intelligent, he only assumes that other persons are moved by and experience the ghostly facsimiles of emotion or pseudoemotion known to him. However quick and rational a person may be and however subtle and articulate his teacher, he cannot be taught awareness of significance which he fails to feel.* He can learn to use the ordinary words and, if he is very clever, even extraordinarily vivid and eloquent words which signify these matters to other people. He will also learn to reproduce appropriately all the pantomime of feeling; but, as Sherrington said of the decerebrated animal,[267] the feeling itself does not come to pass.

Even his splendid logical faculties will, in real life situations, produce not actual reasoning but that imitation of reasoning known as rationalization, for in the synthesis by which reasoning contributes to sound judgment, the sense of value, that is, the value of truth and feeling, cannot be missing. When this is missing, the process is only rationalization, something which, however technically brilliant, does not satisfactorily guide and shape action. And no difference between the two is more fundamental.[57]

When we conceive of the thought, the emotional responses, the general psychic processes, and the behavior of a person in whom is postulated a defect of this sort, we have arrived at something identical or all but identical with the psychopath as he appears in actual life.

When we say that a disorder at deep levels of personality integration prevents experience from becoming adequately meaningful to the subject, we become vulnerable to the accusation of talking nonsense. It is easy indeed to become unclear, if not to appear actually ridiculous, in attempting to express

---

*"Intellect is invisible to the man who has none." (From Schopenhauer's *Essays,* "Our Relation to Others.")

à point, however tentatively, on these fundamental matters. One commentator says of the concept here advanced:

> If that [understanding of the meaning of life] is the disease from which the psychopathic inferior suffers, this term can be applied to most of us and certainly to the reviewer, since, so far as he knows, no one has yet given us an insight into the meaning of life.*

Such a comment is appealing and not without humor, but it scarcely meets the issue in a responsible manner. We need not assume that a normal man understands the ultimate purpose of life or even that he is remotely near final accuracy in his evaluations of his own bits of experience in order to believe that the psychopath is, in comparison, seriously disabled by the specific deficiency we are attempting to formulate.

Although "meaning" or "the meaning of life" can be applied to a philosophic or religious system that attempts to explain man and the universe, it must be obvious that such an application is not intended here. By saying that a good deal of the affective substance which people find in life experiences is lacking in the psychopath's responses, we seek only to point out that he is not adequately moved and that he does not find subjective stimuli to make the major issues of life matter sufficiently to promote consistent striving. Furthermore, he cannot achieve true and abiding loyalty to any principle or any person. It is difficult, perhaps, to express anything about such a matter without inviting misunderstanding. Such an affective alteration of fundamental experience is generally granted in the schizophrenic, who shows superficial indications of it. In the psychopath, although it is so strongly indicated by his conduct, this alteration is well masked by his misleading surface. It should not be said that such an estimate can be scientifically proved in either case, or that any subjective state in another can be so established.

---

*From Book review: The New England Journal of Medicine 225:349, 1941.

59

The concept of masked personality disorder

Let us consider further the concept of disorders or defects that are deeply or centrally located. The contrast between such a pathology and one that is peripheral and visible can be demonstrated readily in speech disorders.

The man whose tongue has been severely mutilated will not be able to pronounce his words clearly. Perhaps he can only mutter unintelligibly. Even a child or a savage can see where the trouble is and understand why function is disrupted. If the hypoglossal nerves are cut, the tongue, although itself unmarred, will not move and words cannot be uttered. An observer may detect the paralysis and in time note that the tongue has shrunk in size. There are, to be sure, some changes discernible at the outer aspect of the organism, but these are less obvious and less gross than the visible swelling, the bruises, and the lacerations that are present when the tongue itself has been directly injured.

Should localized damage occur much farther away in the motor cortex of the brain or in the pyramidal tract, the tongue itself will maintain its normal size and appearance. Although it cannot be voluntarily used to produce speech, or for other purposes, considerable reflex movement may occur. With none of these three lesions have we encroached upon the understanding of language or upon its use except through one of its peripheral instruments, the tongue. All three of these patients can read and think verbally without impairment. All can write as articulately as before.

If localized destruction is visited upon neurons in another part of the brain (let us refer to this area roughly and inexactly as the quadrilateral space of Marie), the tongue remains anatomically sound and able to perform all ordinary movements. The entire physiologic apparatus whereby words are sounded remains intact—intact and controlled by conscious volition. The patient can protrude his tongue and move it from side to side as directed. He can speak also, in contrast to our last two examples, and, unlike the one whose tongue was directly injured, his words may be clearly and accurately pronounced. Often, however, the phrase or sentence he utters will not be what he means to say. Perhaps it will carry little or no suggestion of what he wishes to tell us. Perhaps it will amount to a rough approximation or an awkward circumlocution that indirectly gives us a clue. Perhaps some word irrelevant to his actual thought will be repeated over and over.

Attempting to ask for his pen, he may say, "Ben—Ben—then—then" and, perhaps gesturing with his hand in sign language, at length indicate more to us by the words, "what you write with." Perhaps in attempting to tell us good morning or to inquire about the health of our aunt, he may, to his embarrassment, shout: "Doggone, doggone, son of a bitch, you bastard." This is indeed clear but it has nothing to do with what he has tried to express.

Various degrees of impairment may be found in those aphasias classified by Henry Head as verbal, nominal, or syntactic.[123] Some aphasic patients may utter clear sounds but fail to put syllables together into words. Others may hit upon words but not succeed in making comprehensible sentences or even phrases. Many of those seriously affected by such disorder understand simple statements made by others. Some can communicate with us far better in writing than by the spoken word. In most, however, along with a serious defect in their own meaningful use of speech, we find some impairment in the understanding of spoken or written language. Even those considerably handicapped in reading, speaking, writing, or grasping the significance of what they are told may retain a relatively good use of "inner speech" and may be able still to make silent use of words for thinking or reasoning. Such people are aware of their difficulty and realize in exasperation that they cannot say what they intend and that language once quite familiar has, for them, somehow lost much of what it formerly conveyed.[123]

In discussing these three types of dysarthria we proceeded from the periphery of the functional unit (the injured tongue) inward (the severed hypoglossal nerves) to the relatively central point of the cerebral motor cortex. In the aphasias this entire motor apparatus that produces words is unimpaired, and also unimpaired is the sensory system by which language, written or spoken, is accurately perceived. We confront now a deeper dis-

413

order. In a sense we may say, roughly and imperfectly, that the instrument itself is unimpaired but the player has lost some of his ability to use it accurately for his purposes. Let us modify this and say that the player (if he is to represent something very inexactly suggested by "mind" or "personality") is not in immediate contact with the instrument and does not directly use it as, for instance, a pianist who strikes the keys or man at the telephone who puts the receiver to his ear. In our far from adequate analogy let us assume a complicated system of processes between the hand and the keys, between the ear and the receiver.

To produce speech there must be between the operator and his mechanism for uttering words other instrumentalities of evaluation whereby the words are chosen and used to express his purpose. So too between the correctly received perception (auditory or visual) and its understanding must come processes of recognition and association and integration, the complex shaping of significance that is grasped as a whole, before a real message can be completed. As Suter suggested, speech may be thought of as coming about "as a result of the functioning of a very elaborate kind of reflex arc made up of (1) an afferent, sensory, or receptive part; (2) a central, associative or elaboration part; and (3) an efferent, motor or expressive part."*

Speech disorder resulting from damage to the neural mechanisms of (2), on which depend the elaboration of concepts and the association of words with referents in the person's life experience and designated by Suter as anomia, may be thought of as more central than those chiefly limited to (1) or (3), where the defect is, in a sense, more external.

Henry Head describes under the term semantic aphasia a disorder of language still more central, more (functionally) proximal in the dimension, or area, or direction that (2) serves to indicate. This disorder he believes is related to pathology at, or near, the supramarginal gyrus. Semantic aphasia, according to Head, is "characterized by want of recognition of the ultimate significance and intention of words and phrases . . . loss of power to appreciate or formulate the general conclusion of a connected train of thought."† The person with semantic aphasia "may understand a word or short phrase and can appreciate the various details of a picture but the significance of the whole escapes him."†

In semantic aphasia, in which, so to speak, the lesion is more central

---

*From Suter, Cory: Anomic aphasia, Journal of the American Medical Association **151**:462-468, 1953.
†From Head, Henry: Aphasia in kindred disorders of speech, New York, 1926, The Macmillan Co.

than in other aphasias, the language function can usually produce more words and better phrases than in verbal or syntactical aphasias, but these have far less meaning or use to the patient. The vehicles or vessels of speech are readily made but emerge empty, devoid of the content they ordinarily define. The patient may enunciate clear, grammatical sentences, but they are irrelevant to any intention of his and do not convey even the distorted hints of valid statement often successfully transmitted by the jargon or the circumlocutions of a patient whose aphasia is more peripheral. In the latter, intentions can be realized inwardly and communicated to some degree by gestures or pantomime, or verbal fragments and approximations. In semantic aphasia inner speech or verbal thought is seriously crippled, and the patient usually cannot formulate anything very pertinent or meaningful within his own awareness. He cannot by gestures or verbal approximations hint at his message because he lacks the inner experience on which a message might be formulated. If he could do this, the more peripheral difficulties that mar the speech in verbal aphasia would not lie in his way and his thought would proceed to articulate expression. But he has no inner production of thought and feeling to transmit. The instrumentalities for language are apparently adequate. They do in fact still perform smoothly but more or less reflexly and apart from inner purpose, manufacturing phrases and sentences but doing so automatically. But the language does not represent or express anything meaningful.

It might be said that the very severe inner disorder of language in semantic aphasia is to a considerable degree masked by the mechanical production of a well-constructed but counterfeit speech carried on in some degree of independence by an undirected outer apparatus which has become relatively inaccessible to inner purpose. Like real speech, it appears to represent the inner human intention, thought, or feeling, but actually it is an artifact. Behind the superficially good (clear, grammatical) speech there is little or nothing to be symbolized and conveyed. This stands in contrast to the gross superficial disorder of communication in verbal aphasia in which inner purposes can still be intelligently formulated and, however awkwardly and indirectly, are often communicated with some degree of success to another.

We need not assume Head's interpretation of the aphasias to be entirely and finally correct if it will by analogy help us formulate and clarify a concept of personality disorder, a concept in which the deeper and less obvious levels of function can be compared and contrasted with more superficial aspects of behavior. Let us use the analogy not as evidence for the concept but only as a means of stating it.

Let us consider several familiar types of psychiatric illness with this aim in mind. The patient with a toxic-delirious psychosis (for example, delirium tremens) shows a maximum of disorder in his superficial aspect. He may not recognize his whereabouts and may scream at nonexistent monsters or belabor the empty air with a broomstick to fight off poison-spitting bugs a yard long which he sees pursuing him. As he leaps over the bed or brandishes a chair, wild-eyed, disheveled, and half-clad, any layman can recognize him as ill and no doubt admit his disorder is mental (that he is "crazy"). Nothing conceals his psychosis. Delusions, hallucinations, confusion, loss of basic orientations, and irrational conduct are obvious everywhere in his imme-diate area of contact with the surroundings. Despite the spectacular impres-siveness of his manifestations, he is very likely to recover, perhaps in a few days. Although intense, his pathology is in some respects relatively superficial.

On the other hand, the hebephrenic patient sometimes maintains excel-lent orientation and calmness. Despite hallucinations and delusions which he often keeps largely to himself, he may carry on clerical work without supervision and do so logically and effectively. It is not difficult for the physi-cian to demonstrate convincing evidence of his grave disorder, but this is usually less obvious, less vivid peripherally, let us say, than in the first exam-ple. As a matter of fact, the uninformed layman (especially if a close rela-tive) will sometimes insist for a while that "it can't be his mind, Doc, it must just be his nerves." Members of the family may argue that because he has kept his accounts straight at the store where he worked and showed intelligence about other matters, he must have a relatively minor psychiatric disorder. The outer form of normal behavior may be much better preserved in such a patient than in one with delirium tremens despite the fact that beyond this relatively thin functional shell the basic foundations of his personality are in chaotic devastation and despite the fact that his disorder is maximally malignant, extending deeply into the core of his being.

A patient with early paranoid schizophrenia is likely to be free of those outer manifestations of mental illness that distinguish the hebephrenic. His reasoning powers may be truly excellent, his emotional reactions appro-priate, and his general behavior effective. It might be difficult indeed to find any point at which we can truthfully say his abilities, in the ordinary sense, are impaired by disease. He may be a brilliant and delightful companion at a dinner party and may discuss politics, business, or philosophy with high intelligence and learning. Well concealed beneath all this exterior functional perfection is a serious disorder which may influence him to direct his un-blemished talents toward useless or highly undesirable goals or perhaps to carry out, conscientiously and effectively, disastrous antisocial aims. If we consider personality function somewhat as we did the more circumscribed function of speech, we might say that what is pathologic or defective in the paranoid patient must be more centrally situated, more difficult to discern or to demonstrate from the outside. Yet such a disability is not mild. It is as real and often as serious as hebephrenia. Some paranoid patients, particularly those with paranoia vera, show no signs at all of psychiatric impairment that can be demonstrated regularly. If brought to the courts, they may successfully establish their sanity before judge and jury, sometimes excelling their medical and legal examiners in the exercise of reason. Not rarely they attract supporters or disciples in the community who enthusiastically follow their advice. In such patients, despite the impressive outer layers of unimpaired function, psychosis is genuine and severe.

The delusions of some paranoiacs are circumscribed—confined to conviction about what is indisputably possible or even plausible. A man may, for instance, believe his wife is unfaithful. Sometimes it is difficult to prove objectively that this belief is a delusion rather than a sane mistake, or, indeed, a fact. The pathologic substructure or inner lesion, so to speak, which gives rise to his delusion is not directly accessible to our scrutiny. From that point out, we might say, he behaves rationally. His functions peripheral to this disturbed level may proceed sanely and effectively.

The delusional belief in paranoia, although often not intrinsically absurd or irrational, allows the trained observer to realize that such a patient is psychotic despite the unimpaired operation of his exterior functions. This psychosis is extremely well disguised by the covering layers of sanity. The delusion, once it is recognized, gives us a reliable clue to the extremely serious disorder beneath, somewhat as specific notes in the percussion of a chest reveal indirectly to an internist the presence of a lung cavity despite the unmarred exterior of the body.

In some cases of schizophrenia no delusion or other manifestation technically indicative of psychosis can be elicited. In contrast with paranoia, not even one circumscribed but distinct clue can be offered by the examiner as evidence of a true mental disorder. Under such terms as simple, masked, or ambulatory schizophrenia many of these cases have been described. The psychiatrist who recognizes the psychosis in such a patient is often at a loss to explain his conclusion. He senses a peculiar emotional deficit and distortion and is able to realize that the person does not normally experience and evaluate the basic data of life and that this deviation is of the quality and the degree characteristic of schizophrenia. Let us not deny that the psychiatrist may sometimes erroneously come to such a conclusion. He must rely on a clinical judgment, not on objective scientific evidence. The experienced winetaster may, it is said, detect that his beverage comes from grapes grown on the east rather than the west side of some hill in Touraine. Experts may reliably distinguish in an obscure painting the hand of Benozzo Gozzoli from that of a talented imitator. Perhaps few psychiatrists develop so sure and fine a knack of diagnosing schizophrenia in these cryptic cases. It is true, nevertheless, that experience sometimes enables them to apprehend correctly such a disorder in those who show no objectively demonstrable sign of psychosis. Some of these patients are more dangerous than many who hallucinate, express delusions, and show gross irrationality.

Most of these masked schizophrenics do not present an outer aspect that appears entirely normal. A brittleness, an indefinable peculiarity of manner, fine details of posture or gesture, and nuances of expression and attitude may cumulatively contribute to the psychiatrist's impression. Many subliminal or almost subliminal items of perception may be sensed in such a person and correctly identified with similar real but not quite expressible qualities familiar to the observer because he has previously sensed them in hundreds of closely studied schizophrenic patients who also showed gross and indisputable manifestations of psychosis. What is thus sensed may reveal to the psychiatrist that such a patient is emotionally far out of contact in basic human relations and inadequately influenced by sane motives.

Such patients with schizophrenia suggest in some respects the psychopath in that their major abnormality, their real pathology, is chiefly within and largely concealed by good reasoning and by ability, at least for intervals, to go through the motions of what looks like a sane pattern of life. Occasionally such a patient will attempt to hang himself, address an insulting letter to the President, announce the discovery of perpetual motion, or wander off from home and let no one know whether he is dead or alive for a couple of months, without being able to give any good reason for such acts and apparently without feeling that an explanation is in order. After following for years obviously queer, distorted, and socially restricted, but apparently not psychotic, careers, a few commit without provocation murder or some other tragic misdeed, for which they show little evidence of remorse or other adequate and understandable reactions.

Such patients in some respects, particularly in their central emotional deficit, may seem closer to the psychopath than to the ordinary state hospital schizophrenic. There are, however, important differences. The psychopath's outer mask of mechanically correct peripheral functioning is immeasurably more deceptive. The masked schizophrenic outwardly shows no obvious or expected signs of traditional psychosis, but he does not achieve the socially appealing presence, the warm, easy manners, or the false promise of strong and superior character and human qualities that are so bewildering in the psychopath. Real peculiarities, cool and strange alterations of emotion, social isolation, and a profound and indefinable queerness emerge in outer aspects of the cryptic schizophrene. Such signs, except to the expert, do not suggest psychosis or adequately warn us that gross and malignant alterations exist beneath such a surface. But the evidence of something schizoid, or something queer and not precisely normal, is usually apparent.

The surface of the psychopath, however, that is, all of him that can be reached by verbal exploration and direct examination, shows up as equal to or better than normal and gives no hint at all of a disorder within. Nothing about him suggests oddness, inadequacy, or moral frailty. His mask is that of robust mental health. Yet he has a disorder that often manifests itself in conduct far more seriously abnormal than that of the schizophrenic. Inwardly, too, there appears to be a significant difference. Deep in the masked schizophrenic we often sense a cold, weird indifference to many of life's most urgent issues and sometimes also bizarre, inexplicable, and unpredictable but intense emotional reactions to what seems almost irrelevant. Behind the exquisitely deceptive mask of the psychopath the emotional alteration we feel appears to be primarily one of degree, a consistent leveling of response to petty ranges and an incapacity to react with sufficient seriousness to achieve much more than pseudoexperience or quasi-experience. Nowhere within do we find a real cause or a sincere commitment, reasonable or unreasonable. There is nowhere the loyalty to produce allegiance even to a negative or fanatic cause.

Just as meaning and the adequate sense of things as a whole are lost with semantic aphasia in the circumscribed field of speech although the technical mimicry of language remains intact, so in most psychopaths the purposiveness and the significance of all life-striving and of all subjective experience are affected without obvious damage to the outer appearance or superficial reactions of the personality. Nor is there any loss of technical or measurable intelligence.

With such a biologic change the human being becomes more reflex, more machinelike. It has been said that a monkey endowed with sufficient longevity would, if he continuously pounded the keys of a typewriter, finally strike by pure chance the very succession of keys to reproduce all the plays of Shakespeare. These papers so composed in the complete absence of purpose and human awareness would look just as good to any scholar as the actual works of the Bard. Yet we cannot deny that there is a difference. Meaning and life at a prodigiously high level of human values went into one and merely the rule of permutations and combinations would go into the other. The patient semantically disordered does not, of course, strike sane and normal attitudes merely by chance. His rational power enables him to mimic directly the complex play of human living. Yet what looks like sane realization and normal experience remains, in a sense and to some degree, like the plays of our simian typist.

Tables 1 and 2 may serve to outline or illustrate some points in this discussion. All differences between central and peripheral speech disorders cannot of course be pronounced identical with similar differences between masked and obvious psychiatric disorders.

In Henry Head's interpretation of semantic aphasia we find, however, concepts of neural function and of its integration and impairment that help to convey a hypothesis of grave personality disorder thoroughly screened by the intact peripheral operation of all ordinary abilities. In relatively abstract or circumscribed situations, such as the psychiatric examination or the trial in court, these abilities do not show impairment but more or less automatically demonstrate an outer sanity unquestionable in all its aspects and at all levels accessible to the observer. That this technical sanity is little more than a mimicry of true sanity cannot be proved at such levels. Only when the subject sets out to conduct his life can we get evidence of how little his good theoretical understanding means to him, of how inadequate and insubstantial are the apparently normal basic emotional reactions and motivations convincingly portrayed and enunciated but existing in little more than two dimensions.

What we take as evidence of his sanity will not significantly or consistently influence his behavior. Nor does it represent real intention within, the degree of his emotional response, or the quality of his personal experience much more reliably than some grammatically well-formed, clear, and perhaps verbally sensible statement produced vocally by the autonomous neural apparatus of a patient with semantic aphasia can be said to represent such a patient's thought or carry a meaningful communication of it.

Let us assume tentatively that the psychopath is, in this sense, semantically disordered. We have said that his outer functional aspect masks or disguises something quite different within, concealing behind a perfect mimicry of normal emotion, fine intelligence, and social responsibility a grossly disabled and irresponsible personality. Must we conclude that this disguise is a mere pretence voluntarily assumed and that the psychopath's essential dysfunction should be classed as mere hypocrisy instead of psychiatric disease or deformity?

Let us remember that his typical behavior defeats what appear to be his own aims. Is it not he himself who is most deeply deceived by his apparent normality? Although he deliberately cheats others and is quite con-

Table 1. Speech disorders

PERIPHERAL ⟶ SOMEWHAT PERIPHERAL ⟶ SOMEWHAT CENTRAL ⟶ CENTRAL

DYSARTHRIA			THE APHASIAS			
Injured tongue	Severed hypoglossal nerves	Lesion of motor cortex or pyramidal tract	Verbal aphasia	Syntactic aphasia	Nominal aphasia	Semantic aphasia
Anatomic defect in distal organ of vocal speech	Anatomic lesion less distal but dysfunction still circumscribed to vocal production		Lesions in quadrilateral space of Marie		Lesion at or about angular gyrus	Lesion at or about supramarginal gyrus
			Defect in verbal formulation of language; still a relatively external defect ⟶		More defect of inner speech, of verbal understanding, of silent reasoning	Most extensive and deepest loss of language function; maximal defect of inner speech, but defect less obvious, better disguised by intact superficial functions
Only physiologic mechanisms for speaking impaired			Physiologic mechanisms for speaking and writing entirely unimpaired			

Table 2. Personality disorders

PERIPHERAL ⟶ SOMEWHAT PERIPHERAL ⟶ SOMEWHAT CENTRAL ⟶ CENTRAL

Delirium	Hebephrenic schizophrenia	Paranoid schizophrenia	Paranoid psychosis and paranoia vera	Masked schizophrenia	The psychopath
Psychosis immediately obvious	Psychosis less obvious, better preserved function tending to obscure it; although less obvious, disorder not less severe ⟶			Psychosis not demonstrable, but outer aspects of personality show some apparently minor deviation	Psychosis not technically demonstrable; maximally concealed by outer surface of intact function; manifested only in behavior; may, however, be extremely severe

scious of his lies, he appears unable to distinguish adequately between his own pseudointentions, pseudoremorse, pseudolove, etc., and the genuine responses of a normal person. His monumental lack of insight indicates how little he appreciates the nature of his disorder. When others fail to accept immediately his "word of honor as a gentleman," his amazement, I believe, is often genuine. His subjective experience is so bleached of deep emotion that he is invincibly ignorant of what life means to others.

His awareness of hypocrisy's opposite is so insubstantially theoretical that it becomes questionable if what we chiefly mean by hypocrisy should be attributed to him. Having no major values himself, can he be said to realize adequately the nature and quality of the outrages his conduct inflicts upon others? A young child who has no impressive memory of severe pain may have been told by his mother it is wrong to cut off the dog's tail. Knowing it is wrong he may proceed with the operation. We need not totally absolve him of responsibility if we say he realized less what he did than an adult who, in full appreciation of physical agony, so uses a knife. Can a person experience the deeper levels of sorrow without considerable knowledge of happiness? Can he achieve evil intention in the full sense without real awareness of evil's opposite? I have no final answer to these questions.

Attempts to interpret the sociopath's disorder do not, of course, furnish evidence that he has a disorder or that it is serious. For reliable evidence of this we must examine his behavior. Only here, not in psychopathologic formulations, can we apply our judgment to what is objective and demonstrable. Functionally and structurally all is intact on the outside. Good function (healthy reactivity) will be demonstrated in all theoretical trials. Judgment as well as good reasoning will appear at verbal levels. Ethical as well as practical considerations will be recognized in the abstract. A brilliant mimicry of sound, social reactions will occur in every test except the test of life itself. In the psychopath we confront a personality neither broken nor outwardly distorted but of a substance that lacks ingredients without which normal function in major life issues is impossible.

Any method that offers the possibility of adding objectivity to our appraisals is indeed stimulating and welcome anywhere in psychiatry but particularly so in this more than ordinarily confusing problem.

Simon, Holzberg, and Unger, impressed by the paradox of the psychopath's poor performance despite intact reasoning, devised an objective test specifically to appraise judgment as it would function in real situations, as contrasted with theoretical judgment in abstract situations.[270]

These workers are aware that the more complex synthesis of influences constituting what is often called judgment or understanding (as compared to a more theoretical "reasoning") may be simulated in test situations in which emotional participation is minimum, that rational factors alone by an accurate aping or stereotypy can produce in vitro, so to speak, what they cannot produce in vivo. Items for a multiple choice test were selected with an aim of providing maximal possibilities for emotional factors to influence decision and particularly for relatively trivial immediate gratification impulses to clash with major, long-range objectives. The same items were also utilized in the form of a completion test. The results of this test on a group of sociopaths support the hypothetical interpretation attempted in this book.

If such a disorder does indeed exist in the so-called psychopath, it is not remarkable that its recognition as a major and disabling impairment has been long delayed. Pathologic changes visible on the surface of the body (laceration, compound fractures, etc.) were already being handled regularly by medical men when the exorcism of indwelling demons retained popular favor in many illnesses treated by the internist. So, too, it has been with personality disorders. Those characterized by gross outward manifestations have been accepted as psychiatric problems long before others in which a superficial appearance of sanity is preserved.

Despite the psychopath's lack of academic symptoms characteristic of those disorders traditionally classed as psychosis, he often seems to belong more with that group than with any other. Certainly his problems cannot be dealt with, medically or by any other means, unless similar legal instrumentalities for controlling his situation are set up.

I believe that if such a patient shows himself grossly incompetent in his behavior, he should be so appraised. If, as is true nearly everywhere in our country, it is necessary to say that he is psychotic in order to make attempts at treatment or urgently needed supervision possible for him, the most serious objections are primarily theoretical. Perhaps our traditional definitions of psychosis can stand alteration better than these disordered patients and those about them can stand the present farcical and sometimes tragic methods of handling their problems.

This is not to say that all people showing features of this type should be regarded as totally disabled. It is here maintained that this disorder, like other psychiatric disorders, appears in every degree of severity and may constitute anything from a personality trait through handicaps of varying magnitude, including maximum disability and maximum threat to the peace and safety of the community.

60

Further consideration of the hypothesis

In attempting to account for the abnormal behavior observed in the psychopath, we have found useful the hypothesis that he has a serious and subtle disorder at deep levels disturbing the integration and normal appreciation of experience and resulting in a pathology that might, in analogy with Henry Head's classifications of the aphasias, be described as semantic. Presuming that such a patient does fail to experience life adequately in its major issues, can we then better account for his clinical manifestations? The difficulties of proving, or even of demonstrating direct objective evidence, for hypotheses about psychopathology (or about ordinary subjective functioning) are too obvious to need elaborate discussion here.

If the psychopath's life is devoid of higher-order stimuli, of primary or serious goals and values, and of intense and meaningful satisfactions, it may be possible for the observer to better understand the patient who, for the trivial excitement of stealing a dollar (or a candy bar), the small gain of forging a $20.00 check, or halfhearted intercourse with an unappealing partner, sacrifices his job, the respect of his friends, or perhaps his marriage. Behind much of the psychopath's behavior we see evidence of relatively mild stimuli common to all mankind. In his panhandling, his pranks, his truancy, his idle boasts, his begging, and his taking another drink, he is acting on motives in themselves not unnatural. In their massive accumulation during his career, these acts are impressive chiefly because of what he sacrifices to carry them out. If, for him, the things sacrificed are also of petty value, his conduct becomes more comprehensible.

Woolley, in an interesting interpretation of these patients, compares them with an otherwise intact automobile having very defective brakes.[311] Such an analogy suggests accurately an important pathologic defect which seems to exist. In contrast with an automobile, however, the braking functions of the human organism are built into the personality by reaction to life experience, to reward and punishment, praise and blame, shame, loss, honor, love, etc. True as Woolley's hypothesis may be, it seems likely that more fundamental than inadequate powers to refrain is the inadequate emotional reactivity upon which the learning to refrain must be based. Even with good brakes on his car, the driver must have not only knowledge of but also feeling for what will happen otherwise if he is to use them correctly and adequately.

Some of the psychopath's behavior may be fairly well accounted for if we grant a limitation of emotional capacity. Additional factors merit consideration. The psychopath seems to go out of his way to make trouble for himself and for others. In carelessly marrying a whore, in more or less inviting detection of a theft (or at least in ignoring the probability of detection), in attempting gross intimacies with a debutante in the poorly sheltered alcove just off a crowded ballroom, in losing his hospital parole or failing to be with his wife in labor just because he did not want to leave the crap game at midnight (or at 3 A.M.)—in such actions there seems to be not only disregard for consequences but active impulse to show off, to be not discreet but conspicuous in making mischief. Apparently he likes to flaunt his outlandish or antisocial acts with bravado.

When negative consequences are negligible or slight (both materially and emotionally), who does not like to cut up a little, to make a bit of inconsequential fun, or perhaps playfully take off on the more sober aspects of living? Dignity might otherwise become pompousness; learning, pedantry; goodness, self-righteousness, etc. The essential difference seems to lie in how much the consequences matter. It is also important to remember that inclination and taste are profoundly shaped by capacity to feel the situation adequately. A normal man's potential inclination to give the pretty hatcheck girl $50.00 would probably not reach awareness in view of his knowledge that this would result in his three children's not having shoes or in his having to humiliate himself by wheedling from a friend a loan he will never repay.

If, as we maintain, the big rewards of love, of the hard job well done, of faith kept despite sacrifices, etc., do not enter significantly in the equation, it is not difficult to see that the psychopath is likely to be bored. Being bored, he will seek to cut up more than the ordinary person in order to relieve the tedium of his unrewarding existence. If we think of a theater half-filled with ordinary pubertal boys who must sit through a performance of *King Lear* or of Beethoven's *Ninth Symphony,* we need ask little of either imagination or memory to bring to mind the restless fidgeting, the noisy intercommunication of trivialities, the inappropriate guffaws or catcalls, and perhaps the spitballs or the michievous application of a pin to the fellow in the next seat.

Apparently blocked from fulfillment at deep levels, the sociopath is not unnaturally pushed toward some sort of divertissement. Even weak impulses, petty and fleeting gratifications, are sufficient to produce in him injudicious, distasteful, and even outlandish misbehavior. Major positive attractions are not present to compete successfully with whims, and the major negative deterrents (hot, persistent shame, profound regret, etc.) do not loom ahead to influence him. If the 12-year-old boys could enjoy *King Lear* or the *Ninth Symphony* as much as some people do, they would not be so restless or unruly. If the son of a family long honored in the community (and husband of a wife at her wits' end) felt about going to jail and about being widely known as a jailbird, as most people do, he could not, after dozens of brief incarcerations, drop in on somewhat similar acquaintances (just back at work after their own periods of detention) and gaily twit them with such greetings as, "What kind of a bird can't fly?"

In a world where tedium demands that the situation be enlivened by pranks that bring censure, nagging, nights in the local jail, and irritating duns about unpaid bills, it can well be imagined that the psychopath finds cause for vexation and impulses toward reprisal. Few, if any, of the scruples that in the ordinary man might oppose and control such impulses seem to influence him. Unable to realize what it meant to his wife when he was discovered in the cellar flagrante delicto with the cook, he is likely to be put out considerably by her reactions to this. His having used the rent money for a midnight long-distance call to an old acquaintance in California (with whom he bantered for an hour) also brings upon him censure or tearful expostulation. Considering himself harrassed beyond measure, he may rise from the dining room table in a petty tantrum, curse his wife violently, slap her, even spit on her, and, further annoyed by the sudden weeping of their 6-year-old daughter, throw his salad in the latter's face before he strides indignantly from the room.

His father, from the patient's point of view, lacks humor and does not understand things. The old man could easily take a different attitude about having had to make good those last three little old checks written by the son. Nor was there any sense in raising so much hell because he took that dilapidated old Chevrolet for his trip to Memphis. What if he did forget to tell the old man he was going to take it? It wouldn't hurt him to go to the office on the bus for a few days. How was he (the patient) to know the fellows were going to clean him out at stud or that the little bitch of a waitress at the Frolic Spot would get so nasty about money? What else could he do except sell the antiquated buggy? If the old man weren't so parsimonious he'd want to get a new car anyway!

And why did he (the father) have to act so magnanimous and hurt about settling things last Saturday night down at the barracks? You'd think from his attitude that it was the old man himself who'd had to put up with being cooped in there all those hours with louse-infested riffraff! Well, he'd thanked his father and told him how sorry he was. What else could a fellow do? As for that damned old Chevrolet, he was sick of hearing about it. His grudge passing with a turn of thought, he smiles with half-affectionate, playfully cordial feelings toward the old man as he concludes, "I ought to tell him to take his precious old vehicle and stick it up his _____!"

Lacking vital elements in the appreciation of what the family and various bystanders are experiencing, the psychopath finds it hard to understand why they continually criticize, reproach, quarrel with, and interfere with him. His employer, whom he has praised a few hours before, becomes a pettifogging tyrant who needs some telling off. The policeman to whom he gave tickets for the barbecue last week (because he is such a swell guy) turns out to be a stupid oaf and a _____ meddler who can't mind his own business but has to go and arrest somebody just because of a little argument with Casey in the Midnight Grill about what happened to a few stinking dollar bills that were lying on the bar.

Adolescents who feel need to kick over the traces often seek to do so in unconventional, spectacular, daring, and somewhat shocking acts that sometimes are motivated primarily by impulses of defiance. Similar impulses of defiance no doubt contribute to the psychopath's behavior. Figures representing authority or respectability naturally irk him. They are smug and meddlesome in his eyes and tempt him to show them what he really can do. If he cannot actually remember his parents, on the eve of a whipping, telling him "this is going to hurt me more than it does you," he, like all people, gets the idea. Through the damage he does to himself he has a way of getting back at or disciplining them, along with his wife, his friends, and all sorts of self-righteous people who volunteer to "do him good" and to meddle.[45]

It is not necessary to assume great cruelty or conscious hatred in him commensurate with the degree of suffering he deals out to others. Not know-

427

ing how it hurts or even where it hurts, he often seems to believe that he has made a relatively mild but appropriate reprimand and that he has done it with humor. What he believes he needs to protest against is no small group, no particular institution, set of ideologies, etc., but human life itself. In it he finds nothing deeply meaningful or persistently stimulating, but only some transient and relatively petty pleasant caprices, a terribly repetitious series of minor frustrations, and ennui.

Like many teen-agers, saints, history-making statesmen, and other notable leaders or geniuses, he shows unrest; he wants to do something about the situation. Unlike these others, as Lindner has so well and convincingly stressed, he is a "rebel without a cause."[188] Reacting with something that seems not too much like divine discontent or noble indignation, he finds no cause in the ordinary sense to which he can devote himself with wholeheartedness or with persistent interest. In certain aspects his essential life seems to be a peevish bickering with the inconsequential. In other aspects he suggests a man hanging from a ledge who knows if he lets go he will fall, is likely to break a leg, may lose his job and his savings (through the disability and hospital expenses), and perhaps may injure his baby in the carriage just below. He suggests a man in this position who, furthermore, is not very tired and who knows help will arrive in a few minutes, but who, nevertheless, with a charming smile and a wisecrack, releases his hold to light a cigarette, to snatch at a butterfly, or just to thumb his nose at a fellow passing in the street below.

In his work on obsessive disorder, Straus brings out and develops a concept very germane to the present discussion.[280] Beneath obsessive symptoms he finds indications of a distaste for life as it is ordinarily lived, a nauseous rejection of what is normally most appealing, and an attitude toward the world that finds in our chief sources of joy the equivalent of decay and filth. These observations are interesting and extraordinarily articulate. They seem to elucidate from an independent viewpoint other and important aspects of what has elsewhere been presented as confusion of love and hate.[215]

It is impossible to give briefly an adequate account of what Straus brings out. Its relation to our subject is of interest. The psychopath does not seem to share the obsessive patient's pathologic evaluations, but he also reacts to the milieu of human life as if it had been altered in its essential qualities. The alteration in the psychopath is by no means similar to what Straus depicts. The obsessive patient spends his life desperately trying to avoid what he finds so disgusting and horrible. The psychopath looks as if he is reacting to what is trival by showing that he just doesn't give a damn. Having no major goals or incentives, he may be prompted by simple tedium to acts of folly

428

or crime. Such prompting is not opposed by ordinary compunction or concern for consequences.

The psychopath certainly does not seem to be warding off anything similar to what the obsessive solemnly seeks to ward off with disgust. He may, however, be flouting something very different in an unrecognized or poorly recognized mockery or travesty whereby he demonstrates that he is not emotionally involved.

The lack of aversion to conduct and situations which to the normal man are repulsive is striking and paradoxical in the sociopath. This is no less impressive than the disgust Straus finds in obsessive patients. It might in fact be regarded as an equally basic alteration of the normal reaction but an alteration toward the other extreme. The opposite reactions of depression and manic euphoria have been interpreted as diverse responses to an identical inner pathologic situation.[88] The prude and the pathologically wanton often seem to be influenced chiefly by the same misconception of sexuality as being intrinsically ignoble and, to the female, degrading. So, too, the active life rejection underlying obsession and the indifference to major human values underlying the psychopath's life scheme may themselves be thought of as profoundly pathologic reactions in opposite directions.

A world not by any means identical but with some vivid features of both these underlying situations can be found in Huysman's *Against the Grain*[145] and in Jean-Paul Sartre's *Nausea*.[261] In the satirical novels of Evelyn Waugh, also, an atmosphere difficult to describe sometimes develops—an atmosphere that may give the reader awareness of attitudes and evaluations genuinely illustrative.[299,300,301,302]

In none of this fiction does one find evidence of the obsessive patient's reaction to what he scrupulously rejects as if it were filth. The leading characters depicted therein show a peculiar cynicism which is more conscious and directed and purposive than the behavior of the psychopath. But none of the characters presented show even an approximate awareness of what is most valid and meaningful and natural in human beings. A negative response to life itself, an aversion at levels more basic than ordinary morals or the infraconscious foundations of taste and incentive, is conveyed subtly and impressively.

It is difficult to illustrate by incident, by the expressed attitude of the characters depicted, or by any clearly implied evaluation of the authors the specific quality of what is evoked in these novels as the essence of an unhappy, mutilated, and trivial universe in which all the characters exist. The sense of pathology pervades to levels so deep that rational scrutiny cannot reach and meet the fundamental implications; nor can inquiry satisfactorily demonstrate its precise source. If the actual world or man's biologic scope were that conveyed in these interesting works, it would not be difficult to account for obsessive illness and for the psychopath's career as reasonable reactions to a situation where no course is possible except one profoundly pathologic in one way or another.

Thoughtful contemplation of what is depicted in these works of fiction suggests a world as fundamentally altered as what Straus presents as the world of the obsessive. In the effective and terse implication of general emotional incapacity in these characters, the authors succeed in evoking awareness of a sort of quasi-life restricted within a range of staggering superficiality. This, rather than those aspects of the works that apparently brought them popularity, may deserve high literary appraisal as concise and valuable communications of something that is by no means easy to convey in direct language. Such a superficiality and lack of major incentive or feeling strongly suggest the apparent emotional limitations of the sociopath.

In his discussion of what arouses disgust in obsessive patients, Straus brings out memorable points. Not by literal falsification of objective facts but by seeing and feeling these facts in a pathologic mode is the world altered. He says:

> Curls on a head look lovely and attractive, but the same hair found in the soup is disgusting; perhaps we should like to cut one of these curls as a souvenir, but we should be disgusted to collect the hair left in a comb. Saliva spit out is disgusting, an expression of our contempt, but on fresh lips and tongue the saliva is not disgusting. Separation from the integrity of the living organism turns the physiognomy from delight to digust. This transition indicates a transition from life to death; it signifies decay. Disgust is directed more against decay, the process of decomposition, than against the dead. A skeleton, a mummy, may be frightening, even horrible, but not as disgusting as a cadaver which has just been brought from a river to the morgue.*

Through the writings of Jonathan Swift excellent illustration is given of a peculiar distortion of those sympathetic relations which constitute the very essence of biology. It is not the charm of a lovely woman that attracts Swift's attention but the fact that she has sweat pores, excretions, etc. Similar pathologic preoccupations with decay have also been noted by Havelock Ellis and cogently discussed.[83,84] To the psychopath the basic axioms of life must seem different from what they seem to normal people and also very different

---

*From Straus, Erwin: On obsession, New York, 1948, Nervous and Mental Disease Monographs.

from what they seem to people with severe obsessive disorders. Obsessive patients, as pointed out by Straus, are unable to appreciate what is normally obvious about many positive aspects of experience. This underlying and often unrecognized attitude can be better illustrated than described.

Let us consider briefly an item that is vividly pertinent:

A young man who apparently was not quite happy in his marriage had been seen occasionally with other women. According to rumor he had been or was about to be unfaithful to his wife. A cousin, also married and a few years older, was, in my presence, attempting to bring the other fellow to his senses. The counselor was a man of remarkable learning and intellect. He did not approach the problem by harping on conventional morality or the personal injustice that the other's wife might be done. Maintaining a light touch, half-teasing in his remarks but also seriously trying to be helpful, he spoke of how often young married men drift astray. He made, in a playful, unmoralizing style, some good arguments for avoiding adultery. Then, as if to diminish the temptations which he felt might be troubling the young man, he said: "Remember that when you kiss a girl you are sucking on the end of a tube twenty-five feet long and that the other end is filled with - - - -."*

Exposition or further discussion can contribute little or nothing to the remark as it stands. Whether the estimated length of the gastrointestinal tract is accurate or not has little pertinence. No one can argue with the literal truth of the counselor's statement. But who can avoid wondering about what might have led to the arrival at such a conception of a woman's kiss? And to such a response to such a stimulus?

What Straus and Havelock Ellis have brought out is not discernible in reactions of the psychopath. It is, as a matter of fact, somewhat veiled in the reactions of most obsessive patients. Observation of the psychopath makes it increasingly plain that he is not reacting to the surroundings that are ordinarily assumed to exist. I cannot clearly define the specific milieu which such a patient encounters and to which his reactions are related. There is much to suggest that it is a less distinctly or consistently apprehended world than what Straus describes as the inner world of the obsessive patient. It is my belief that it is a world not less abnormal and probably more complexly confusing. We should remember, however, that we have no direct evidence to prove that a deficiency or distortion of this sort exists in the unconscious core of the psychopath. We can only say that his behavior strongly and consistently suggests it. This discussion has been based, of course, on a hypothesis

---

*The speaker did not have symptoms of obsessive-compulsive neurosis or any features of the psychopath.

that the psychopath has a basic inadequacy of feeling and realization that prevents him from normally experiencing the major emotions and from reacting adequately to the chief goals of human life.

There are other theories that attempt to explain the disorder without taking into consideration the question of such a defect. Alexander has assumed that the psychopath's behavior arises from forces similar to those which in the psychoneurotic are by many believed to be the fundamental cause of his distressing symptoms.[9,11] Postulating unconscious conflict and repressed impulses also in the psychopath, he was led to believe that the asocial, unprofitable, and self-damaging acts of the psychopath are purposive and unconsciously motivated expressions of the conflict. In the classic neurosis, subjective symptoms develop and the patient complains of weakness, headache, or obsessions or develops compulsive rituals, conversion paralysis, blindness, etc. As these manifestations are thought to be reactions of the organism to inner stress, reactions that serve the purpose of protection, relief of anxiety, and gratification (by substitution or displacement, etc.) of rejected or frustrated impulses, so, too, according to Alexander, the pathologic behavior of the other type of patient is an acting out of impulses similarly neurotic. Thus interpreted, the psychopath has, in a sense, genuine and adequate reasons (like the neurotic for his symptoms) for the apparently foolish and uncalled-for things he does that damage himself and others. He himself does not know the reasons or clearly recognize his aims or the real nature of the impulses, and his acts do not constitute a wise solution for his problem; but the acts, according to Alexander, are purposive. This concept of the psychopath as acting out the neurotic problem (in contrast with the more passive development of ordinary symptoms) has been generally accepted by psychoanalysts.[88,185,193,213] It is an interesting concept but it rests chiefly on psychoanalytic theories and assumptions about the unconscious and not upon regularly demonstrable evidence.

Some interpretations of schizophrenia[88] assume that it is largely through the relatively undamaged remnants of the personality that the positive features of the psychosis emerge. If the process is complete, if the personality has, so to speak, entirely dissolved in the underlying id, the machinery to express most of the usual symptoms will be lacking. In response to stress and conflict, what remains of the personality produces, by familiar mechanisms, most of what is generally regarded as characteristic of the disorder. The more fundamental feature, and the one that particularly distinguishes schizophrenia from the psychoneuroses, is the disintegration of the personality.[96] In the psychopath we maintain there is also a generalized disorder of the personality that can be compared with schizophrenia and contrasted with ordinary psychoneurosis (in which the personality is "intact" and the organism maintains "sane" social relations, etc.). It cannot be said that the disorder is that of schizophrenia, but in the whole of the patient's life we find such inadequacy of response, such failure of adaptation, that it seems plausible to postulate alterations more fundamental and more extensive than in classic psychoneurosis.

Beyond the symptomatic acts of the psychopath, we must bear in mind his reaction to his situations, his general experiencing of life. Typical of psychoneurosis are anxiety, recognition that one is in trouble, and efforts to alter the bad situation. These are natural ("normal") whole personality reactions to localized symptoms. In contrast, the severe psychopath, like those so long called psychotic, does not show normal responses to the situation. It is offered as an opinion that a less obvious but nontheless real pathology is general, and that in this he is more closely allied with the psychotic than with the psychoneurotic patient. The pathology might be regarded not as gross fragmentation of the personality but as a more subtle alteration. Let us say that instead of macroscopic disintegration our (hypothetical) change might be conceived of as one that seriously curtails function without obliterating form.

In addition to outwardly visible demolition or shattering in material structures, other changes may occur. These may be intracellular and leave the appearance unchanged but greatly alter the substance. Colloidal variations in concrete may rob it of its essential properties although the appearance of the material remains unaltered. Steel under certain conditions is said to crystallize and lose much of its strength. The steel so affected looks the same as any other and no outer evidence of the molecular rearrangment which has so greatly altered the substance can be detected. For the purpose of analogy, one can consider not only intracellular or molecular but also intramolecular changes. Let us think of the personality in the psychopath as changed in some such way. The form is perfect and the outlines are undistorted. But being subtly and profoundly altered, it can successfully perform only superficial activities or pseudofunctions. It cannot maintain important or meaningful interpersonal relations. It cannot fulfill its purpose of adjusting adequately to social reality. Its performance can only mimic these genuine functions.

Karl Menninger, in *Man Against Himself*,[213] picturesquely developed the argument that antisocial behavior sometimes represents an indirect search for punishment, a veiled but essentially self-destructive activity. The hypothesis of an active "death instinct" advanced by Freud is, in this dramatic study, applied to many types of disorder.[8,96] In localized symptoms, as well as in broad maladjustments, self-damaging impulses are interpreted as fulfilling their negative purpose.

In the patients presented here the general pattern of life seems to be more complex. Although thefts are sometimes committed, checks forged, and frauds perpetrated under circumstances that invite or even assure detection, similar deeds are also frequently carried out with shrewdness and foresight that are difficult to account for by such an interpretation. It is also characteristic for the real psychopath to resent punishment and protest indignantly against all efforts to curtail his activities by jail sentences or hospitalization. He is much less willing than the ordinary person to accept such penalties. In the more circumscribed symptoms of acting out, in many of the disorders referred to by Fenichel[88] as impulse neuroses, the unconscious but purposive quest for punishment might more plausibly be conceived of as a major or regular influence.[255] The validity of such an assumption, however, whether or not it is plausible, must be determined by what actual evidence can be produced to establish it, and not by mere surmises and inferences about what may or may not be in the unconscious.

61

Aspects of regression

The persistent pattern of maladaptation at personality levels and the ostensible purposelessness of many self-damaging acts definitely suggest not only a lack of strong purpose but also a negative purpose or at least a negative drift. This sort of patient, despite all his opportunities, his intelligence, and his plain lessons of experience, seems to go out of his way to woo misfortune.[46] The suggestion has already been made that his typical activities seem less comprehensible in terms of life-striving or of a pursuit of joy than as an unrecognized blundering toward the negations of nonexistence.[8,213]

Some of this, it has been suggested, may be interpreted as the tantrumlike reactions of an inadequate personality balked, as behavior similar to that of the spoiled child who bumps his own head against the wall or holds his breath when he is crossed. It might be thought of as not unlike a man's cutting off his nose to spite not only his face, but also the scheme of life in general, which has turned out to be a game that he cannot play. Such reactions are, of course, found in nearly all types of personality disorder or inadequacy. It will perhaps be readily granted that they are all regressive. Behavior against the constructive patterns through which the personality finds expression and seeks fulfillment of its destiny is regressive activity although it may not consist in a return, step by step, or in a partial return to the status of childhood and eventually of infancy. Such reactions appear to be, in a sense, against the grain of life or against the general biologic purpose.

Regressive reactions or processes may all be regarded as disintegrative, as reverse steps in the general process of biologic growth through which a living entity becomes more complex, more highly adapted and specialized, better coordinated, and more capable of dealing successfully or happily with objective or subjective experience. This scale of increasing complexity exists at points even below the level of living matter. A group of electrons functioning together make up the atom which can indeed be split down again to its components. The atoms joining form molecules which, in turn, coming together in definite orderly arrangement, may become structurally coordinating parts of elaborate crystalline materials; or, in even more specialized and complex fashion, they may form a cell of organic matter. Cells of organic matter may unite and integrate to form the living organism we know as a jellyfish. Always the process is reversible; the organic matter can decompose back into inorganic matter.

Without laboriously following out all the steps of this scale, we might mention the increasing scope of activity, the increasing specialization, and the increasing precariousness of existence at various levels up through vertebrates and mammals to man. All along this scale it is evident that failure to function successfully at a certain level necessitates regression or decomposition to a lower or less complicated one. If the cell membrane of one epithelial unit in a mammalian body becomes imporous and fails to obtain nutriment brought by blood and lymph, it loses its existence as an epithelial cell. If the unwary rabbit fails to perceive the danger of the snare, he soon becomes in rapid succession a dead rabbit, merely a collection of dead organs and supportive structures, protein, fat, etc., and, finally, inorganic matter. The fundamental quest for life has been interrupted, and, having been interrupted, the process goes into reverse.

So, too, the criminal discovered and imprisoned ceases to be a free man who comes and goes as he pleases. A curtailment in the scope of his functioning is suffered—a regression in one sense to simpler, more routine, and less varied and vivid activities. The man who fails in another and more complex way to go on with life, to fulfill his personality growth and function, becomes what we call a schizophrenic. The objective curtailment of his activities by the rules of the psychiatric hospital are almost negligible in comparison with the vast simplification, the loss of self-expression, and the personal disintegration which characterize his regression from the subjective point of view. The old practice of referring to the extremely regressed schizophrenic as leading a vegetative existence implies the significance that is being stressed.

Regression, then, in a broad sense may be taken to mean movement from richer and more full life to levels of scantier or less highly developed life. In other words, it is relative death. It is the cessation of existence or maintenance of function at a given level.

The concept of an active death instinct postulated by Freud[96] has been utilized by some[8,213] to account for socially self-destructive reactions. I have never been able to discover in the writings of Freud or any of his followers real evidence to confirm this assumption. In contrast, the familiar tendency to disintegrate, against which life evolves, may be regarded as fundamental and comparable to gravity. The climbing man or animal must use force and purpose to ascend or to maintain himself at a given height. To fall or slide downhill he need only cease his efforts and let go. Without assuming an intrinsic death instinct, it is possible to account for active withdrawal from positions at which adaptation is unsuccessful and stress too extreme. Whether regression occurs primarily through something like gravity or through impulses more self-contained, the backward movement (or ebbing) is likely to prompt many sorts of secondary reactions, including behavior not adapted for ordinary human purposes but, instead, for functioning in the other direction. The modes of such reactivity may vary, fall into complex patterns, and seek elaborate expression.

In a movement (or gravitational drift) from levels where life is vigorous and full to those where it is less so, the tactics of withdrawal predominate. People with all the outer mechanisms of adaptation intact might, one would think, regress more complexly than can those who react more simply. The simplest reaction in reverse might be found in a person who straightway blows out his brains. As a skillful general who has realized that the objective is unobtainable withdraws by feints and utilizes all sorts of delaying actions, so a patient who has much of the outer mechanisms for living may retire, not in obvious rout but skillfully and elaborately, preserving his lines. The psychopath as we conceive of him in such an interpretation seems to justify the high estimate of his technical abilities as we see them expressed in reverse movement.

Unlike the general with the retreating army in our analogy, he seems not still devoted to the original contest but to other issues and aims that arise in withdrawal. To force the analogy further we might say that the retiring army is now concerning itself with looting the countryside, seeking mischief and light entertainment, etc. The troops have cast off their original loyalties and given up their former aims but have found no other serious ones to replace them. But the effective organization and all of the technical skills are retained.

F. L. Wells has expressed things very pertinent to the present discussion. A brief quotation will bring out useful points:

> The principle of substitutive reactions, sublimative or regressive in character, has long been known, but Kurt Lewin's (1933) experi-

mental construction of the latter is especially apt, if not unquestionable mental hygiene. A child, for example, continually impelled to open a gate it is impossible for him to open, may blow up in a tantrum, grovel on the ground, till the emotion subsides sufficiently for him to become substitutively occupied, as with fragments of gravel and other detritus he finds there, by which he forgets his distress about the gate. Lewin, perhaps unaware of the status of this and allied observations (and their symbols) in psychiatric history, gives it the name "going out of the field": the background is that enunciated by Woodworth and by James before him, not to say Adolf Meyer, Janet, Jung, and the psychoanalytic group generally. The human personality has the adaptive property of finding satisfactions at simpler levels when higher ones are taken away, fortunately so if this keeps him out of a psychosis, otherwise if it stabilizes him in contentment at this lower level ("going native") or if the satisfactions cannot be found short of a psychosis (MacCurdy, 1925, p. 367). All such cases have the common regressive factor of giving up the higher-level adjustment (opening the gate) with regressive relief at a lower level (playing with the gravel).*

Another illustration given by Wells emphasizes features of the concept that are valuable to us:

> Consider, for example, the group of drives that center about the concept of self-maintenance, the "living standards" of civilization. This means the pursuit of the divers means to surround oneself with the maximum of material comfort in terms of residence, food, playthings, etc., for the purchase of which one can capitalize his abilities. That the normal individual will do this to a liberal limit is taken in the local culture as a matter of course, probably more liberally than the facts justify. For this pursuit involves a competitive struggle beset also with inner conflicts (e.g., ethical), which by no means everyone is able to set aside. Among regressions specific to this category are those undertakings of poverty common to religious orders, but this regression is quite specific, since these orders often involve their members in other "disciplines" from which the normal individual would flee as far (Parkman, 1867, Chap. 16). It is quite certain, though hard to demonstrate objectively, that many an individual in normal life regresses from these economic conflicts only in less degree. He does not take the vow of poverty like the monastic, nor does he dedicate himself to the simplified life of the "South Sea Island" stereotype, but he prefers salary to commission, city apartment to suburban "bungalow," clerical work to (outside) sales.*

---

*From Wells, F. L.: Social maladjustment: adaptive regression (chap. 18). In A handbook of social psychology, Worcester, Mass., 1935, Clark University Press.

A thought expressed by William James in 1902 and quoted by Wells deserves renewed attention:

> Yonder puny fellow however, whom everyone can beat suffers no chagrin about it, for he has long ago abandoned the attempt to "carry that line," as the merchants say, of Self at all. With no attempt there can be no failure; with no failure no humiliation. So our self-feeling in this world depends entirely on what we back *ourselves* to be and do. It is determined by the ratio of our actualities to our supposed potentialities; a fraction of which our pretentions are the denominator and the numerator our success: thus, Self-esteem = Success/Pretensions. Such a fraction may be increased as well by diminishing the denominator as by increasing the numerator. To give up pretensions is as blessed a relief as to get them gratified; and where disappointment is incessant and the struggle unending, this is what men will always do. The history of evangelical theology, with its conviction of sin, its self-despair, and its abandonment of salvation by works, is the deepest of possible examples, but we meet others in every walk of life. . . . How pleasant is the day when we give up striving to be young—or slender! Thank God! we say, *those* illusions are gone. Everything added to the self is a burden as well as a pride. . . .*

Something relevant to the points now under consideration may be found also in Sherrington's comment on reactions (or inlaid precautions) against unbearable pain or stress in the human organism. He says:

> Again in life's final struggle the chemical delicacy of the brain-net can make distress lapse early because with the brain's disintegration the mind fades early—a rough world's mercy towards its dearest possession.†

There are, it seems, many ways for this to occur without signs of any change which we yet have objective means to detect, chemically or microscopically. Such changes may occur under the stimulus of agents that do not have direct physical contact with the brain or with any part of the body.

Withdrawal, or limitation of one's quest in living, appears in many forms. The decision for taking such a step may be consciously voluntary, but it seems likely that many influences less clear and simple may also play a part. In the earliest years of human life a great deal of complicated shaping may occur, with adaptive changes to promote survival by an automatic refusal (in-

---

*From James, William: Cited in Wells, F. L.: Social maladjustment: adaptive regression (chap. 18). In A handbook of social psychology, Worcester, Mass., 1935, Clark University Press.
†From Sherrington, Charles: The brain and its mechanism, London, 1934, Cambridge University Press.

ability) to risk one's feelings (response) in the greatest subjective adventures. In adult life such decisions sometimes emerge in clear deliberation.

A man seen many years ago needed and sought understanding from his wife in a relationship which, for many reasons, they had not been able to achieve. None of his problems were related to those of the psychopath. Had he been a little more like these patients, the particular disappointment, loneliness, and distress which influenced him could never have arisen. In a note he refers to a recent failure to reach her after some years of complexly emotional alienation.

Two things emerged in my awareness after an hour of outward harmony; of nothing but conciliatory affection in her words, or in mine: (1) the way her mind closed automatically at the only point possible for me to enter; (2) the total absence of cruelty, or even of intention, in the response that settled the issue. I cannot endure that again. I can make myself believe that it doesn't matter. I will live by myself and nothing will hurt me any more. I apologize for cancelling the appointment.

Such words, standing apart from the situation, convey little or nothing of the distress from which the person withdrew. Perhaps they will illustrate the act of turning away.

The activity of the psychopath seems in some respects to accomplish a kind of protracted and elaborate social and spiritual suicide. From this point of view his behavior suggests that he finds greater and more desirable accomplishment (or relief) in this regressive process than is offered by such an act as promptly killing himself.[46] Perhaps the complex, sustained, and spectacular undoing of the self may be cherished by him. He seldom allows physical suicide to interrupt it. Be it noted that such a person retains high intelligence and nearly all the outer mechanisms for carrying on the complicated activities of positive life. It is to be expected then that his endeavors in the opposite (regressive) emotional direction will be more subtle and far-reaching than those of a less highly developed biologic entity. The average rooster proceeds at once to leap on the nearest hen and have done with his simple erotic impulse. The complex human lover may pay suit for years to his love object, approaching her through many volumes of poetry, through the building up of financial security in his business, through manifold activities and operations of his personality functions, and with aims and emotions incomparably more complicated and more profound than that of the rooster. When complexly organized functions are devoted to aimless or inconsistent rebellion against the positive goals of life, they may enable the patient to woo failure and disintegration with similar elaborateness and subtlety. His

440

conscious or outer functioning may at the same time maintain an imitation of life that is uniquely deceptive.

Perhaps the emptiness or superficiality of a life without major goals or deep loyalties, or real love, would leave a person with high intelligence and other superior capacities so bored that he would eventually turn to hazardous, self-damaging, outlandish, antisocial, and even self-destructive exploits in order to find something fresh and stimulating in which to apply his relatively useless and unchallenged energies and talents.

Like so much of what is often called dynamic interpretation of psychiatric disorder and of human behavior, these thoughts are purely speculative and without the slightest support of evidence. They are offered with no pretense whatsoever of constituting a scientific explanation.

62

Surmise and evidence

If, in the so-called psychopath, we have a patient profoundly limited in ability to participate seriously in the major aims of life, how, we might inquire, did he get that way? Reference has been made to the traditional viewpoint from which it was assumed that an inborn organic defect left these people "constitutionally inferior" or "moral imbeciles," etc. Such a congenital defect, it must be readily admitted, may exist and may account for the failure to experience life normally and hence to react sanely.

During the earlier decades of the twentieth century this concept of the psychopath prevailed. It was widely believed that these patients, often called *constitutional inferiors,* came almost exclusively from families loaded with *stigmata of degeneration* and *signs of neuropathic taint.*[124] As time passed it was noted that typical psychopaths were also seen in families of very respectable, ethical, and successful people and were entirely free from all physical *stigmata of degeneration.* Many pointed out that some of the statistical studies giving evidence of hereditary factors are not as reliable as they were once thought. Even the famous studies of the Jukes and the Jonathan Edwards families have been severely criticized and called fallible by some.[285]

As already mentioned, Healy[125,126] long ago pointed out that antisocial behavior often seemed to occur as a response to unhappy life situations, and Alexander formulated such disorder in psychoanalytic terms as a purposive acting out of unconscious pathologic conflicts.[9,11]

The concept of acting out, in lightly disguised symbolic deeds, might be vividly illustrated in the case reported here in which a man responded to what is often spoken of as being in the doghouse by putting on his dog's collar and spectacularly caricaturing canine behavior.* Another response to a similar situation can be found in the patient who literally got into a kennel at the veterinarian's and so exhibited himself.† Although these incidents picturesquely illustrate Alexander's concept of acting out, they do not in themselves constitute evidence of an unconscious conflict which he has assumed causes the behavior. Neither patient showed any reaction that would support belief in the presence of inner, unconscious feelings of guilt or of the type of conflict attributed to sociopaths in such interpretations. The assumption of such guilt in these two patients must be made purely on faith in the theory.

Many other psychiatrists have attempted to explain the psychopath in terms of psychogenic causation. The studies of Greenacre led her to conclude that the confusing influence of a stern, authoritarian father and an indulgent or frivolous mother is common in the early background of the psychopath. It is plausible to feel that such an influence might contribute to rebellious reactions and to a defective development of conscience and of ordinary social and personal evaluations.[107] Karpman, in his extensive work with character and behavior disorders, offers the opinion that in most cases a psychogenic etiology can be established if adequate investigation is made.[166,167,168,169] A relatively small percentage of those we call psychopaths, he believes, are not so motivated. These, presumably disordered because of inborn or constitutional defect, he distinguishes from the majority and calls anethopaths.[167]

Knight's studies of severe alcoholics, many of whom were considered psychopaths, led him to believe that they often had "a parental background characterized by inconsistency and lack of unanimity in parental discipline resulting in conflicting unstable identifications in the son."* A weak, pampering mother in combination with a domineering father whose severity was fitful and inconsistent appeared frequently in the background of Knight's cases. He feels that important causal relations between this early situation and the subsequent disorder are likely.[174,175] Knight says:

> Innumerable personality shadings and accents are possible from a son's reaction to such parental management, but one regular result seems to be the fostering of excessive passive demands and expecta-

---

*P. 203.
†Pp. 215 to 216.

tions in the son, such passive, childish, feminine wishes being in marked conflict with masculine strivings inculcated by the father and by the cultural ideology absorbed from schooling and from contacts with other males.*

Adelaide Johnson has expressed a strong conviction that the delinquency of a child or teen-ager is sometimes caused by the parents' own *unconscious* impulses toward antisocial conduct. The child or teen-ager, she tells us, is craftily used as a pawn and unconsciously encouraged in theft, arson, sexual promiscuity, violence, or sexual perversion in order to fulfill the parents' unconscious emotional needs to carry out such conduct themselves.[154,155,156] According to this formulation, the child, even after he has become an adult, remains unconscious of the parents' adverse influence and of his real motives for antisocial conduct. Furthermore, Johnson reports that the parents are often unwilling to give up their vicarious criminal satisfactions and that they may actively block the psychiatrist's attempts at therapy. Such an explanation has been accepted as a common cause for the sociopath's disorder by a number of prominent psychiatrists.[235]

Perhaps there are delinquents and sociopaths in whom such influences play an important part. Let us remember, however, that some methods of trying to determine what is in the unconscious may allow us unwittingly to project items from our theories into the assumed motivation of the patient and also of his parents. If persistent but unconscious antisocial impulses are really active in the parents, we might also ask ourselves if such tendencies might have been conveyed to the offspring by hereditary factors. I think it very unlikely that the parents of the patients presented here and of the others studied by me found satisfaction, unconsciously or otherwise, in the persistent misconduct of their sons and daughters.

Lindner[188] devoted almost an entire volume, *Rebel Without a Cause,* to the detailed report of one psychopath studied by hypnoanalytic methods. He believed that through processes of preverbal memory he was able to obtain from the patient a true report of significant and traumatic experiences which he dated as occurring at 6 or 8 months of age. Lindner gives a detailed and ingenious explanation of how he believes these experiences caused the patient to develop seriously disturbed relations with his parents and eventually to adopt the typical role of the sociopath. Despite the strong convictions of Lindner, his excellent presentation, and the superb title of his book, *Rebel Without a*

---

*From Knight, Robert: The psychoanalytic treatment in a sanatorium of chronic addiction to alcohol, Journal of the American Medical Association 111:1443-1448, 1938.

Cause, there is much that makes me skeptical about the significance of experiences reported as having occurred at such an early age and about the validity of what may be recalled through preverbal memory or established chiefly by the interpretation of symbols and dreams.

One reason for my skepticism is derived from startling and at times fantastic accounts of events in infancy or very early childhood occasionally given to me by my own patients. Let us consider briefly two examples:

One man, 35 years of age, told in vivid detail, under repeated hypnotic investigations, of having been brutally snatched away from the mother's lactating breast by the father, who replaced him and nursed her—forcibly, brusquely, but thoroughly—meanwhile immobilizing her despite her struggles, protests, and screams. Conscious and very overt incestuous impulses toward the mother during his early years and frank and bitter murderous wishes toward the father were spontaneously expressed and with vehemence. Vivid conscious desires to "crawl up into my mother's womb" were enthusiastically voiced. Much more material equally impressive was elicited, including particularly traumatic details about his reactions to sexual relations between the parents which he claimed to have witnessed frequently during the first year of his life and which he described in spectacular detail. Almost any of his dreams could be interpreted by popular methods to confirm the presence of persistent oedipal problems, as well as problems often ascribed to oral and anal phases of development.

A 17-year-old boy claimed similarly unusual experiences. Many details emerged suggesting profound bewilderment, hate, fear, maximal insecurity and subtly and grossly incestuous drives that arose from experiences reported as occurring at the age of three years. These centered about a partial and mystified sensing of major unhappiness in the mother, who sometimes shrieked, wept, or appeared to be at the point of death because of something she complained of to the father, whom she called vile, merciless, a fraud, and a fiend. No clear understanding arose from his repeatedly being taken along by the father (apparently as a screen against the mother's suspicion) on adulterous ventures. He offered details of the scene in which, left to play on the floor of an adjoining room, he overheard much that puzzled him. He described very convincingly a grandfather's clock in the place of rendezvous behind which he sometimes hid so that he could obtain a view of the copulating couple. He claimed that stresses and confusions of the most drastic nature affected him during this period.

Some, but by no means all, of this material impressed me from the first as probably representing fabrication or fantasy confused with memory rather than accurately recalled facts. In the two cases just mentioned, as investiga-

445

tion proceeded, so many implausible events were recounted that it became evident none could be accepted as necessarily factual. Anything the examiner chose to seek was readily produced by the patient and elaborated with marvelous conviction. This proclivity in some patients may play a significant part in explaining how conscientious therapists find confirmation for widely differing and sometimes contradictory theories during prolonged investigations of a patient's infantile experiences and unconscious attitudes. It has tended to make me increasingly cautious about accepting as necessarily true historical data even from much later periods of life from patients of this type. It has often been noted that the psychopath will very convincingly report entirely false incidents and attitudes in others, particularly in parents, that tend to put responsibility for his difficulties upon them.

It is also true that experiences ordinarily withheld or deeply repressed in other people are often quickly and readily divulged by these patients. Disgraceful and extremely uninviting deeds are sometimes reported with a relish that suggests pride in them. Although shame and terrible conflict are sometimes claimed in such matters and superficial indications of such claims may be impressive, I am unable to feel that I regularly get at any level with the patient in which such affects are major or even quite real. This is a factor deserving constant attention, for it can enter very subtly into material obtained from patients of this sort. The point most difficult to corroborate, in my own experience, is the actual or innermost personal reaction of these patients to the events they report. It is more difficult than with others to tell what the events mean to them.

Some comments made by Jenkins are pertinent, it seems to me, to the question of whether or not psychopaths are acting out a conflict based upon unconscious feelings of guilt.

> Effective challenge to a basic faith always causes pain and a reaction ridden with emotion in which the issues can easily become clouded . . . . This challenge has been felt by some of the defenders of the modern psychodynamic faith which, at least initially, tended to a narrow conception that functional mental disorders and maladjustments are always due to conflicts within the personality. To enlarge this concept with a realization that morbid conditions and gross maladjustments may be due primarily to a *lack* of conflict within the personality represents a readjustment of thinking which is apparently beyond the flexibility of many professional persons. There is of course, a semantic problem involved. It was not difficult for mankind to understand poisoning, for it is easy to grasp the proposition, "what he ate made him sick." The understanding of the vitamin deficiency

diseases was more difficult because of the greater semantic difficulty of the proposition, "what he did not eat made him sick."[120] Yet this second proposition is as true and as necessary to any adequate consideration of illness as is the first. In the same way many of our dynamically oriented colleagues have great difficulty with the proposition, "The conflict he does not have makes him a psychopath." This concept is true and necessary, but requires at least a flexible application of classical psychodynamic theory.

Theories are advantageous when they stimulate some resourceful new attack on a problem. They are handicapping when they make it difficult for us to recognize important facts. . . .

. . . If indeed we must get into the area of theory—and this is not entirely avoidable—I should like to propose that psychopaths differ from psychoneurotics and indeed contrast with them in their most important characteristics. The typical psychopath and the typical psychoneurotic are, in some important regards, on opposite sides of the normal. Where the psychoneurotic suffers from excessive inner conflict, the psychopath makes others suffer from his lack of inner conflict. Only the person who does not come in contact with serious cases of this sort, or whose mind is literally imprisoned by his faith in a theory can brush aside this fundamental difference.*

I have become increasingly convinced that some of the popular methods presumed to discover what is in the unconscious cannot be counted upon as reliable methods of obtaining evidence. They often involve the use of symbolism and analogy in such a way that the interpreter can find virtually anything that he is looking for. Freud, for instance, from a simple dream reported by a man in his middle twenties as having occurred at 4 years of age drew remarkable conclusions. The 4-year-old boy dreamed of seeing six or seven white wolves sitting in a tree. Freud interpreted the dream in such a way as to convince himself that the patient at 18 months of age had been shocked by seeing his parents have intercourse three times in succession and that this played a major part in the extreme fear of being castrated by his father which Freud ascribes to him at 4 years of age. No objective evidence was ever offered to support this conclusion. Nor was actual fear of castration ever made to emerge into the light of consciousness despite years of analysis.[54,97]

Faithfully following Freud's method of establishing proof by analogy, a prominent psychiatrist in his recent book *Beyond Laughter*[109] has given us a remarkable interpretation of the drum majorette. Most of us are likely

---

*From Jenkins, Richard L.: The psychopathic or antisocial personality, Journal of Nervous and Mental Disease **131**:318-332, 1960.

to think that the average man's pleasant reaction to these well-built, sparsely clad young ladies who prance happily and often somewhat sexily before the band at football stadiums can be pretty well accounted for by tastes and impulses quite obvious in nearly anyone's consciousness. These, according to the interpretation in *Beyond Laughter,* must be considered as superficial or perhaps even as the result of reaction formation. The lissome girl, we are solemnly told, stands out before the grouped band just as an erect penis stands out before the larger mass of the body. This analogy is taken as evidence that interest and excitement about the provocative lass do not lie primarily in the fact that any ordinary man would find her attractive. In our unconscious she is said to be equated with the erect male organ, and it is maintained that men really feel toward her, as she stands projected before the group, as they *unconsciously* feel toward the penis of another male. Our positive reactions toward her, we are told, arise from our unrecognized and unaccepted homosexuality. No corroborative evidence is offered, nor any doubt expressed, about this interpretation. It is soberly offered as a fact, presumably discovered by science.[109]

The Dutch psychiatrist Peerbolte[246] uses a similar method of analogy to establish what he considers satisfactory evidence of emotional trauma during embryonic or fetal life. A patient dreams that she is in a chapel and that the figure of Christ with a wooden leg walks toward her. The interpreter concludes that this indicates that she was frightened and shaken up by her father's penis when those who were to become her parents had intercourse while she was a fetus in her mother's uterus.

Distrust for such glib use of the popular methods of interpretation has been strongly expressed by a few prominent and well-qualified psychoanalysts. Masserman, in a delightful article, gives us an important lesson in his brilliant satire, "The Psychosomatic Profile of an Ingrown Toenail." Let us quote from this article.

> Consider, I said, the toenail. Anthropologists have pointed out that man's mind developed when his arms were freed of the task of locomotion so that he could walk about the earth in an upright position, manipulating its resources and thinking about the heavens. Moreover, osteologists tell us that all of this in turn depended upon the hallux and its toenail. But libidinally speaking, the nail represents even more than this. Actually, it is the most protuberant part of the body, hard and rounded; in locomotion it describes a most suggestive to-and-fro movement—obviously, then, it is a basic penile symbol displaced, for a change, downward. But let us also remember the anatomic origin of this important little phallus, namely the *nail-bed*— also a most significant term. This in turn consists of an invagination

448

of vascular tissue into a zone called, with intuitive propriety, the *stratum germinativum* or *matrix*—a region consummately feminine in its conformation, physiology, and import. Here, then, we have a psychosomatically significant microcosm; a womb-equivalent ever generating a masculine imago which normally goes forth to meet, explore, and conquer the external world.

But now consider what happens when this normal functioning is disrupted by frustration and conflict; when, specifically, the erect nail is stubbed and traumatized, or is too long opposed by unyielding reality in the form of a repressive shoe. Clinically and perhaps personally we know the effects all too well: the nail, particularly at the peripheral portions of its individuality (or more technically, its "ego boundaries") turns about and digs its way back into the flesh of its origin. To those properly indoctrinated with psychosomatic understanding, however, a much deeper significance can be discerned in this process. It will be obvious, indeed, that the counter-cathected ungual masculinity, blocked from its exteriorizing libidinal outlets, introverts upon itself and eventually even seeks final regression through the mechanism of re-encapsulation and vascularization—i.e., a return to uterine existence. This formula, derived as it is by analogic thinking enlightened by metapsychologic insight, could of course stand on its merits alone about as well as others derived from similar research endeavors; fortunately, however, it can be further validated by objective clinical observation. Thus, it can be demonstrated that analysands of both sexes with ingrown toenails actually do have masculine aspirations and intra-uterine fantasies, and the mere fact that analysands *without* ingrown toenails have the same unconscious dynamisms serves merely to emphasize once again how the study of the abnormal can reveal profound truths about all mankind.*

The material just quoted is from a lecture that Masserman gave to point out, by a playful reduction to absurdity, some of the overenthusiastic and unreliable uses of dynamic methods in psychology and psychiatry. Let us quote also his comments on the audience's reaction to his lecture:

Here I ended my Lecture on Psychosomatics, rewarded by what I was sure was an understanding gleam in the eye of some of my listeners and trusting that, though I lacked the ribaldry of a Rabelais or the subtlety of a Voltaire, I might still have aroused a healthy whimsy of doubt about some of the verbal gymnastics that pass for serious thinking and investigation in the field. Imagine my consternation, therefore, when on meeting some of the members of the audience days and weeks later I was actually congratulated on the clinical and analytic perspicacity with which I had derived the specific

*From Masserman, Jules H.: Faith and delusion in psychotherapy, the ur-defenses of man, American Journal of Psychiatry **110**:324-333, 1953.

dynamic formula for the etiology and possible therapy of that hitherto unexplored psychosomatic disorder—onychocryptosis, or ingrown toenail!*

In dwelling on the pitfalls and possibilities of error that we face in attempts to explain the sociopath's disorder on a psychogenic basis, I do not mean to discount sober efforts to accomplish this by realistic methods. Let us, however, be cautious and tentative and try always to distinguish surmise from evidence.

I have noted incidents in the early life of some sociopaths that might serve as factors likely to promote rebellion against society, distort the normal aims of life, interfere with the development of basic values, and go far, perhaps, toward accounting for much of the behavior so familiar to all who know them well. Some of these early experiences might indeed go far toward explaining their emotional status that has been so effectively and succintly summarized by William and Joan McCord in their excellent book. They say:

> The psychopath feels little, if any, guilt. He can commit the most appalling acts, yet view them without remorse. The psychopath has a warped capacity for love. His emotional relationships, when they exist, are meager, fleeting, and designed to satisfy his own desires. These last two traits, guiltlessness and lovelessness, conspicuously mark the psychopath as different from other men.†

But similar experiences also can be demonstrated in the background of many well-adjusted, happy, and successful adults. In a few of the cases reported here an impressive account was given of incidents and reported reactions (with indications of emotion) that could theoretically be said to explain emotional withdrawal (despite maintenance of excellent rational contact) from the areas or levels of living in which severe hurt, deep joy, genuine pride, shame, dignity, and love are encountered and experienced. Protest reactions, loss of insight, an acting out of unconscious impulses, a behavioral caricature, or a diatribe against life and its (for the psychopath) subjective emptiness could be interpreted as major causal factors in the disorder we encounter clinically. Such interpretations may be correct, but usually there are more elements of assumption or speculation than of evidence in what is offered in support of the argument.

A very large percentage of the psychopaths I have studied show back-

---

*From Masserman, Jules H.: Faith and delusion in psychotherapy, the ur-defenses of man, American Journal of Psychiatry 110:324-333, 1953.
†From McCord, William, and McCord, Joan: Psychopathy and delinquency, New York, 1956, Grune & Stratton. Reprinted by permission.

grounds that appear conducive to happy development and excellent adjustment. Whatever part psychogenic factors may play, I am inclined to believe that there may be an important relationship between the abstruse, paradoxically compounded, and ambivalent nature of the influences and the complex and deeply masked nature of the disorder such factors may shape. If such a relationship exists, it may to some degree explain the special difficulties we have encountered in obtaining from the psychopath convincing subjective information about what has happened and about how he was affected by it.

In the patients presented here, social service reports and all ordinary information usually indicated normal and helpful family attitudes and general environments. The families themselves often impressed the examiner as good, healthy, wise, and eminently well-adjusted people whose children were particularly fortunate because of what they could offer as parents. When opportunities arose, as they sometimes did, to learn more of matters inward, subtle, and deeply personal, the observer was sometimes led to suspect that even in these apparently superior parents there were attitudes, frustrations, emotional confusions, and deficiencies that might have played a masked but crucially adverse role in the infinite complexities and paradoxes of parent-child relationships.

This is not to say that the parents were wrongly judged as conscientious or as superior people or that in many important respects they were not well adjusted. Despite conscientiousness and a good deal of wisdom and success, characteristics may exist which could subtly but trenchantly distort the milieu of an infant or a child.[254]

People may be fair, kind, and genial, may hold entirely normal or even admirable attitudes about all important matters and yet unknowingly lack a simple warmth, a capacity for true intimacy that seems to be essential for biologic soundess (substantiality) in some basic relationships. There are men and women of whom it might correctly be said that it is impossible for them ever to become really personal. This aspect (or ingredient) of human experience is difficult to describe or to signify accurately. We do not encounter it squarely in thinking but feel it in perceptive modes or at reactive levels not readily translatable into speech.[104] Let us remember, however, that such qualities may be found in parents of those who are not sociopaths.

Some who show only superior qualities in all their activities as citizens, in their work, and in all definable responsibilities feel little need for the sort of specific attachment and affective closeness which perhaps constitute the core of deep and genuine love. They also seem to have little perception of such a need in others. There are people who show in changeless formality, poise, and cool "sensible attitudes" outer indications of what is being discussed, but it is not they who concern us at present. In others, genial informality and manifestations of more than ordinary warmth may prevail in relatively super- ficial friendships and routine social contacts, in professional and business associations, at dinner parties, and at club meetings. Where intimacy is normally limited they may be spontaneous and show cordiality as real as anything appropriate for such occasions. Their inner formality and remote- ness is not encountered until the observer approaches areas of privacy, deep levels of personal affect that ordinarily are only reached in relations between mates, between parent and child, or in the few other very intimate and cher- ished friendships or sharings of personal understanding and feeling that man never achieves in wholesale lot. Parents of this sort may give an impression of affording each other and the child all that is ideal, and affording it in abundance. One such parent will, however, leave the other (if normal) so deprived in essential needs that the child may be turned to for the exclusive and possessive intimacy normal between mates but full of pathologic poten- tialities in the other relationship.

The observations reported by Kanner in his study of infantile autism illus- trate some of the points that are being discussed here.[163] In the brilliant and outstandingly successful parents of these seriously disabled infants a com- plex and profound emotional deficiency was regularly encountered. During all my years of experience with hundreds of psychopaths, however, no type of parent or of parental influence, overt or subtle, has been regularly demon- strable.

Both hereditary factors and influences of the frustrating, or antisocial, environment seem evident in the development of delinquency in many of the patients described long ago by Healy.[124] In the background of the intelligent, charming psychopath who appears in a family of prominent, ethical, and successful citizens, it is often far more difficult to find convincing evidence to account for his disorder on either basis. If an inborn biologic defect exists and plays an important part in such a psychopath's disorder, it is not neces- sary to assume that the defect is hereditary. Perhaps it may be the result of a subtle failure in maturation, an agenesis of unknown etiology. A much simpler and more grossly manifested defect of this sort is familiar in the pathology of congenital cerebral palsy. It is well known that encephalitis may be followed by changes in behavior and personality that cause some who have suffered from it to become indistinguishable from the psychopaths we have been discussing and that these changes may occur without any physical signs of neurologic damage.

Many psychiatrists[39,200,289] have continued to express the conviction that some organic injury or deficiency underlies the psychopath's dysfunction. Although no neurologic lesion has been regularly demonstrated in the typical psychopath, it is also true, as Thompson reminds us, that no satisfactory proof of psychogenic factors as the cause of his disorder has been established. Referring to formulations of the psychopathology in terms of environmental influences, he says:

> Here too much is missing that might give us a rational explanation which would be subject to scientific scrutiny, and which would meet the postulates of science necessary for validity.*

Numerous observers have reported records of electroencephalographic abnormality in psychopaths.[105,177,269] Others have failed to confirm these findings of a specific abnormality.[101,271] At present many believe there are non-specific but definitely abnormal electroencephalographic findings in a significant percentage of psychopaths.[81,134,135,289]

If a neurologic defect does exist in the psychopath, it is also quite possible that influences in the milieu may play an important part also in shaping his pattern of life. It seems to me likely that such a defect, if present, must be one that affects complex mechanisms of integration in a subtle and abstruse manner. Some of the superior capacities encountered so often in psychopaths suggest that their difficulties might arise not only from deficiencies but possibly, even if rarely, by misused assets.

It seems reasonable to believe that in differences lie varying susceptibilition to failure or to psychiatric disorder. Such susceptibilities may not necessarily be defects or intrinsically negative qualities. May not superior emotional responses contribute to a boy's developing maternal attachments that can prove crippling in the degree to which he has capacity for loyalty? May not the precociously brilliant child, because of his advancement, encounter deep personal and social problems earlier than the average? And, will he, perhaps, sustain trauma that he might have avoided with additional experience? Such experience may be available to the mediocre child who, in his slower progress, meets the confusing situation a little later. Those whose feelings are highly developed may be more susceptible to hurt than others. The goals of the superior person often demand of him complicated choices and sacrifices that the average person never has to face. Disillusion and suffering because of frustrations escaped by most of his fellows might, it seems reasonable to think, in the child of great talent and potentiality, stimulate attitudes of withdrawal and cynical rejection or other pathologic reactions. Exceptional

---

*From Thompson, G. N.: The psychopathic delinquent and criminal, Springfield, Ill., 1953, Charles C Thomas, Publisher.

talent or capacity seems almost regularly to call for exceptional achievement or fulfillment and to put the subject under extraordinary responsibility and into situations peculiarly complex. Courage and initiative lead man not only to take physical risks but sometimes also into subjective ventures of many sorts with many dangers.

What we value in some as steadfastness may arise from potentialities that, through different shaping, emerge in others as incorrigibility, inelasticity, or perhaps as those elements which may make a psychiatric disorder irreversible. Granting the likelihood of great variation in the basic potentialities of the organism, let us not forget that in so complex a matter as personality maturation and social adjustment not only defects but talents also may contribute to conflict, to confusion, to distortion of the life pattern, and, perhaps, to serious clinical disorder.

If what is good or wise or sound comes, or appears to come, mixed, so to speak, with what is untrue or deleterious and is identified in a single concept, and designated by the same term, peculiar difficulties may be promoted. Such difficulties, it seems reasonable to think, might be especially disturbing to the superior child. Conscientious acceptance of what is most necessary for normal growth and development may, under these circumstances, sometimes necessitate commitments to what must later be rejected if the organism is to survive. The deeper the capacity for loyalty, the more profound may be the stress, confusion, and eventual disillusionment.

The psychopath's inner deviation from the normal impresses me as one subtly masked and abstruse. So, too, it has often seemed that interpersonal and environmental factors, if they contribute to the development of his disorder, are likely to be ones so disguised superficially as to appear of an opposite nature. Something pertinent to this concept may be conveyed by the words that follow:

> Everything spiritual and valuable has a gross and undesirable malady very similar to it and possessing the same name. Only the very wise can distinguish between them.*

I do not believe that the cause of the psychopath's disorder has yet been discovered and demonstrated. Until we have more and better evidence than is at present available, let us admit the incompleteness of our knowledge and modestly pursue our inquiry.

---

*From Thompson, D. L.: Address at banquet, meeting of the American Psychiatric Association, Montreal, 1949.

This disease is beyond my practice.
          —The doctor in *Macbeth*

63

Illness and misconduct

A good deal has already been said about the difficulties and disappointments arising in our efforts to treat these patients generally known as psychopaths. A few more points will be added presently to the opinions already
expressed, but if we are to make any progress therapeutically it seems first
necessary to clarify some broader issues.

Aside from the intrinsic obdurateness of the disorder which we find in
the patient himself, there exist surrounding difficulties and absurdities that
have made it quite impossible even to approach the central problem in any
way except one that axiomatically predetermines defeat. Challenged by what
is perhaps the most difficult therapeutic task in psychiatry, the physician is
denied ordinary access to the area in which the task must be accomplished.
It is only in exceptional instances that the therapist can get his hands on
the patient, and even then he has little more opportunity to take useful
measures than would a surgeon called upon to remove the gallbladder of a
jackrabbit in full flight. Our medical, legal, and social concepts are so formulated and our institutions so devised that it is usually impossible to bring the
psychopath into the range of treatment. Nor is it usually possible for him to
be brought under control of any agency that can protect him or others from

the damaging effects of his disorder.[47,49] This point is emphasized by Thompson in a helpful study:

> . . . The administrative officers of penal institutions attempt to have such individuals transferred to mental hospitals because they believe them to be mentally ill. Knowing how little they can do for them and what difficult problems they are, the superintendents of mental hospitals attempt to get rid of them as soon as possible and transfer them back to the prison as "not psychotic." Pushed from prison to hospital and back again, wanted in neither, the psychopathic delinquent is essentially the orphan of both penology and psychiatry.*

The exceptional patients who commit felonies and are convicted come, it is true, under the legal restraints of prison. These, in my opinion, constitute a proportion approximately equivalent to the proportion of schizophrenic patients who might obtain treatment or come under protective control if nothing could be done about schizophrenia until the patient with this illness had carried out felonies and these had been legally established. Like the patient with traditionally recognized psychosis, the psychopath cannot be counted on to seek treatment and even less to submit voluntarily to protective measures.

Two crucial points confront us in any attempt to deal practically with the disorder which has engaged our attention: (1) the question of distinguishing between illness (true disability) and willful or culpable misbehavior and (2) the question of legal responsibility or competency. These two matters are deeply interwoven and bring us eventually to the same basic problem. It will be helpful, however, to approach our problem through these two channels. Let us take them in order.

It has already been pointed out that in earlier times many types of dangerous or bizarre conduct which today are regarded as illness were attributed to witchcraft, demon possession, or other supernatural agencies.[216,285,313,314] Along with and subsequent to this interpretation we find the practice of attributing misfortune, ordinary physical and psychiatric diseases, etc., to sin or some other form of voluntary wrongdoing. Those conditions earliest recognized as having a medical aspect are the ones in which injury, symptoms (somatic or psychic), and other outward features are most obvious. The overtness rather than the real degree of seriousness seems to have been the chief clue in these determinations. The medical practitioner was called upon to help with the mangled leg or the carbuncle while exorcism and other mystic rites

---

*From Thompson, G. N.: The psychopathic delinquent and criminal, Springfield, Ill., 1953, Charles C Thomas, Publisher.

were still the only measures provided for the patient suffering from such obscure pathology as leukemia or Addison's disease. Even when ideas still prevailed that wrongdoing was the primary cause of disease, treatment by the physician was accepted as an appropriate step to take in dealing with some of these afflictions.[50,313] The compound fracture that followed a fall was treated by the surgeon during times when the fall was regarded as the result of a sorcerer's spell. So, too, salvarsan was administered to the patient with syphilis even by those who regarded him as ill primarily because of his voluntary wrongdoing.

After overt and vividly macroscopic expressions of psychosis (running naked through the streets and wildly shouting out messages received from the dead, arguing that one's body lacks an anus, one's blood is pure pus, etc.) had for some time been accepted as illness, decades passed before the masked or cryptic schizophrene and the well-oriented, careful, and brilliantly reasoning paranoiac could count on so regular or so early medical attention as they receive today. We have not yet learned to distinguish such patients very readily and they sometimes remain without treatment or any protective social measures until their disorder is far advanced. Murder or some other tragic consequence may be necessary to bring them to examination and eventually to what treatment is available for their condition.

Forms or expressions of illness are not necessarily less serious, less dangerous, or less genuine because the superficial appearance of the patient reveals less obvious signs of a disorder. One of the factors contributing to our present difficulty in distinguishing the aspect of illness in the psychopath is, I believe, not dependent on the degree of whatever disorder he shows but on its type or nature.

Few (sane) theologians, philosophers, or jurists would contend today that present concepts of disease and methods of dealing with it, whether manifested in a predominantly somatic aspect or otherwise, have damaged religion or made nonsense of moral values. When something can be done to help the situation in its medical aspect, this is done without waiting to reach agreement on nonmedical absolutes, however important these ultimate questions may be for each of us.

The patient with pneumonia might not have become ill if he had not suffered exposure while he was out in severe weather robbing the bank. Another patient's hemorrhoids may or may not be related to his lazy habits of sitting around all day or to his becoming constipated and then unwisely taking powerful laxatives advertised in the papers. Here we may find a patient whose anxiety seems to be, in part at least, caused by a (cowardly) fear of accepting the responsibilities (and opportunities) of a new job and also by an old pathologic (wrong) tendency to rely on his mother for support and protection.

A man in severe agitated depression may say all his viscera have rotted until the stench is lethal and that his neighbor's crops wither under his glance. His throat may show deep lacerations from his last desperate attempt at suicide. No one questions the plain fact that he is ill and gravely ill. Some psychopathologists believe that he is ill primarily (or largely) because of his unconscious hate for those he loves and his impulses to destroy them.[2,3,88] Even those who hold this belief agree that therapy is appropriate. It is also agreed that he must be supervised and protected, if necessary against his own will and judgment.

Just who or what (in a final philosophic showdown) is to blame for these situations is difficult indeed for anyone to say. That they are pathologic conditions deserving every available measure for their correction is not as difficult to determine.

An important point to express and, if possible, to establish is this: medical attention or any other practical step to help or ameliorate misfortune or pain must not wait for a threshing out on philosophic, metaphysical, and religious planes of the ultimate whys and wherefores, the final determining of blame or responsibility. It is possible and practicable to meet these emergencies at another point.

Reasons have been expressed already for the opinion that the psychopath differs fundamentally from the ordinary criminal or rascal.* Whether or not this argument is valid, let us seek a remedy for what obviously demands attention. Not only a patient's welfare but that of the community must be given consideration in any step we decide to take.

Many types of behavior formerly regarded as voluntary wrongdoing or the just results of sin are now classed as disease. This does not prove that eventually all wrongdoing will be plainly revealed as disease and all conduct necessarily evaluated at a level at which good and bad are nonexistent. There are, however, indications that medical, legal, and social remedial steps are often useful in dealing with situations that we have not yet assayed and may never unanimously assay in final terms of ethics.

Let us remember, however, that there are good reasons to believe that this tendency to reclassify wrongdoing as illness has in recent decades gone too far—perhaps in some instances to the point of absurdity. Some commentators use the term sickness, or illness, glibly in referring to the cause of any bank robbery, embezzlement, forgery, murder, income tax fraud, or viola-

---

*Pp. 276 to 282.

tion of traffic laws. The assumptions that underlie this practice are not usually supported by any actual evidence from psychiatric investigation but depend entirely upon the arbitrary choice of a term to exonerate those who have perpetrated antisocial acts.

It has become exceedingly popular to say routinely that crime is not the fault of the criminal but of society. Many commentators also insist that there is no such thing as a bad child but only bad parents. All this tends logically to promote the feeling that a person can do no wrong and need take no responsibility for his own misconduct, however deplorable or harmful to himself or to others. Suppose I want to rob a bank. Well, why not? If I do, I am not to blame. The blame instead will be put on society, or on my parents, or perhaps on a teacher in the first grade who traumatized me by discipline and must now be responsible for my rebellious self-expression. If we need other scapegoats to exonerate all criminals of any possible guilt, we might blame the grandparents, who from this viewpoint must in turn have been responsible for the evil in the criminal's parents. Arguments approximately as glib and unrealistic as these are to be found today in scientific literature.[56] In trying to understand or estimate the sociopath, let us avoid these gratuitous and so often far-fetched assumptions. Is it possible that we have sometimes gone to extremes during recent years in this direction to a degree comparable to the follies of witchcraft in another?

64

Legal competency and criminal responsibility

It has been mentioned that the psychopath does not often cooperate willingly in treatment over any considerable period of time and that he also seems to be remarkably free from the ordinary legal and penal restraints that prevent others from repeatedly carrying out antisocial activity. Questions of legal competency and criminal responsibility play a fundamental part in the efforts of society to cope with sociopaths. Let us consider these concepts more closely.

The term *competency* in connection with our present problem is pertinent to questions of legal commitment, which is a procedure by which the psychiatric patient can, when necessary, be placed under treatment and appropriate restrictions even if this has to be done against his will and, if necessary, by force. Responsibility seems in many respects to be another aspect of the same thing. The incompetent person has been legally pronounced unable to look after his own affairs or make his own decisions about crucial matters. If a person is held to be legally responsible by a court, he is then considered to be culpable for any crime or other misdeed he may have committed and hence subject to legal penalties. Many assumptions, some of them about matters on which few entirely agree, lurk in various degrees of disguise in the almost limitless implications of these terms.

Probably most laymen, and perhaps some physicians, think of both incompetency and a lack of legal responsibility as identical with psychosis or *insanity*. As so helpfully pointed out by Davidson,[68] this is incorrect, or at least incomplete and sometimes misleading. According to the law, Uncle John's will may be entirely valid, although he insisted for years that he talked with his dead grandmother and was diagnosed as having schizophrenia. Every psychiatrist knows people who hallucinate and are delusional but who should not be deprived of their liberty and sent against their will to institutions. A good example is offered in a 50-year-old woman who for fifteen years has carefully listened to a voice from her stomach which she "knows" is real and which often directs her. Advice given by the voice has on the whole been quite sensible and practical—never irrational! She has for a decade come at intervals to the outpatient clinic. So far as can be ascertained, her life has been undisturbing to others, and she has, with fair competency, carried out her own affairs.

It is true, nevertheless, that nearly everywhere in the United States it is usually necessary for medical evidence to establish the presence of a "psychosis" and for the court to pronounce a patient "insane" before he can be committed or in any way handled therapeutically or prophylactically against his wishes. Mental deficiency, it is true, may also serve as a basis for such action, although it is sometimes the practice to say that the degree of deficiency is so great as to render the patient psychotic. There are those who will argue that nevertheless he does not have a "psychosis."

The technicalities of procedure vary from state to state. Items redolent of necromancy, and in which the glow of witch fires is still reflected, are not uncommon in these doings. In my native state the patient was until only a few years ago "charged with being a lunatic." Most physicians and jurists would perhaps agree that for practical purposes incompetency, in the sense of making legal commitment advisable, indicates a disability (disorder) of such degree that the patient cannot be counted on to make a (normally) correct appraisal of his condition and (therefore) to choose what treatment or protection he needs.

In considering the questions that arise concerning legal competency and responsibility, let us remember that the determination of competency, on which commitment depends, is usually carried out by a few selected experts—a lunacy commission. On the other hand, as Cumming so well emphasized, questions of responsibility on which terms of imprisonment or even the death penalty may depend are determined by a jury of twelve laymen.[64] Usually when a person is legally adjudged incompetent, it is on the basis of his being psychotic. Sometimes, however, a person who is plainly psychotic may be held legally responsible because he is considered as knowing the nature and quality of his criminal deed and that it is wrong.

A case referred to by Guttmacher is illustrative. Let us quote from his interesting discussion:

> Spencer married a woman who had been raped about six years before. The man was found guilty of rape and was given a sentence of five years. They usually give longer sentences in Maryland, but he got five years. Spencer's wife, a very frail person, died without medical attention while this man was serving his penitentiary sentence. The cause of death was not determined, but Spencer was sure that her death was the result of the rape, which had occured six years before, about three years before he had married her. The idea possessed him that his wife was not going to be able to rest in her grave unless she was really avenged, and he decided that it was his mission in life to right this great wrong. A few months after this man had been released from the penitentiary, Spencer went up to him and asked him to take a walk. They started walking down the road together, and Spencer was overheard by some people who passed to say, "You have been responsible for my wife's death. I hear voices at times telling me that I must kill you. Her spirit will never rest unless I carry out this request. I know that I am likely to hang for it and it's the wrong thing for me to do, but there is nothing else left for me to do." Whereupon he killed him. He pleaded insanity and the court, upheld by the court of appeals, ruled that he was not insane. The court of appeals said it was clear that the witness heard Spencer say that he was doing what he knew to be wrong and that he would be punished. That was all that the court needed to know in order to satisfy itself that he was a responsible agent.*

The patient discussed by Guttmacher, despite the hallucinations which would surely have caused most psychiatrists to call him psychotic, was regarded as "responsible" because of his own statement to the effect that it was wrong to commit murder. An important question must be asked. Just how much knowing of the quality and nature of the act, just how much and what sort of evaluation and emotional appreciation of it, is proved or indicated by such a statement from a man who is hallucinating?

It is not unusual to find patients with schizophrenia who can pronounce correct verbal judgments about matters they fail to evaluate sanely or react to normally. Recently a man was examined who had almost succeeded in strangling his wife to death. He "knew" this act was wrong at the time, was not apparently angry with her, and was glad he had been prevented from killing her. He had felt influences "from within" which were more effective in determining his decisions and acts than the impulse to avoid murder and

---

*From Guttmacher, Manfred: Criminal responsibility, Bulletin of the U. S. Army Medical Department 8:681-694, 1948.

to have his wife remain alive. This patient, who also had hallucinations and was obviously psychotic and schizophrenic, apparently did not attempt murder because of deficiency in the "intellectual" concept of right and wrong but probably because his personality was so altered that appreciation, the emotional significance, etc., of the act was (otherwise) diminished or disordered. Another patient with schizophrenia may recognize his child, say that he loves his child, express all the correct attitudes "intellectually" about the situation, and still be so disordered in his responses that he will let the child drown or burn to death without making ordinary efforts to save him.

In contrast with these, the psychotic paranoiac as he plans an assassination may be able to feel strong hate and destructiveness (to experience criminal intent) similar in degree and quality to that of the normal man.

In the case discussed by Guttmacher, definite evidence of irrationality was demonstrable. But the contrary evidence of a localized rationality at the crucial point of being able to express an opinion that to kill the man was wrong was accepted as proof that he knew the nature and quality of the act. It might be said that here we have a "lesion of the intellect" demonstrated, but the lesion was not demonstrated to be in such a place as to prevent the man from making the rational statement about his deed.

Many psychiatrists and jurists have protested against the M'Naghten Rules and have insisted that judgment should be made not on cognition (knowing) alone but that other aspects of the personality should be considered. In response to this criticism, the concept of "irresistible impulse," an alleged abnormality of the will, was advocated years ago and has been adopted as law in some parts of the United States.

This theory of "irresistible impulse" so often advanced by the defense in questions of criminal responsibility deserves a brief discussion. As traditionally interpreted, the M'Naghten Rules obviously center examination on an assumed intellectual faculty.[113] The concept of a pathologic and genuinely irresistible impulse attempts to center it on another assumed and discrete faculty, a hypothetical will.

> Seventeen of our states . . . recognize that it is not only a question of whether a man knows that what he is doing is wrong, but [also] whether his will power is sufficiently undermined by mental disorder that he cannot adhere to the right, in which case he is not considered a responsible agent.*

Hall believes that even where the irresistible impulse test is recognized in theory, it is not often respected in practice.[113]

---

*From Guttmacher, Manfred: Criminal responsibility, Bulletin of the U. S. Army Medical Department 8:681-694, 1948.

Nothing could be more obvious than the follies that arise when an attempt is made to localize illness in a hypothetical volition dismembered from the integrate of human functioning. Arguments as to whether an impulse is pathologically strong or whether what resists it is pathologically weak soon become little more practical or more enlightening than arguments about priority between the hen and the egg. As Hall points out, it has been said that if legal questions are determined on such a basis "you will soon make irresistible an impulse which now is resistible and resisted because of penal law."* A prominent psychiatrist is quoted as saying,

> From a psychological point of view, the impulse could not have been resistible, since the act was carried out in accordance with the impulse. It is difficult for me to conceive of an impulse which is resistible but not resisted.*

Attempts to apply the M'Naghten Rules to a concept of faculty psychology vividly illustrate the weaknesses of faculty psychology. Attempts, within the confining framework of its assumptions, to examine not only an *intellect* but also a *will* are unlikely to be helpful since in neither pursuit can we encounter a reality of experience but only a verbal concept.

Many psychiatrists over several decades have been extremely bitter in their criticism, and sometimes in their ridicule, of the M'Naghten Rules which for over a hundred years have constituted the chief legal guide in determining criminal responsibility. As given by Hall, the essential points of the M'Naghten Rules lie in this statement:

> To establish a defense on the grounds of insanity, it must be clearly proved that at the time of the committing of the act the party accused was labouring under such a defect of reason from disease of the mind as not to know the nature and quality of the act he was doing or, if he did know it, that he did not know he was doing what was wrong.*

Some of this criticism of the traditional rules has apparently been based on the wish by expert witnesses to express the opinion in psychiatric terms rather than in those familiar to the law and to laymen. Violent denunciation of the rules has also apparently been related to the concept of psychic determinism so vigorously espoused by Freud and very popular among psychiatrists for several decades. This doctrine is regarded by many as one of Freud's most important discoveries and as a foundation stone of dynamic psychiatry.[195] Although it is often assumed to be a fact established by psycho-

---

*From Hall, Jerome: Mental disease and criminal responsibility, Columbia Law Review 45:677-718, 1945.

analytic research, we may note that Freud and all his followers have produced no scientific evidence whatsoever to support it. It remains purely an assumption.

A truly logical conclusion from psychic determinism would, of course, abolish the concept of personal responsibility altogether and along with it the basis of law and all the value judgments that underlie ethical conduct and even rudimentary civilization. Let us bear in mind, however, that those who profess allegiance to the doctrine almost never follow it to the inevitable conclusions it logically demands. There are many, nevertheless, who respond to its influence sufficiently to arrive at peculiar and interesting assumptions. Some of these are now popularly regarded as the essence of a liberal and scientifically enlightened mind. Going part of the logical way, but not all the way, they conclude that when crimes are committed, it is never the fault (responsibility) of the criminal but, inevitably, the fault of society.[56]

Zilboorg, one of those who have vigorously criticized the law, and the M'Naghten Rules especially, has this to say:

> When they all individually and jointly [judges, lawyers, and jury] ask me whether the defendant in the dock is in my opinion insane, I must candidly state, if I am to remain true to my professional knowledge and faithful to my oath, first, that I do not understand the question, and, second, that since I don't understand the question, I do not know whether the defendant is insane or not. I admit the situation is embarrassing and puzzling to all concerned, but it is beyond my knowledge and power to remedy or alleviate it.*

Continuing a discussion of what he considers to be the basic differences between medical man and jurist, Zilboorg goes on to say:

> We have reached a rather disquieting parting of the ways. This is undesirable from both your [the jurist's] point of view and mine. Your rules are unintelligible to me, and my inability to follow them is unintelligible to you.*

It is a matter of no little importance that joint action be continued, that every effort at cooperation be made to fit our social instrumentalities to the needs of the patient. It is important that new knowledge and understanding be used in these efforts. It is doubtful, as Hall points out, that the substitution of psychiatric terminology for the legal phrases would be of much practical or immediate help. To quote from Hall again:

> Imagine that, instead of a judge's instructions in terms of prevailing rules he said ". . . essential to the psychopathic personality may be

---

*From Zilboorg, G.: Mind, medicine and man, New York, 1943, Harcourt, Brace & Co., Inc.

a defective organization of the autotely . . . and unsatisfactory adjustment of the heterotely."* . . . If, instead of "knowledge" or "understanding," "control," or "act," the language of the law ran in terms of *id, ego,* and *super-ego,* the psychiatrists would understand, but would many lay persons be much enlightened even after they were informed that the *"id"* is the "true unconscious," that the *"ego"* is that part of the mind that is "regulated by the reality principle," and that the *"super-ego"* is a sort of inner monitor synonymous with conscience?†

It seems likely that Hall's suggestions offer more hope for common understanding and for effective action. (The need for such action is particularly urgent and obvious so far as psychopaths are concerned.) He suggests that concepts generally agreed upon in psychiatry be utilized to "implement the M'Naghten Rules."† It is doubtful if any psychiatrist today conceives of personality function only in the abstractions of faculty psychology. The human being as we know him is integrated. We do not find him "thinking" without also "feeling." We do not observe acts of volition altogether free of emotion. Continuing, Hall clarifies the very point on which he feels agreement may be reached and which intelligent action may follow:

> This view of the participation of the rational functions, including evaluation, does not imply any depreciation of the role of the instincts in normal conduct. For consistently with this theory, one asserts the fusion of various aspects of the self. This means that moral judgment ("knowledge of right and wrong") is not reified as an outside, icy spectator of a moving self; on the contrary, the corollary is that value judgments are permeated with the color and warmth of emotion, as is evidenced by the usual attitudes of approval that coalesce with right decisions. Indeed all action, especially that relevant to the penal law, involves a unified operation of the personality . . . . The M'Naghten Rules provide an analytical device for dissecting this action.†

If these rules can be thus used by the jurist, it seems obvious that as psychiatrists we can venture honest and sensible opinions on whatever evidence of medical impairment we find that may alter such a "knowing." When no longer dismembered and falsified in two-dimensional aspect but considered in all that we sometimes imply by "appreciation," "realization," "normal evaluation," "adequate feeling," "significant and appropriate experiencing," etc., the term does not restrict us solely to a discussion of the patient's reasoning abilities in the abstract.

---

*From Kahn, Eugen: Psychopathic personalities, New Haven, 1931, Yale University Press.
†From Hall, Jerome: Mental disease and criminal responsibility, Columbia Law Review **45**:677-718, 1945.

In very impressive and helpful studies over a period of many years, Hall[113,114,115,116,117] has brought out from the viewpoint of our legal co-workers in this area facts, appraisals, and suggestions which I feel can enable us to deal honestly and more effectively with questions of legal responsibility and competency. He has also politely but convincingly demonstrated some of the confusion contributed by us as psychiatrists to important issues. Interestingly enough, Hall demonstrates in our own psychiatric writings examples of the very dogmatism, the archaic and unrealistic approaches, and the adherence to dubious theory at the expense of vital fact which we have so readily ascribed to the law and its interpreters and so vigorously denounced.

If the jurist and the psychiatrist would approach our problem from the viewpoint expressed by Hall, it seems to me that much nonsense and tragedy could be avoided. After referring to typical arguments between those who argue for "reason" as a criterion and those who in contradiction emphasize "will," he says:

> Opposed to these views and avoiding their particularistic fallacies is the theory of the integration of the self . . . . In terms of this theory any interaction with the environment is integrated in the sense that the various functions of personality coalesce and act as a unit. Although it is useful to distinguish the important "modes" or attributes of such action, the various functions are not actually separate. On the contrary, the affective, the cognitive, and the conative functions as well as all others interpenetrate one another. Thinking (knowing, understanding) e.g., fuses with tendencies to action and it is permeated also in varying degrees by the warmth of the emotions . . . . Hence it is arbitrary and formalistic to assert that the psychotic's rational functions, including his knowledge of right and wrong, are unimpaired. There is only a certain awareness, a bare calculation unsupported by the strong pillar of sensitivity that, in normal adults, effects identification with a prospective victim or stimulates a vivid imagining of other consequences of the intended behavior; in short, the psychotic's conduct is unaccompanied by actual understanding of the moral significance of his action.*

Despite the excellent points made by Hall, vigorous criticism of the law and particularly of the M'Naghten Rules has continued over the decades, chiefly from psychiatrists but also from jurists. Many of those who have expressed such bitter dissatisfaction with the M'Naghten Rules welcomed the Durham Rule as a tremendous and triumphant step forward. This rule pro-

---

*From Hall, Jerome: Mental disease and criminal responsibility, Columbia Law Review 45:677-718, 1945.

nounced by Judge Bazelon in 1954 is to the effect that a defendant must not be held criminally responsible "if his unlawful act was the product of mental disease or mental defect."* Speaking of the Durham Rule, Fortas has said, "Its importance is that it is a charter—a Bill of Rights for psychiatry."† Judge Bazelon received official honors and a certificate of commendation from the American Psychiatric Association. Along with many psychiatrists, prominent legal scholars have enthusiastically expressed the conviction that "science", "scientific facts", and "the latest knowledge of human behavior" have made the M'Naghten Rules obsolete. They apparently assume that all this psychiatric enlightenment can now be freely applied to legal problems.

On the other hand, Hall and some other critics have expressed fear that the Durham Rule might lead to the destruction of our jury system in criminal trials and turn over questions of guilt and responsibility to narrow experts who, however adequately trained in their limited field, may not really qualify as all-knowing judges on such questions and all that they involve. Hall[115] and Cumming[64] express the fear that various unproved and widely differing theories might be utilized by psychiatric witnesses to make arbitrary and absolute judgments that would have little relation to scientific fact. They also develop arguments that illustrate the danger of leaving such complex value judgments on such imponderables as the judgment of criminal responsibility solely to any experts known today. Although it is maintained by some that psychiatrists now have a scientific method of arriving at such a decision, the points made by Hall and Cumming raise grave doubts about this assumption and suggest that this is an area not yet proved accessible to methods that are genuinely scientific. Forcing the methods of science, or a caricature of these methods, into areas which science is not equipped to deal with does not endow judgments in these areas with validity, whatever words we may use to state the case. This specious and misleading practice has sometimes been called *scientism*.[56]

It is interesting to note that over sixty years ago Grasset[106] brought forth under the term "physiological responsibility" a concept very similar to that embodied in the Durham Rule. Grasset advocated that the judgment of responsibility be made merely on whether or not the capability of the organism is impaired. In this old concept he avoids decisions about free will versus determinism. He also refuses to confine his inquiry to disparate conceptual

---

*From Hall, Jerome: The M'Naghten Rules and proposed alternatives, Journal of the American Bar Association **59**:960-964, 1963.
†From Fortas, Abe: Implications of Durham's case, American Journal of Psychiatry **113**:575-582, 1957.

abstractions such as "knowing," "feeling," or "will." Instead he keeps his attention on the integrated reality of human functioning.

It has been customary over the decades for lunacy commissions to pronounce psychopaths competent and for juries to pronounce them sane and responsible. It is in the concept of competency that we meet our primary problems when we attempt to provide any improvement in methods of dealing with the psychopath. It is difficult to examine the most important aspects of competency, however, without becoming entangled with essential implications of legal responsibility. If we attempt to make pronouncements about responsibility, we are likely, unless we take particular care to signify what we are talking about, to find ourselves submerged in metaphysics and attempting solutions of ultimate philosophic and religious problems. However important or transcendent these problems may be and however we may solve them for ourselves, we are not, as psychiatrists, qualified to solve them as experts. We are, let us say, not *responsible* to serve in such a role nor are we *competent*.

In approaching questions of competency in the psychopath, it is plain that he shows no defect in theoretical reasoning and that he lacks all the outer or peripheral manifestations of psychosis and usually even of minor psychiatric disorder. If, however, we consider the record of his actual performance, we nearly always find ample evidence to say that he is socially incompetent in the sense that he cannot carry out a sane plan of life or avoid repeated antisocial acts and other acts seriously damaging to himself.

McDougall long ago expressed a succinct and practical opinion on the essential question of competency:

> In practice the criterion adopted is: Can the patient be trusted to look after his affairs without undue risk to himself and others? And there is no other criterion.*

As the reader must, I believe, agree, this sensible criterion, although regularly applied to any patient who has ever shown a delusion or a hallucination, is not in practice applied to those who lack these and some other traditionally accepted signs of "a lesion of the intelligence." If this criterion should be applied to psychopaths, it would not be difficult to commit them and keep them under satisfactory control.

Karl Menninger, also, in referring primarily to questions of liability for punishment, has made a point that should be helpful if we apply it to the commitment of patients who are not charged with crime. "The psychiatrist,"

---

*From McDougall, William: An outline of abnormal psychology, London, 1926, Methuen & Co.

he says, "asks not 'Is that man responsible?' but 'Of what is he capable or incapable?' "*

Despite the cogency of this position, it is not the common practice of psychiatrists, if the patient is diagnosed as psychopathic personality, to ask themselves such a question. Or, if they ask it, they arrive at a strange answer, and by extraordinary methods.

In estimating competency in most matters, intelligence as manifested in verbal reasoning carries a good deal of weight, but few who survive as adults continue to make the estimate entirely on this basis. Judgment is often spoken of as a matter somewhat different from and far more complicated than intelligence and is in general regarded as better demonstrated in behavior than in talk. In the old Stanford-Binet psychometric test we find the question, "Is it better to judge a man by his actions or by his words?" The normal 10-year-old child is supposed to answer this correctly. What disturbing thoughts may arise from this apply, I believe, as accurately to us in our role as psychiatrists as to legal authorities.

Despite the widespread and sometimes bitter disagreement among psychiatrists and at times among legal scholars, most patients with psychosis who need treatment and who need restraint can be legally committed and controlled. Although many psychopaths are, in my opinion, far more disabled than a large proportion of committed psychotic patients and in far greater need of control, it is very difficult to have such a patient committed. Before any important step toward solving the problems created by psychopaths can be taken, some legal means of controlling their antisocial, heedless, self-damaging, and irresponsible behavior must be devised.

If the new Durham Rule devised by Judge Bazelon is followed, the question of competency in the psychopath would depend chiefly on whether his abnormality was correctly defined as a "mental disease or mental defect." It has long been customary in psychiatry and law to distinguish sharply between this abnormality and all the conditions to which the terms "mental disease" or "mental defect" are applied. Few psychiatrists could doubt that crimes committed by a psychopath are the product of his aberration. The psychiatrist-witness's opinion would, inevitably it seems, depend on whether or not he classified this aberration as mental. This decision, it seems to me, would in turn substantially depend on whether or not this term is limited in its meaning to an assumed disparate faculty of cognition. Thus, as far as the psychopath is concerned, it would appear that the psychiatrist in court is faced with essentially the same decision, whether he testifies under the

_____
*From Menninger, Karl: The human mind, New York, 1947, Alfred A. Knopf, Inc.

M'Naghten Rules or the Durham Rule. Either may be interpreted narrowly and confined to mere cognition or more broadly, as Jerome Hall[113] suggests that the M'Naghten Rules be interpreted. Decisions based on the M'Naghten Rules depend on the interpretation of the word "know," and with the Durham Rule, on the interpretation of "mental disease or defect." It is hardly conceivable to me that a psychiatrist would arrive at anything but the same conclusion by either test in his opinion about a psychopath. Despite some very important achievements in the last half-century, psychiatry does not today, in my opinion, possess newly discovered and well-established facts which afford a scientific answer to the ultimate questions that arise in determining responsibility.[56]

Whatever rule is followed, when a psychopath is involved, the issue will be determined by whether the estimation of his legal competency is based on outer appearance and the peripheral mechanisms of function or on his amply demonstrated incapacity to lead an adequate or socially acceptable life and on the serious inner pathology that only emerges in his actual performance as a member of the social group.

65

Treatment or control

More than two decades ago, while preparing the first edition of this book, I was profoundly impressed by two difficulties that stood in the way of dealing effectively with the psychopath. One of these was his apparent immunity, or relative immunity, from control by law. The other was his lack of response to psychiatric treatment of any kind.

Today both of these difficulties exist and, it seems to me, with little alteration. Let us consider first the question of legal control, of the problems that arise when steps are taken to protect the community and the patient from his misconduct. It is only on very unusual occasions that a psychopath can be committed as legally incompetent, and even when this occurs it is not likely that he can be kept long under medical supervision. Let us consider an example:

After years of expensive, fruitless, heartbreaking, and faithful efforts to keep him out of disaster, the family of a young (and in most respects typical) psychopath succeeded in having him pronounced incompetent and sent to a state hospital. Such an event is rare enough to suggest the miraculous. Unlike most psychopaths, this patient had shown strong indications that he might murder one or more members of his family. This and the prodigious obviousness of his disability and his danger to the community strangely enough overbalanced the customary psychiatric concepts in this isolated instance, and he was admitted to be socially incompetent. There is no denying that this procedure was incorrect according to clearly defined medical rules.

After a few weeks of study he was found not to show any of the technical signs of irrationality (none of which had ever been suspected), diagnosed as a "psychopathic personality," and sent home as "sane and competent."

One of the psychiatrists at the hospital who had participated in this procedure explained his attitude as follows. He believed that this particular patient, no matter what his proper diagnosis might be, was more seriously disabled than a great many of the patients who would spend the rest of their lives in the institution. He also believed that the discharged patient was more dangerous to the community and more difficult to care for at home than, perhaps, half of those in the state hospital. The members of the staff, he felt, were motivated in their action by several impulses, directed by several judgments.

First of all, it was not in accordance with official psychiatric concepts to call such a patient psychotic. It was also against the rules of the hospital to keep a nonpsychotic patient against his will. There was, in addition, in some members of the staff a tendency to resist efforts to slip in or palm off on the hospital these psychopaths who are considered technically not eligible for care. There was opinion expressed about how crowded the place was already and about the dangers of being overrun with psychopaths if an exception was made and this one kept. Some felt it would not serve the cause of justice if this man were admitted by the staff of the state hospital to have mental disability, because this appraisal would be utilized in the future dozens or hundreds of times to help him evade legal penalties for the antisocial acts they, like everyone else, realized he would continue.

There are not a few among those in charge of our state hospitals who feel that, with conditions as they stand, it would be more fitting for persons of this sort, when segregation or supervision of some type is urgently necessary, to be placed not in our present psychiatric institutions but in reformatories or prisons. Some who take this position feel that psychiatric care and many of the services and facilities now available in our mental hospitals could and should be made available to the group of psychopaths whom they prefer, nevertheless, to have come into the general framework of our penal institutions.

As our evidence has shown, I hope, the psychopath notoriously avoids the petty and temporary restraints that might be legally imposed. Those imprisoned for serious crimes return at length no less prone to continue these crimes. Even when under life sentence, the psychopath tends more readily than others to obtain parole and become again a social menace. Not only can he (perhaps involuntarily) mimic sanity in superlative fashion but also moral rebirth, salvation, absolute reform, transformation into a supercitizen, etc. Among many examples one patient stands out:

This brilliant and charming young man, when in his early twenties, murdered another without provocation. Despite a typical record of psychopathic behavior, he so impressed the authorities that parole was granted after a few years. That which, if properly understood, would have warned the parole board against the extreme danger of releasing this man was interpreted as a mitigating factor, as grounds for giving him another chance. Apparently emotional handicaps and personality symptoms had played a part in his unfortunate deed. This, they reasoned, made him less culpable and more deserving of leniency. Like nearly all of his kind, he now showed no superficial signs of nervous or mental disorder (as this is generally understood) but indications of great promise. He inspired trust and confidence and gave a convincing (theoretical) demonstration of reform, self-control, trustworthiness, sound ethics, and high ideals. Shortly after his release he again committed murder, this time of a woman and again with no discernible motivation of any consequence.

Although some protection to society is afforded by dealing out sentences of varying length to such offenders on the assumption that they are normal and to be punished in accordance with the degree of blame their crimes are judged to deserve, such protection is not reliable. The assumption that they will thereby learn their lesson and become safe inhabitants of the community is an assumption at sharp variance with simple facts. Poorly adapted as our present methods are to prevent the repetition of crime, we find them rapidly approaching travesty and farce when we look for what security they offer against initial crimes of tragic magnitude. An example will make the point clear:

In big letters on the front page of newspapers all over the United States the *"Bestial Sex Slaying"* of an 11-year-old girl by a boy 17 years of age is proclaimed. Details of torture and dismemberment follow. The horrible impact of impulses perverted from the aims of Eros and fused with those of hate and brutality arouses disgust and vengefulness in millions upon millions. Additional articles point out that the murderer, now remarkably callous and undisturbed by his act, had, over a period of many years, shown gross maladjustment and indifference to social values, to ordinary aims, and to the rights of others. He had on several occasions been placed in a reform school and kept for various periods determined in accordance with the legally estimated seriousness of his antisocial acts and with the amount of punishment these were officially regarded as deserving.

Had this boy expressed a few delusions or reported even once that he heard an imaginary voice (like many people who are quite harmless), he could have been hospitalized as long as hospitalization was regarded by experts as advisable. Lacking these and the other accepted technicalities which are presumed to determine competency and sanity, he could not be held in any institution beyond the arbitrary term to which he had been sentenced. His conduct had so strongly indicated that he could not without danger to others be left unrestricted in the community that his parents protested to the authorities against his release from custody. They urged that he be kept in the institution and gave adequate reasons for their plea. The authorities had no means of heeding this warning—no legal grounds for an alternative to the technically correct procedure of dismissing the patient. The regrettable results reflected in newspaper headlines soon followed.

If such patients could be evaluated in terms of their behavior and committed, like other psychiatric patients, not to limited terms of confinement but for indeterminate periods, the community would obviously obtain far better protection. The patient could then be held until his condition, as appraised by experts, indicated that he could be released with safety to himself and others. Let us grant that even the best of experts is not likely to prove infallible in such an appraisal. Even the wisest and most experienced psychiatrist may be misled by the appearance of profound change in the true sociopath who will later show himself to be as dangerous as before.

Some practical help might be afforded in controlling the sociopath by the general application of laws designed to increase progressively the penalty and term of confinement for those who repeatedly demonstrate by antisocial acts that they have not learned through experience and that they are still dangerous to the community. Some of these principles are embodied in the Greenstein Act (Pennsylvania),[253] which is so designed that the psychopath, as well as other disordered but generally neglected persons who commit legal offenses, can be dealt with by safer as well as more rational and humane methods. The need for similar changes throughout the nation is urgent.

Persons who show evidence of schizophrenic illness or of almost any other psychiatric disorder (excepting that of the psychopath) can, through existing facilities, usually be reached and sensibly dealt with before any legal offense against others is committed. In addition to the valuable contribution offered through the Greenstein Act, I believe there is also need for some means of committing psychopaths on the primary basis of their demonstrated disability and need. Perhaps all or nearly all of these patients will in the demonstration of their disorder commit antisocial acts by which they might, through facilities such as those afforded by the Greenstein Act, be reached. It is nevertheless true that very serious disability or gross maladjustment may, as in other psychiatric patients, be obvious despite the relatively trivial nature of the offenses which usually bring the psychopath into court.

Relatives, long confused about the nature of this problem, often sacrifice themselves grievously to keep the patient out of court, to prevent his going to jail, to spare his reputation (and perhaps their own, also), and to give him every advantage in the vain hope he will soon change his ways. Effective and rational handling of many patients would be expedited if relatives could initiate legal action for commitment through the same courts and agencies set up to deal with other psychiatric patients, and in the same way, without having prior conviction of the patient for legal offense as an obligatory condition, a prerequisite, to such steps. If the same procedure followed in dealing with other mental illness could be utilized without what many relatives would regard as "branding him a criminal," etc., many advantages in addition to those afforded by the Greenstein Act would result.

Would this jeopardize the liberties of the citizen? Would it enable unscrupulous relatives, psychiatrists, and jurists to deprive people of the right to make their own decisions concerning treatment, hospitalization, etc., without sufficient cause? Would just about anyone whose conduct did not suit his neighbors (or his spouse, or his old maid aunt) find himself in danger of being declared psychiatrically ill and put away indefinitely?

These are, indeed, important considerations. As pointed out so well by Hall[115] and Cumming,[64] among others, a basic safeguard of freedom provided by law exists in the right to trial by a lay jury. The law, with good reason it seems, is firmly resistant to encroachments upon the jury's responsibility. It looks with distrust upon any movement which may tend to place into the hands of an expert or specialist final decisions which might deprive a citizen of his liberty or arbitrarily determine the length of his incarceration whether it be in prison or in a psychiatric institution. This is very probably the chief reason why it has been so difficult to devise legal measures to bring sociopaths under better control. Urgent as the need is for better control of these patients, we must recognize the grave danger which the law must take pains to avoid and try to work patiently with our legal colleagues toward some better solution of a very subtle and complex problem.

Over a period of many years I have remained discouraged about the effect of treatment on the psychopath. Having regularly failed in my own efforts to help such patients alter their fundamental pattern of inadequacy and antisocial activity, I hoped for a while that treatment by others would be more successful. I have had the opportunity to see patients of this sort

who were treated by psychoanalysis, by psychoanalytically oriented psychotherapy, by group and by milieu therapy, and by other variations of dynamic
method. I have seen some patients who were treated for years. I have also
known cases in which not only the patient but various members of his family
were given prolonged psychotherapy. None of these measures impressed me
as achieving successful results. The psychopaths continued to behave as
they had behaved in the past.

Among such patients I recall a young millionaire whose family was able
to place him in an institution where every possible resource of psychiatry
was available, including psychoanalysis by one of the best-qualified men in
our country. Everyone was eager that the patient stay as long as advisable
and that every means of therapy be utilized, however expensive, time-con-
suming, or protracted. Despite these apparent advantages nothing of importance was accomplished. At first the patient expressed great determination
to obtain help and to get well. Evidence of such a desire steadily diminished,
and eventually it became apparent that he had no real interest in the goals he
had set for himself and of which he spoke for a while so eloquently. After a
long and tremendously expensive period of hospitalization he left, apparently
without regret, discontinued all pretense of seeking treatment, and returned
to his familiar ways of behavior.

I am impressed also with the recollection of another patient, a woman
in her thirties, for whom almost limitless wealth and strong family cooperation provided every therapeutic advantage. I referred her, long ago, to a
colleague outstanding as a leader not only in psychiatry but also in psychoanalysis. Everything conceivable that might be needed in the most ambitious
plans for treatment was available. After a careful study of the patient, this
able and honest physician advised against any prolonged therapeutic endeavor, since he felt that the chances for substantial benefit were not sufficient
to justify the attempt.

These two swallows do not, of course, make a summer, but they are
typical of many other similar cases I have observed over the years.

For a while I had hoped that long-term treatment might be more effective if the patient could be induced voluntarily or constrained by commitment procedures to remain with the therapist for enough time to give his
methods a thorough and adequate trial. I am no longer as hopeful that any
methods available today would be successful with typical sociopaths. I have
now, after more than two decades, had the opportunity to observe a considerable number of patients who, through commitment or the threat of
losing their probation status or by other means, were kept under treatment
not only for many months but for years. The therapeutic failure in all such

patients observed leads me to feel that we do not at present have any kind of psychotherapy that can be relied upon to change the psychopath fundamentally.

Nor do I believe that any other method of psychiatric treatment has shown promise of solving the problem. Physical methods of therapy including electric shock have been attempted.[66] Prefrontal lobotomy, topectomy, and transorbital lobotomy have been used in a few patients with severe disorder.[16,67,127,178,220] Some encouragement was expressed by a few observers about the effects of these measures, but apparently they have not proved to be a real solution of the problem.

I wish I could be optimistic about the accomplishments of psychiatry in treating and curing the psychopath. Some spokesmen for mental hygiene movements and for greater extensions of psychiatric influence tend to credit us, I fear, with far more power and effectiveness than we have really attained. Hundreds of millions of dollars are being spent to promote mental hygiene and psychiatric care. Many seem to believe that if we only had enough psychiatrists, or enough dynamically oriented psychiatrists, all problems of mental health, crime, and delinquency could be solved.[43] This claim is seldom made directly in such absolute terms, but the implication plainly underlies many eloquent appeals for more and more funds from the state and federal governments.[43,171] Some of the more zealous spokesmen even seem to feel that psychiatry has recently made such profound discoveries and devised such effective methods of eliminating not only illness and crime but also prejudice, superstition, and human error that we can and should settle racial and international problems and even revise the basic standards of morality.[43,190]

Despite these enthusiastic and at times embarrassing claims in our behalf, our actual achievements should encourage profound modesty. So far no statistical evidence has been obtained to support a belief that our most ambitious, protracted, dynamic, and reputedly scientific methods of psychotherapy have proved more effective even in the psychoneuroses than the warmhearted but unpretentious methods used over the years by kind and wise physicians in the general practice of medicine.[41,56,86,260,287] There is, of course, no evidence of this sort to demonstrate or to indicate that psychiatry has yet found a therapy that cures or profoundly changes the psychopath.[112]

If we have not yet devised adequate legal methods of controlling these destructive people and do not at present have a therapy to offer that has been demonstrated as effective, what, then, can we do?

Let us try to promote a general understanding of the serious nature of the psychopath's abnormality and of its strong tendency to persist despite all efforts toward correction or treatment. Let us cooperate with our legal colleagues in efforts to devise a more effective means of keeping sociopaths under adequate control. The degree of control should, insofar as possible, be regulated by the need, that is, by the degree of disability that the patient continues to demonstrate. Let us recognize psychopaths as differing greatly from the psychotic and psychoneurotic patients for whom our present hospitals and clinics have been designed and our current methods of treatment or control established.

It is urgent and obvious that we devise some more effective means of restraining these people in their persistently destructive careers. Henderson says: "It is amazing and almost paralyzing to realize the extent to which some of these cases may go before any action can be taken legally or medically to exert adequate control."*

If a proper general understanding could be reached that such people have a serious psychiatric abnormality and are not likely under prevailing conditions to become better, and if this fact could be disseminated, their families might be able to reconcile themselves better to a major problem and seek more realistic ways of dealing with it.

By systems of parole, probation, and supervision designed specifically for patients of this type and devised to meet the sort of problems they present, it is probable that reasonably effective guidance could be maintained after hospitalization and, when necessary, restraint be applied pertinently and effectively. We must remember that under present conditions nearly all psychopaths are entirely on their own in the community and that the few with whom society gets any opportunity at all to deal fall under one or the other of two methods. Neither of these methods was evolved with any cognizance of the psychopath, but each for quite a different sort of problem.

On one hand, the existing psychiatric hospitals, parole arrangements, mental hygiene clinics, etc., are set up to meet situations that arise in dealing with (legally) psychotic and psychoneurotic patients. With patients in these two groups, our methods, imperfect as they may be, are relevant to the situation. By them much is accomplished.

On the other hand, we have the penal system with its preordained terms of restraint graded arbitrarily in what, perhaps during the last century, was agreed upon as a proper dosage of punishment for this or that misdeed. Such punishments were presumably considered as having corrective (and perhaps prophylactic) effect on antisocial tendencies. Whatever efficacy this method may show for dealing with citizens in general, it has demonstrated year after

---

*From Henderson, D. K.: Psychopathic states, New York, 1939, W. W. Norton & Co., Inc.

year its lack of success in controlling the grave problems that continually multiply about the psychopath.[253] Largely inaccessible to ordinary social agencies, this type of patient capers, reels, or plunges along his disastrous course.

Without medicolegal apparatus to reach him, without social instrumentalities designed to cope with his problems or those he makes for others, and with no general recognition even of his presence, we find ourselves emulating the ostrich and its proverbial tactics of evasion.[47] When the situation becomes too alarming or too monumentally fantastic for us to continue these tactics and when it cannot any longer be blandly ignored, we find ourselves fumbling between the only two methods available, neither of which, we find immediately, is applicable to the real issues we confront.[48] Psychiatrists finding it impossible under existing circumstances to continue any long-range plans are hardly to be blamed if they tend to regard these people as birds of passage through their institutions, that is, as patients in name only who seek temporary refuge there from other legal restraints, create much confusion and disorder, then leave when it suits their whim or convenience, to continue in their former maladjustment.

Turning now to penal facilities, now to psychiatric institutions, relatives, friends, doctors, lawyers, or the community at large, all find themselves at a loss, somewhat as if they were trying to measure areas in kilowatts or color in inches. Since the fire extinguisher did not particularly help the child's fever, which has become alarming, we gravely decide to apply a plaster cast. There are no really appropriate remedies available.

Without restraint and without any effective treatment, the psychopath continues, progressively accumulating in his social wake woe, confusion, despair, farce, and disaster, beyond any measure of these things I can convey. Exonerations in courts on the grounds of "insanity" are followed by discharges from hospitals because "no nervous or mental disease" is found. Sometimes when incompetency cannot be medically or legally established, common sense attempts a compromise and, perhaps unofficially, shows recognition of an aberration through leniency of judgment or an assumption of mitigating circumstances with the practical result of reducing terms of confinement in proportion to the degree of dangerous abnormality evident. This all too frequently amounts to diminishing whatever protection is offered the public directly in proportion to the degree of menace indicated by the disorder.

We must remind ourselves once more of the gross and tragic misunderstanding that determined legal and medical attitudes toward patients suffering from ordinary types of psychosis in past centuries before we can realize the monstrous inefficacy of our present methods of dealing with psychopaths.

Pinel, who is so justly venerated by the world today, did not discover any cure or any satisfactory treatment for the psychotic patients whom he liberated from the chains and dungeons into which they were thrown by a society that could not realize they were ill but assumed them merely evil and vicious. Indeed, a hundred or more years passed before any regular therapy even remotely effective became available for patients in most psychiatric institutions. Even if another hundred years should pass before we discover a truly effective method of treatment for psychopaths, we must make a beginning by reappraising them as Pinel did by reappraising psychotic patients and revising methods for their care. Such a step in understanding these other patients must be made before we can hope to progress far toward the solution of their problem. Let us without delay recognize them for what they are and begin more realistically to plan medical and social facilities through which they can be intelligently treated or, at the very least, through which they will not be mistreated or left without control to endanger the community.

In properly set-up hospital units and through adequate outpatient control, efforts might be made to utilize the excellent abilities of these patients and to provide whatever degree of supervision is found necessary to keep them occupied and out of trouble. This supervision would, as with other socially disabled patients, vary widely with various persons.

Such institutions and other community facilities and the regular practice of committing suitable patients to their supervision would soon bring new viewpoints to countless parents who, in shame and grief, blush over what they take to be the deeds of wickedness and depravity of their children and who wreck their own lives and fortunes seeking to protect, to rehabilitate, and to reform them. Women might learn in time not to sacrifice so readily their fortunes, their life plans, their grief, and their energy in indefatigable and fruitless struggles to support and nurse and pamper maturity into husbands and lovers whose profound disorder makes such maturity (by such means) impossible.

In speaking of hospital units and other facilities for parole and supervision, I do not propose that vast and expensive institutions be built in addition to those designed for patients with the traditional problems of psychiatry. I suggest rather that psychopaths be recognized clearly as a separate group and dealt with by rules and methods specifically adapted to cope with their problems and their behavior. Units for their care might be maintained in our existing institutions. It seems possible that such a step might lead to substantial economies instead of an additional burden of expense to the public. Vast sums of money are now being disbursed daily by the state to bring psychopaths repeatedly through due processes of the law, and all to no avail. At great cost relatives send them hopefully for treatment in expensive hospitals, which they leave on personal whim or prankish impulse. Enormous sums are wasted in futile efforts to reestablish them in business and to compensate victims for their continual follies. It is doubtful that the cost of even a most elaborate setup of hospital units and outpatient facilities, which I do not propose, would equal the financial loss they now inflict, in addition to their socially damaging effects upon the community.

Even if no really adequate therapeutic measure should become available in the foreseeable future, it seems reasonable to hope that with facilities specifically designed for the direction and control of the sociopathic group these people might be maintained at a better level of adjustment despite the continued need of support and restriction. Even if we cannot count on curing their disorder, the goal of bringing about improvement in adjustment is not to be despised.

Impressed by points of similarity between the psychopath and the spoiled child, some psychiatrists have maintained that promising therapeutic possibilities might lie in establishing a really effective control whereby the patient would regularly, promptly, and persistently experience the logical results of (1) socially acceptable conduct and (2) irresponsible and destructive conduct. Mangun[200] has reported encouraging results from such a program and Woolley[311] also has expressed hopefulness about this approach to the problem.

Is it not our responsibility as psychiatrists to agree, despite all our notable differences about etiology, terminology, technicalities of method, etc., that such patients as those discussed here need medical reappraisal?

My proposals and opinions may be in many respects incomplete, superficial, or erroneous. It is too much to ask that the viewpoint of any one observer in so complex and confusing a matter be generally accepted as final. The whole field of psychiatry, by its very nature, abounds in questions still unanswered and about which diverse opinions naturally exist and arguments inevitably arise. If we cannot agree that the psychopath has anything like a "psychosis" or even a "mental disorder," can we not all agree that some means is urgently needed of dealing more realistically with whatever it is that may be the matter with him? If some practical means of controlling the psychopath can be devised, perhaps, eventually, we may find his disorder to be not altogether beyond our practice.

Appendix

Statistics obtained from the records of one federal psychiatric hospital give these facts concerning the prevalence of psychopaths among the general group of mental patients. It is a hospital of 1,067 beds devoted exclusively to the diagnosis and treatment of mental disorders.* During the period under consideration, from February 9, 1935, to June 12, 1937, there were 857 new admissions. These patients, after several weeks of observation, careful physical, neurologic, and psychiatric examination, and study of social service reports, were given diagnoses by a staff of ten psychiatrists. A review of the records over this period shows the following distribution of diagnoses among the 857 patients admitted:

Dementia praecox	212
Dementia paralytica	139
Psychopathic personality	102
Chronic alcoholism	60
Chronic alcoholism with deterioration	41
Psychosis with mental deficiency	31
Manic depressive psychosis	28
Psychosis, type undetermined	27
Epilepsy	26
Psychosis with cerebral arteriosclerosis	24
Psychoneurosis	20
Other organic brain disease	19
Mental deficiency	15
Acute alcoholic hallucinosis	14
Toxic psychosis	11
Traumatic psychosis	10
Psychopathic personality with psychotic episodes	8
Psychosis with pellagra	8
Drug addiction	8
No nervous or mental disease	7
Syphilis of the central nervous system	7
Other psychoses with alcohol	6

*All comments on the policies and practices of the Veterans Administration apply to the period (1935-1937) when these patients were observed by me and do not apply to current policies and practices.

Psychosis with somatic disease	6
Encephalitis lethargica	4
Senile psychosis	3
Acute alcoholism	3
Involutional melancholia	2
Traumatic neurosis	2
Korsakoff's psychosis	2
Meningitis, tuberculous	2
Meningitis, pneumococcic	1
Hyperthyroidism	1
Progressive muscular atrophy	1
Multiple sclerosis	1
Huntington's chorea	1
Psychosis with endocrine dyscrasia	1
Tabes dorsalis	1
Paranoia	1
Cerebral gumma	1
Paranoid condition	1

These statistics are not, of course, to be taken as typical for all psychiatric hospitals. They represent the admissions in a hospital maintained by the federal government through the Veterans Administration for the care of ex-service men. The majority of the patients were veterans of World War I, although Spanish-American War veterans, a very few Civil War veterans, former soldiers discharged from peacetime service, and young men from the Civilian Conservation Corps are represented in the figures given.

The group now being considered consists then chiefly of men with an average age level in the early forties. The hospital is located on the southeastern seaboard. Most of the patients are drawn from the adjacent states, but every section of the country is represented.

Several factors must be weighed before any attempt is made to draw conclusions from the bare figures given above. The general policy in federal hospitals maintained for the treatment of veterans differs considerably from the policy of state hospitals. Although patients classed as chronic alcoholics and psychopaths are not considered eligible for treatment and, according to regulations, should not be admitted, the authorities try at all times to give the veteran the benefit of any doubt and are undoubtedly more lenient in general than those at the state hospitals. Consequently, many patients who turn out to be psychopaths pure and simple and who probably would not be accepted at state hospitals are taken into federal hospitals.

On the other hand, this very factor, the policy of giving the veteran every possible benefit of doubt, tends to make the proportion of psychopaths appear lower among this group of 857 patients than if the same group were diagnosed elsewhere. Since those who are put in this classification do not draw compensation, being considered by law responsible for their own maladjustment, the Veterans Administration insists that the diagnosis be made only on the most convincing evidence and when the possibility of other psychiatric conditions for which compensation is paid is thoroughly ruled out. As everyone who deals with such questions knows, it is often extremely difficult to rule out "neurasthenia," "hysteria," "psychasthenia," and posttraumatic neuroses when these conditions are claimed by patients eager for pension money. Taking into consideration the fact that the psychopath is almost invariably just the sort of person who will bend his efforts to get everything possible from the government, or from any other source, and that he is entirely unscrupulous and often very clever in doing so, the difficulty will be still further appreciated.

In my frank opinion some of the patients listed here in the psychoneurotic and posttraumatic groups are really psychopaths and nothing more. Men who had sustained skull injuries and have records of concussion, whether the injury dates from army service or not, were nearly always given the advantage of the possibility that their maladjustment resulted from cerebral trauma. Everyone knows that although personality changes sometimes follow such injuries, they by no means always follow. This is known, of course, to the psychiatrists in the federal hospitals. Yet it cannot be denied that with so strong a policy prevailing, to eschew even the remote possibility of injustice to a veteran, many received the posttraumatic diagnosis who would otherwise have been called psychopaths.

The same thing is true when a question of psychoneurosis is concerned. When a patient has once been called psychoneurotic, any change which would deprive him of his compensation brings protest and calls for further examinations, not to speak of the strong political pressure which is sometimes exerted. Without meaning to accuse any psychiatrist in the Veterans Administration service of responding to such pressure, I believe that such conditions cannot but tend on the whole to make all cases about which there is an honest doubt gravitate from the psychopathic personality group to one of the others.

No doubt it is better to let one hundred guilty men go unpunished than to hang one who is innocent, and so this policy in regard to diagnosis may be justifiable. Nevertheless, it must be considered as a factor in the statistics under discussion.

There was another important influence that worked against making a diagnosis of psychopathic personality in the group of patients considered here. Often the need for hospitalization was plain and urgent. Sometimes the patient had for years continuously demonstrated his inability to conduct himself or his affairs without constant supervision. Occasionally such patients were a serious and immediate danger to the lives of others. Under such circumstances the necessity to admit the patient to the hospital and to keep him there was compelling. The diagnosis of psychopathic personality, with its implication of a person legally sane, does not qualify a patient for admission and leaves him free to depart form the hospital at will if he is admitted. The practical and often imperative necessity to keep such patients under supervision serves, in my opinion, as an influence to make conscientious physicians on the staff try to place the patient's disorder on some other basis and, whenever even the slightest possibility of any other causal factor can be invoked, to make some other diagnosis. Usually when such other factors, for instance, slight trauma to the head, diabetes, or possible alcoholic deterioration, can be established, they are recent in appearance, and the folly and misconduct are of many years prior duration. Yet this new possibility is seized on as a practical expedient. I do not mention this tendency to condemn it, for, after all, it is vitally important to hospitalize these patients and to keep them under supervision. As a factor in the present statistics, however, it cannot be ignored.

For my purposes many other patients in the 857 listed may be added to the 102 in the psychopathic personality group. The forty-one patients described as having chronic alcoholism with deterioration and the fourteen patients with acute alcoholic hallucinosis were nearly all, in varying degree, of the same type as the group of 102 patients. This is to say that aside from their temporary hallucinosis or their more recent deterioration, the fundamental personality disorder was the same. Most of those listed under the heading "chronic alcoholism with deterioration" were, as a matter of fact, also given the secondary diagnosis of "psychopathic personality." I believe that few, if any, people who use alcohol to such an extent that they have to be confined for treatment in psychiatric institutions are normal. As brought out elsewhere, it is believed that a large proportion of such people, in the absence of other nervous or mental disorders, properly belong in the psychopathic personality group.

Here, again, the benign policy of the Veterans Administration comes into play. It is not customary to make the diagnosis of psychopathic personality unless the condition is pronounced and inescapable, the intention being to spare veterans whenever possible the stigma that is felt by some to go with this term.

Most of the patients diagnosed as having chronic alcoholism with deterioration showed very little deterioration indeed. There is no doubt that their maladjustment, which extended back many years, resulted primarily from a personal inadequacy, whatever complicating factors may have been added by the deterioration. My belief is that some physicians tend to see evidence of deterioration in the poor judgment and bizarre conduct which are notoriously typical of the psychopath pure and simple. Not even those who spend their lives dealing with mental mechanisms in others are entirely free from similar factors in themselves, and it is a well-known human tendency to explain things such as the fantastic behavior of these patients on a tangible basis, such as damaged brain structure, instead of on the ill-defined basis of psychopathic personality, a term implying something far less clearly understood than schizophrenia or any of the other psychoses.

The seven patients classed as "no nervous or mental disease" had also a history of excessive drinking and maladjustment strongly suggestive of psychopathic personality, or at least of what I mean to define as such, in a milder degree. A few of these, it must be granted, may have been merely cases of neurotic drinking.

Leaving out all patients who, aside from their major conditions, were probably psychopaths and also those patients in whom a typically psychopathic maladjustment was explained on some other basis (such as psychoneurosis or traumatic condition) but including the alcohol and drug addicts, a formidable proportion of this material qualifies for consideration.

    102 diagnosed as having psychopathic personality
      60 diagnosed as having chronic alcoholism
      41 diagnosed as having chronic alcoholism with deterioration
      14 diagnosed as having acute alcoholic hallucinosis
       8 diagnosed as having psychopathic personality with psychotic episodes*
       3 diagnosed as having acute alcoholism
       8 diagnosed as having drug addiction

These 236 patients, more than one-fourth of the total, probably represent in varying degree the type of character inadequacy and personality disorder which is the subject of the present discussion. If we count only one-half of the 134 patients not diagnosed primarily as psychopaths, these, with the unquestionably psychopathic patients, give us a total of 169 patients, almost one-fifth of all who were admitted. The question of whether or not the term psychopathic personality is an ideal one and suitable to all these patients I am willing to leave unanswered at present. Since there is considerable disagreement among groups of psychiatrists in state and federal hospitals as to just how much maladjustment is necessary for a patient to deserve such a

---

*These are considered here on the basis of their usual condition without reference to their behavior in the alleged episodic "psychotic" periods.

diagnosis, some preferring to apply it only in extreme cases, there is no reason to insist here on its wider application. Standard textbooks do not make clear to what precise degree the person must be affected to be justifiably placed in this category. With due apologies then to those who would restrict this term, I ask leave to use it for the type of person who is now being considered. There is no other accepted term available. Whatever these people may be called, they are not normal.

If we consider, in addition to these patients (nearly all of whom have records of the utmost folly and misery and idleness over many years and who have had to enter a psychiatric hospital), the vast number of similar people in every community who show the same behavior pattern in milder form but who are sufficiently protected and supported by relatives to remain at large, the prevalence of this disorder is seen to be appalling.

References

1. Abraham, Karl: Selected papers, London, 1927, Institute of Psychoanalysis and Hogarth Press.
2. Abraham, Karl: Melancholia and the development of the libido. Cited in Masserman, J. H.: Principles of dynamic psychiatry, Philadelphia, 1946, W. B. Saunders Co.
3. Abraham, Karl: Selected papers, London, 1949, The Hogarth Press, Ltd., pp. 418-501.
4. Abrahamson, David: The mind and death of a genius, New York, 1946, Columbia University Press.
5. Adams, J. D.: Speaking of books, The New York Times Book Review, March 15, 1953.
6. Adler, Alfred: The neurotic constitution, London, 1921, Kegan Paul, Trench, Trubner & Co., Ltd.
7. Alcoholics Anonymous, New York, 1939, Works Publishing Co.
8. Alexander, Franz: The need for punishment and the death instinct, International Journal of Psychoanalysis 10:260, 1929.
9. Alexander, Franz: The neurotic character, International Journal of Psychoanalysis 2:292-311, 1930.
10. Alexander, Franz: Opinion cited in Healy, William, Bronner, A. F., and Bowers, A. M.: The structure and meaning of psychoanalysis, New York, 1938, Alfred A. Knopf, Inc., p. 304.
11. Alexander, Franz: Fundamentals of psychoanalysis, New York, 1948, W. W. Norton & Co., Inc.
12. Alexander, Franz, and Healy, William: The roots of crime, New York, 1935, Alfred A. Knopf, Inc.
13. Allen, Clifford: Modern discoveries in medical psychology, London, 1937, The Macmillan Co.
14. Astor, Mary: The incredible Charlie Carewe, Garden City, New York, 1960, Doubleday & Co., Inc.
15. Bailey, Pearce: The present outlook of neurology in the United States, Journal of the Association of American Medical Colleges 24:214-228, 1949.
16. Banay, R. S., and Davidoff, L.: Apparent recovery of a sex psychopath after lobotomy, Journal of Criminal Psychopathology 4:59-66, 1942
17. Barnard, Allen: The harlot killer, New York, 1953, Dodd, Mead & Co., Inc.
18. Beerbohm, Max: Zuleika Dobson, London, 1911, William Heinemann, Ltd.
19. Bender, L., and Yarrell, Z.: Psychoses among the followers of Father Divine, Journal of Nervous and Mental Disease 87:418-449, 1938.
20. Bergler, Edmund: The myth of a new national disease, Psychiatric Quarterly 22:66-88, 1948.
21. Bett, W. R.: The infirmities of genius, New York, 1952, Philosophical Library.
22. Billings, Edward G.: A handbook of elementary psychobiology and psychiatry, New York, 1939, The Macmillan Co.

23. Book review: The New England Journal of Medicine **225**:349, 1941.
24. Boss, M.: Meaning and content of sexual perversions, New York, 1949, Grune & Stratton.
25. Bradley, A. C.: Shakespearean tragedy, New York, 1926, The Macmillan Co.
26. Brady, M. E.: The strange case of Wilhelm Reich, May 26, 1947, New Republic. Reprinted in Bulletin of the Menninger Clinic **12**:61-67, 1948.
27. Brickner, Richard: Is Germany incurable? Philadelphia and New York, 1943, J. B. Lippincott Co.
28. Bromberg, W., and Cleckley, H. M.: The medico-legal dilemma, Journal of Criminal Law, Criminology, and Police Science **42**:729-745, 1952.
29. Bromberg, W., and Thompson, C. B.: The relation of psychosis, mental defect, and personality types to crime, Journal of Criminal Law and Criminology **28**:1, 1937.
30. Bronte, Emily: Wuthering heights, New York, 1939, Dodd, Mead & Co., Inc.
31. Brown, J. F.: The psychodynamics of abnormal behavior, New York, 1940, McGraw-Hill Book Co., Inc., pp. 246, 247.
32. Brussel, James A.: Father Divine: holy precipitator of psychoses, American Journal of Psychiatry **92**:215-223, 1935.
33. Bulliet, C. J.: Apples and madonnas, New York, 1935, Covici-Friede, Inc.
34. Burlingame, C. C.: Hard facts about psychiatry, Journal of the American Medical Association **113**:337-380, 1939.
35. Burman, B. L.: The cult of unintelligibility, The Saturday Review, Nov. 1, 1952.
36. Byrne, Donn: O'Malley of Shanganagh, New York, 1924, The Century Co.
37. Caldwell, Erskine: Tobacco road, New York, 1932, Gosset & Dunlap.
38. Caldwell, John M.: Neurotic components in psychopathic behavior, Journal of Nervous and Mental Disease **99**:134-148, 1944.
39. Campbell, John D.: Everyday psychiatry, Philadelphia, 1945, J. B. Lippincott Co.
40. Carpenter, Edward: The intermediate sex, London, 1908, George Allen & Unwin, Ltd.
41. Cheney, Clarence O., and Landis, Carney: A program for the determination of the therapeutic effectiveness of psychoanalytic method, The American Journal of Psychiatry **91**:1161-1165, 1935.
42. Chesterton, G. K.: Humor. In Encyclopaedia Britannica, ed. 14, 1929.
43. Chisholm, Brock: The re-establishment of peacetime society, Psychiatry **9**:3-20, 1946.
44. Chornyak, J.: Some remarks on the diagnosis of the psychopathic delinquent, American Journal of Psychiatry **97**:1326-1340, 1941.
45. Cleckley, Hervey: The so-called psychopathic personality, Journal of the Medical Association of Georgia **11**:466-472, 1941.
46. Cleckley, Hervey: Sematic dementia and semi-suicide, Psychiatric Quarterly **61**:521-529, 1942.
47. Cleckley, Hervey: The psychosis that psychiatry refuses to face, Journal of Criminal Psychopathology **6**:117-130, 1944.
48. Cleckley, Hervey: The psychopath, a problem for society, Federal Probation **10**:22-25, 1946.
49. Cleckley, Hervey: The psychopath viewed practically (chap. 11). In Seliger, R. V., Lukas, E. F., and Lindner, R. M., editors: Contemporary criminal hygiene, Baltimore, 1946, Oakridge Press, pp. 194-217.
50. Cleckley, Hervey: Antisocial personalities (chap. 12). In Pennington, L. A., and Berg, Irwin A., editors: An introduction to clinical psychology, New York, 1948, The Ronald Press Co., pp. 249-264.

51. Cleckley, Hervey: Common sources of confusion in psychiatric matters, Journal of the Southern Medical Association 42:341-343, 1949.
52. Cleckley, Hervey: Psychopathic personality. In Branham, V. C., and Kutash, E. B., editors: Encyclopedia of Criminology, New York, 1949, Philosophical Library.
53. Cleckley, Hervey: The mask of sanity, Postgraduate Medicine 9:193-197, 1951.
54. Cleckley, Hervey: The caricature of love, New York, 1957, The Ronald Press Co.
55. Cleckley, Hervey: Psychopathic states (chap. 28). In Arieto, Silvano, editor: American handbook of psychiatry, New York, 1959, Basic Books, Inc.
56. Cleckley, Hervey: Psychiatry: science, art, and scientism (chap. 5). In Schoeck, Helmut, and Wiggins, James W., editors: Psychiatry and responsibility, vol. 2, Princeton, 1962, D. Van Nostrand Co., Inc., pp. 567-588.
57. Clutton-Brock, Arthur: Evil and the new psychology, The Atlantic Monthly, March, 1923, pp. 298-308.
58. Cory, D. W.: The homosexual in America, New York, 1951, Greenberg.
59. Council on Pharmacy and Chemistry (report of the council): Cancer and the need for facts, Journal of the American Medical Association 139:93-98, 1949.
60. Craig, Maurice: Psychological medicine, Philadelphia, 1926, P. Blakiston's Son & Co.
61. Critchley, MacDonald: The trial of Neville George Clevely Heath, London, 1951, William Hodge & Co., Ltd.
62. Cruvant, B. A., and Yochelson, L.: The psychiatrist and the psychotic psychopath, American Journal of Psychiatry 106:594-598, 1950.
63. Culpin, Millais: Recent advances in psychoneuroses, Philadelphia, 1931, P. Blakiston's Son & Co.
64. Cumming, Joseph B.: The role of the psychiatrist in criminal trials, The American Journal of Psychiatry 115:491-497, 1958.
65. Curran, D., and Mallinson, P.: Recent progress in psychiatry; psychopathic personality, Journal of Mental Science 90:266-286, 1944.
66. Darling, H. F.: Shock therapy in psychopathic personality, Journal of Nervous and Mental Disease 101:247-250, 1945.
67. Darling, H. F., and Sanddal, J. W.: A psychopathologic concept of psychopathic personality, Journal of Clinical and Experimental Psychopathology 13:175-180, 1952.
68. Davidson, Henry A.: Orientation to forensic psychiatry, Archives of Neurology and Psychiatry 57:730-755, June, 1947.
69. Diagnostic and statistical manual, mental disorders, Washington, D. C., 1952, American Psychiatric Association Mental Hospital Service.
70. Dickens, Charles: David Copperfield, New York, P. F. Collier.
71. Diethelm, O.: Treatment in psychiatry, New York, 1936, The Macmillan Co.
72. Dingle, E. J.: Borderlands of eternity, Los Angeles, 1941, Econolith Press.
73. Dostoyevsky, Fyodor: Crime and punishment, New York, 1922, The Macmillan Co.
74. Dostoyevsky, Fyodor: Crime and punishment, New York, 1922, The Macmillan Co., pp. 438-448.
75. Dostoyevsky, Fyodor: The brothers Karamazov, New York, 1922, The Macmillan Co.
76. Dostoyevsky, Fyodor: The idiot, New York, 1926, The Macmillan Co.
77. Dostoyevsky, Fyodor: Stavrogin's confession, New York, 1947, Lear Publishers, Inc.
78. Dowden, Edward: Shakespeare, his mind and his art, New York, 1918, Harper & Brothers.

79. Dubois, R. S.: The treatment of psychopathic personality, Connecticut State Medical Journal 10:640-644, 1946.
80. Editorial: The tide has turned, The Saturday Review, Aug. 30, 1952.
81. Ehrlich, S. K., and Keogh, R. P.: The psychopath in a mental institution, Archives of Neurology and Psychiatry 76:286-295, 1956.
82. Ellis, Havelock: Studies in the psychology of sex, Philadelphia, 1920, F. A. Davis Co.
83. Ellis, Havelock: Studies in the psychology of sex, vol. 6, Philadelphia, 1920, F. A. Davis Co., pp. 118-142.
84. Ellis, Havelock: Introduction to Huysmans, J. K.: Against the grain, New York, 1931, Hartsdale House.
85. English, O. S., and Pearson, H. J. P.: Common neuroses of children and adults, New York, 1937, W. W. Norton & Co., Inc.
86. Eysenck, H. J.: The uses and abuses of psychology, London, 1953, Penguin Books.
87. Faulkner, William: Sanctuary, New York, 1931, Jonathan Cape & Harrison Smith.
88. Fenichel, Otto: The psychoanalytic theory of neurosis, New York, 1945, W. W. Norton & Co., Inc.
89. Ferenczi, S.: Thalassa: a theory of genitality, New York, 1938, The Psychoanalytic Quarterly, Inc., pp. 20-36.
90. Fillmore, C.: Health and prosperity, Unity 98:1-5, 1943.
91. Fodor, N.: The search for the beloved, Psychiatric Quarterly 20:570-602, 1946.
92. Fortas, Abe: Implications of Durham's case, American Journal of Psychiatry 113:575-582, 1957.
93. Freud, Sigmund: Introductory lectures on psychoanalysis, London, 1923, George Allen and Unwin, Ltd., pp. 322-327.
94. Freud, Sigmund: Three contributions to the theory of sex, Washington, 1930, Nervous and Mental Disease Publishing Co.
95. Freud, Sigmund: Neurosis and psychosis. In Collected papers, vol. 2, London, 1942, Hogarth Press, pp. 250-254.
96. Freud, Sigmund: The ego and the id, London, 1942, Hogarth Press.
97. Freud, Sigmund: Collected papers, vol. 3, London, 1943, Hogarth Press.
98. Freud, Sigmund: Psycho-analytical notes upon an autobiographical account of a case of paranoia (dementia paranoides). In Collected papers, vol. 3, London, 1943, Hogarth Press, pp. 387-470.
99. Freud, Sigmund: From the history of an infantile neurosis. In Collected papers, vol. 3, London, 1946, Hogarth Press, pp. 473-605.
100. Freud, Sigmund: The most prevalent form of degradation in erotic life. In Collected papers, vol. 4, London, 1946, Hogarth Press, pp. 203-216.
101. Gibbs, F. A., and Bagchi, B. K.: Electroencephalographic study of criminals, American Journal of Psychiatry 102:294-298, 1945.
102. Gide, André: Corydon, New York, 1950, Farrar, Straus & Co.
103. Glueck, Sheldon, and Glueck, Eleanor J.: Five hundred criminal careers, New York, 1930, Alfred A. Knopf, Inc.
104. Goldfarb, H.: Effects of psychological deprivation in infancy and subsequent stimulation, American Journal of Psychiatry 102:18-33, 1945.
105. Gottlieb, J. S., Ashby, M. C., and Knott, J. R.: Studies in primary behavior disorders and psychopathic personality. Part II. The inheritance of electrocortical activity, American Journal of Psychiatry 103:823-827, 1947.
106. Grasset, Joseph: The semi-insane and the semi-responsible, New York, 1907, Funk and Wagnalls Co.
107. Greenacre, P.: Conscience in the psycopath, American Journal of Orthopsychiatry 15:495-509, 1945.

108. Greenspan, H. G., and Campbell, J. D.: The homosexual as a personality type, American Journal of Psychiatry 101:682-689, 1945.

109. Grotjahn, Martin: Beyond laughter, New York, 1957, The Blakiston Division, McGraw-Hill Book Co., Inc.

110. Guttmacher, Manfred: Criminal responsibility, Bulletin of the U. S. Army Medical Department 8:681-694, 1948.

111. Guttmacher, Manfred: Pseudopsychopathic schizophrenia, Archives of Criminal Psychodynamics (special psychopathy issue), 502-508, 1961.

112. Hakeem, Michael: A critique of the psychiatric approach to crime and correction, Crime and Correction 23:650-682, 1958.

113. Hall, Jerome: Mental disease and criminal responsibility, Columbia Law Review 45:677-718, 1945.

114. Hall, Jerome: Principles of criminal law, Indianapolis, 1947, The Bobbs-Merrill Co.

115. Hall, Jerome: Responsibility and law: in defense of the M'Naghten Rules, Journal of the American Bar Association 42:917-919, 1956.

116. Hall, Jerome: The M'Naghten Rules and proposed alternatives, Journal of the American Bar Association 59:960-964, 1963.

117. Hall, Jerome: Science, common sense, and criminal law reform, John F. Murray Endowment Lecture, College of Law, State University of Iowa, Iowa City, Oct. 18, 1963.

118. Hamburger, Christian, Sturup, G. K., and Dahl-Iversen, E.: Transvestism, Journal of the American Medical Association 152:391-396, 1953.

119. Hamilton, Edith: Faulkner: sorcerer or slave? The Saturday Review, July 12, 1952.

120. Hardin, G.: The threat of clarity, American Journal of Psychiatry 114:392-396, 1957.

121. Hart, Bernard: The psychology of insanity, New York, 1928, The Macmillan Co.

122. Hayakawa, S. I.: Language in action, New York, 1940, Harcourt, Brace & Co., Inc.

123. Head, Henry: Aphasia in kindred disorders of speech, New York, 1926, The Macmillan Co.

124. Healy, William: The individual delinquent, Boston, 1915, Little, Brown & Co.

125. Healy, William: New light on delinquency and its treatment, New Haven, 1936, Yale University Press.

126. Healy, William, and Bronner, A. F.: Delinquents and criminals, New York, 1926, The Macmillan Co.

127. Heath, R. G., and Pool, J. L.: Treatment of psychoses with bilateral ablation of a focal area of the frontal cortex, Psychosomatic Medicine 10:254-256, 1948.

128. Henderson, D. K.: Clinical recollections and reflections: alcoholism and psychiatry, Edinburgh Medical Journal 43:717, 1936.

129. Henderson, D. K.: Psychopathic states, New York, 1939, W. W. Norton & Co., Inc.

130. Hendrick, Ives: Facts and theories of psychoanalysis, New York, 1941, Alfred A. Knopf, Inc.

131. Hendrick, Ives: Facts of theories of psychoanalysis, New York, 1941, Alfred A. Knopf, Inc., pp. 168-190.

132. Henry, G. W.: Essentials of psychiatry, ed. 2, Baltimore, 1938, Williams & Wilkins Co.

133. Henry, G. W.: Sex variants: a study of homosexual patterns, New York, 1941, Paul B. Hoeber, Inc.

134. Hill, D.: EEG in episodic psychotic and psychopathic behavior, Electroencephalography and Clinical Neurophysiology 4:419-442, 1952.

135. Hill, D., and Pond, D. A.: Reflections on one hundred capital cases submitted to electroencephalography, Journal of Mental Science **98**:23-43, 1952.

136. Hill, Paul: Portrait of a sadist, New York, 1960, Avon Book Division, The Hearst Corporation.

137. Himwich, Harold E.: Chap. 1 in Emerson, Haven: Alcohol and man, New York, 1935, The Macmillan Co., p. 13.

138. Hinsie, L. E., and Campbell, Robert J.: Psychiatric dictionary, New York, 1960, Oxford University Press.

139. Hoch, Paul, and Polatin, Phillip: Pseudoneurotic forms of schizophrenia, Psychiatric Quarterly **23**:248-276, 1949.

140. Hughes, Richard: A high wind in Jamaica, New York, 1930, Harper & Brothers.

141. Hugo, Victor: Les miserables, New York, P. F. Collier.

142. Hunt, J. McV., and Cofer, C. N.: Psychological deficit (chap. 32). In Hunt, J. McV., editor: Personality and the behavior disorders, New York, 1944, The Ronald Press Co.

143. Hurn, P. D., and Waverly, L. R.: The truth about Wagner, New York, 1930, Frederick A. Stokes Co.

144. Huxley, Aldous: Point counter point, New York, 1929, Doubleday, Doran & Co., Inc.

145. Huysmans, J. K.: Against the grain, New York, 1931, Hartsdale House.

146. Huysmans, J. K.: La bas, Paris, Les Editions du Courrier Graphique.

147. Hyde, H. M.: The trials of Oscar Wilde, London, 1948, William Hodge & Co., Ltd.

148. Ibsen, Hendrik: Peer Gynt (translated by William Archer), New York, 1907, Charles Scribner & Sons.

149. Ingham, S. D.: Some neurologic aspects of psychiatry, Journal of the American Medical Association **111**:665-668, 1938.

150. Jackson, Charles: The lost week end, New York, 1944, Farrar & Rinehart, Inc.

151. James, Henry: The turn of the screw, New York, 1930, Modern Library.

152. Jellinek, E. M.: Alcohol addiction and chronic alchololism, New Haven, 1942, Yale University Press.

153. Jenkins, Richard L.: The psychopathic or antisocial personality, Journal of Nervous and Mental Disease **131**:318-332, 1960.

154. Johnson, Adelaide M.: Sanctions for superego lacunae of adolescents. In Eissler, K. R., editor: Searchlights on delinquency: new psychoanalytic studies, New York, 1949, International Universities Press.

155. Johnson, Adelaide M.: Juvenile delinquency (chap. 42). In Arieto, Silvano, editor: American handbook of psychiatry, New York, 1959, Basic Books, Inc., pp. 840-856.

156. Johnson, Adelaide M., and Szurek, S. A.: Etiology of the antisocial behavior in delinquents and psychopaths, Journal of the American Medical Association **154**:814-817, 1954.

157. Johnson, Wendell: People in quandaries, New York, 1946, Harper & Brothers.

158. Jones, A. B., and Llewellyn, L. J.: Malingering, Philadelphia, 1917, P. Blakiston's Son & Co.

159. Jones, Ernest: Opinion cited in Healy, William, Bronner, A. F., and Bowers, A. M.: The structure and meaning of psychoanalysis, New York, 1938, Alfred A. Knopf, Inc.

160. Joyce, James: Finnegan's wake, New York, 1945, The Viking Press.

161. Jung, Carl: The psychology of dementia praecox, Washington, D. C., 1936, Nervous and Mental Disease Publishing Co.

162. Kahn, Eugen: Psychopathic personalities, New Haven, 1931, Yale University Press.

163. Kanner, Leo: Problems of nosology and psychodynamics of early infantile autism, The American Journal of Orthopsychiatry **19**:416-426, 1949.

164. Kappers, C. W. A.: Phenomena of neurobiotaxis as demonstrated by position of motor nuclei of the medulla oblongata, Journal of Nervous and Mental Disease **50**:1-16, 1916.

165. Karpman, Benjamin: The individual criminal, Washington, D. C., 1935, Nervous and Mental Disease Publishing Co.

166. Karpman, Benjamin: The principles and aims of criminal psychopathology, Journal of Criminal Psychopathology **1**:187-218, 1940.

167. Karpman, Benjamin: On the need for separating psychopathy into two distinct types: the symptomatic and the idiopathic, Journal of Criminal Psychopathology **3**:112-137, 1941.

168. Karpman, Benjamin: Perversions as neuroses, Journal of Criminal Psychopathology **3**:180, 1941.

169. Karpman, Benjamin: A yardstick for measuring psychopathy, Federal Probation **10**:26-31, 1946.

170. Karpman, Benjamin: The myth of the psychopathic personality, American Journal of Psychiatry **104**:523-534, 1948.

171. Karpman, Benjamin: Criminal psychodynamics: a platform, Archives of Criminal Psychodynamics **1**:3-100, 1955.

172. Kelsey, D. E. R.: Phantasies of birth and prenatal experiences recovered from patients undergoing hypnoanalysis, The Journal of Mental Science **99**:216-223, 1953.

173. Kinsey, A. C., Pomeroy, W. B., and Martin, C. E.: Sexual behavior in the human male, Philadelphia, 1948, W. B. Saunders Co.

174. Knight, Robert: The psychodynamics of chronic alcoholism, Journal of Nervous and Mental Disease **86**:538-548, 1937.

175. Knight, Robert: The psychoanalytic treatment in a sanatorium of chronic addiction to alcohol, Journal of the American Medical Association **111**:1443-1448, 1938.

176. Knight, Robert: A critique of the present status of the psychotherapies, Bulletin of the New York Academy of Medicine **25**:100-114, 1949.

177. Knott, J. R., and Gottlieb, J. S.: The electro-encephalogram in psychopathic personality, Psychosomatic Medicine **5**:139-142, 1943.

178. Kolb, L. C.: An evaluation of lobotomy and its potentialities for future research in psychiatry and the basic sciences, Journal of Nervous and Mental Disease **110**:112-148, 1949.

179. Korzybski, Alfred: Science and sanity, Lancaster, Pa., 1941, The Science Press Printing Co.

180. Krafft-Ebing: Psychopathia sexualis, New York, 1924, Physicians and Surgeons Book Co.

181. Kuprin, Alexandre: Yama (translated by Bernard Guilbert Guerney), New York, 1929, The Modern Library.

182. Lawrenson, Helen: The cool cat era, Park East, Jan., 1953.

183. Levin, Harry: James Joyce, Norfolk, Conn., 1941, New Directions Books.

184. Levin, Harry: Introduction to Curtis, Mina, editor: Letters of Marcel Proust, New York, 1949, Random House.

185. Levin, M.: The dynamic conception of psychopathic personality, Ohio State Medical Journal **36**:848-850, 1940.

186. Levin, Meyer: Compulsion, New York, 1956, Simon & Schuster.

187. Liddell, H. S.: Conditioned reflex method and experimental neurosis (chap. 12). In Hunt, J. McV., editor: Personality and the behavior disorders, New York, 1944, The Ronald Press Co., pp. 398-412.

188. Lindner, Robert: Rebel without a cause, New York, 1944, Grune & Stratton, Inc.
189. Lindner, Robert: Stone walls and men, New York, 1946, Odyssey Press.
190. Lindner, Robert: Prescription for rebellion, New York, 1952, Rinehart & Co., Inc.
191. Lombroso, Cesare: The man of genius, New York, 1910, Charles Scribner's Sons.
192. London, L. S.: Mechanisms in paranoia, Psychoanalytic Review 18:394-412, 1931.
193. Lorand, Sandor: Psychoanalysis today, New York, 1944, International Universities Press, Inc.
194. Lowery, Lawson G.: Delinquent and criminal personalities. In Hunt, J. McV., editor: Personality and the behavior disorders, New York, 1944, The Ronald Press Co.
195. Ludwig, Arnold M.: The other side of the coin, The New Physician 9:56-58, 1960.
196. McCord, William, and McCord, Joan: Psychopathy and delinquency, New York, 1956, Grune & Stratton.
197. McDougall, William: An outline of abnormal psychology, London, 1926, Methuen & Co., p. 373.
198. McWilliams, Carey: Southern California country, New York, 1946, Duell, Sloan & Pearce, Inc.
199. Major, Ralph H.: Faiths that healed, New York, 1940, D. Appleton-Century Co.
200. Mangun, C. W.: The psychopathic criminal, Journal of Criminal Psychopathology 4:117-127, 1942.
201. Mann, Thomas: The magic mountain (translated by H. T. Lowe-Porter), New York, The Modern Library.
202. Mann, Thomas: Stories of three decades, New York, 1936, Alfred A. Knopf, Inc.
203. Mann, Thomas: Introduction to Dostoevsky: The short novels, New York, 1951, Dial Press.
204. March, Harold: Gide and the hound of heaven, Philadelphia, 1952, University of Pennsylvania Press.
205. Marmor, J. M., and Pumpian-Mindlin, E.: Toward an integrative conception of mental disorder, Journal of Nervous and Mental Disease 111:19-29, 1950.
206. Masserman, Jules H.: Behavior and neurosis, Chicago, 1943, University of Chicago Press.
207. Masserman, Jules H.: Principles of dynamic psychiatry, Philadelphia, 1946, W. B. Saunders Co.
208. Masserman, Jules H.: Faith and delusion in psychotherapy, the ur-defenses of man, American Journal of Psychiatry 110:324-333, 1953.
209. Maugham, Somerset: Of human bondage, Garden City, N. Y., 1915, Garden City Publishing Co.
210. Maughs, Sydney: A concept of psychopathy and psychopathic personality—its evolution and historical development, Journal of Criminal Psychopathology 2:329-356, 465-499, 1941.
211. Mauriac, Francois: Proust's way, New York, 1950, Philosophical Library.
212. Menninger, Karl: Discussion of Knight, Robert: The psychoanalytic treatment in a sanatorium of chronic addiction to alcohol, Journal of the American Medical Association 111:1443-1448, 1938.
213. Menninger, Karl: Man against himself, New York, 1938, Harcourt, Brace & Co., Inc.
214. Menninger, Karl: Recognizing and renaming "psychopathic personalities," Bulletin of the Menninger Clinic 5:150-156, 1941.
215. Menninger, Karl: Love against hate, New York, 1942, Harcourt, Brace & Co., Inc.
216. Menninger, Karl: The human mind, New York, 1947, Alfred A. Knopf, Inc.

217. Mental Deficiency Committee of the Royal Medico-Psychological Association: Journal of Mental Science **82**:247-257, 1937.
218. Meredith, George: The ordeal of Richard Feveral, New York, 1896, Charles Scribner's Sons.
219. Meredith, George: The ordeal of Richard Feveral, New York, 1896, Charles Scribner's Sons, p. 302.
220. Mettler, F. A., editor: Selective partial ablation of the frontal cortex; correlative study of its effects on human psychotic subjects, New York, 1949, Paul B. Hoeber, Inc.
221. Meyer, Adolf: Reports of the New York State Pathological Institute, Utica, N. Y., 1904-05, p. 20.
222. Meyer, Adolf: Inter-relations of the domain of neuropsychiatry, Archives of Neurology and Psychiatry **8**:111-121, 1922.
223. Meyer, Adolf: Leading concepts in psychobiology (ergasiology) and psychiatry (ergasiatry), Proceedings of the Fourth Conference on Psychiatric Education, National Committee for Mental Hygiene, 1938, pp. 267-301.
224. Meyer, Adolf: Objective psychology or psychobiology with subordination of the medically useless contrast of mental and physical, Proceedings of the Fourth Conference on Psychiatric Education, National Committee for Mental Hygiene, 1938, pp. 307-313.
225. Meyer, Adolf: In Sladen, F. J., editor: Psychiatry and the war, Springfield, Ill., 1943, Charles C Thomas, Publisher, pp. 359-378.
226. Michelet, Jules: Satanism and witchcraft, New York, 1946, The Citadel Press.
227. Millay, Edna St. Vincent: A few figs from thistles, New York, 1932, Harper & Brothers.
228. Mitchell, Margaret: Gone with the wind, New York, 1936, The Macmillan Co.
229. Molnar, Ferenc: Liliom, The Theatre Guild Anthology, New York, 1936, Random House.
230. Muncie, Wendell: Psychobiology and psychiatry, St. Louis, 1948, The C. V. Mosby Co.
231. Newsweek, May 14, 1956, p. 38.
232. Nicole, J. E.: Psychopathology, Baltimore, 1947, Williams & Wilkins Co.
233. Nomenclature and method of recording diagnosis, U. S. War Department Technical Bulletin, T. B. Med. No. 203, Washington, D. C., 1945.
234. Nordau, Max: Degeneration, New York, 1907, D. Appleton & Co.
235. Noyes, Arthur P., and Kolb, Lawrence C.: Modern clinical psychiatry, ed. 6, Philadelphia, 1963, W. B. Saunders Co.
236. O'Neill, Eugene: Strange interlude, New York, 1928, Boni & Liveright.
237. Outlines for psychiatric examinations, Albany, N. Y., 1943, The New York State Department of Mental Hygiene.
238. Pach, Walter: Vincent Van Gogh, New York, 1936, Artbook Museum.
239. Parkhurst, Helen Huss: Beauty, New York, 1930, Harcourt, Brace & Co., Inc.
240. Parson, Donald: Glass flowers, Boston, 1936, John W. Luce & Co.
241. Partridge, G. D.: A study of fifty cases of psychopathic personality, American Journal of Psychiatry **7**:953-974, 1928.
242. Partridge, G. D.: Psychopathic personalities among boys in a training school for delinquents, American Journal of Psychiatry **8**:159, 1928.
243. Partridge, G. D.: Psychopathic personality and personality investigation, American Journal of Psychiatry **8**:1053, 1929.
244. Partridge, G. D.: Current conceptions of psychopathic personality, American Journal of Psychiatry **10**:53-99, 1930.

245. Pearson, Hesketh: Oscar Wilde, his life and wit, New York, 1946, Harper & Brothers.
246. Peerbolte, M. L.: Psychotherapeutic evaluations of birth-trauma analysis, psychiatric Quarterly **25**:589-603, 1951.
247. Penrose, Lionel S.: Mental defect, New York, 1934, Farrar & Rinehart, Inc.
248. Pescor, M. J.: Abnormal personality types among offenders, Federal Probation **12**:3-8, 1948.
249. Prayers answered, Unity **98**:73-76, 1943.
250. Praz, Mario: The romantic agony, London, 1951, Oxford University Press.
251. Preu, P. W.: The concept of psychopathic personality (chap. 30). In Hunt, J. McV., editor: Personality and the behavior disorders, New York, 1944, The Ronald Press Co., pp. 922-937.
252. Proust, Marcel: Remembrance of things past, New York, 1934, Random House.
253. Psychiatrically deviated sex offenders, report no. 9, Committee on Forensic Psychiatry, Group for the Advancement of Psychiatry, Topeka, Kan., 1949.
254. Ribble, Margaret A.: Infantile experience in relation to personality disorder (chap. 20). In Hunt, J. McV., editor: Personality and the behavior disorders, vol. 11, New York, 1944, The Ronald Press Co., pp. 621-651.
255. Roche, P. Q.: Masochistic motivations in criminal behavior, Journal of Criminal Psychopathology **4**:431-444, 1942.
256. Rosen, J. N.: The treatment of schizophrenic psychosis by direct analytic therapy, Psychiatric Quarterly **21**:3-37, 117-119, 1947.
257. Sadler, William: Theory and practice of psychiatry, St. Louis, 1936, The C. V. Mosby Co., pp. 880-885.
258. Sadler, William: Modern psychiatry, St. Louis, 1945, The C. V. Mosby Co., p. 169.
259. St. Luke: **23**:34, King James Bible.
260. Salter, Andrew: The case against psychoanalysis, New York, 1963, The Citadel Press.
261. Sartre, Jean Paul: Nausea, New York, 1949, New Directions.
262. Schilder, Paul, and Bender, Lauretta: Impulsions: specific disorder of the behavior of children, Archives of Neurology and Psychiatry **43**:990-1008, 1940.
263. Scott, Natalie Anderson: The story of Mrs. Murphy, New York, 1947, E. P. Dutton & Co., Inc.
264. Shakespeare, William: Othello, London, 1853, Henry D. Bohn.
265. Shakespeare, William: King Lear, London, 1853, Henry E. Bohn.
266. Shakespeare, William: King Henry IV, London, 1853, Henry E. Bohn.
267. Sherrington, Charles: The integrative action of the nervous system, New Haven, 1923, Yale University Press.
268. Sherrington, Charles: The brain and its mechanism, London, 1934, Cambridge University Press.
269. Silverman, D.: The electroencephalogram of criminals, Archives of Neurology and Psychiatry **52**:38-42, 1944.
270. Simon, Benjamin, Holzberg, J. D., and Unger, J. F.: A study of judgment in the psychopathic personality, Psychiatric Quarterly **25**:132-150, 1951.
271. Simon, Benjamin, O'Leary, J. L., and Ryan, J. J.: Cerebral dysrhythmia and psychopathic personalities, Archives of Neurology and Psychiatry **56**:677-685, 1946.
272. Smith, W. D., and Helwig, F. C.: Liquor, the servant of man, Boston, 1939, Little, Brown & Co.
273. Solomon, J. C.: Adult character and behavior disorders, Journal of Clinical Psychopathology **9**:1-55, 1948.
274. Southard, C. O.: Truth ideas of an M.D., Kansas City, Mo., 1943, Unity School of Christianity.

275. Sprague, George S.: Varieties of homosexual manifestations, American Journal of Psychiatry **92**:143-154, 1935.

276. Stevenson, G. H.: Armchair psychiatry, Psychiatric Quarterly **23**:71-82, 1949.

277. Stevenson, G. H., and Geoghegan, J. J.: Prophylactic electroshock: five-year study, American Journal of Psychiatry **107**:743-748, 1951.

278. Stone, Simon: The Miller delusion, American Journal of Psychiatry **91**:593-623, 1934.

279. Storch, A.: The primitive archaic forms of inner experiences and thought in schizophrenia, Washington, D. C., 1924, Nervous and Mental Disease Publishing Co.

280. Straus, Erwin: On obsession, New York, 1948, Nervous and Mental Disease Monographs.

281. Strecker, E. A.: Some thoughts concerning the psychology and therapy of alcoholism, Journal of Nervous and Mental Disease **86**:191-205, 1937.

282. Strecker, E. A., and Appel, K.: Discovering ourselves, New York, 1939, The Macmillan Co.

283. Strecker, E. A., and Chambers, F. T.: Alcohol—one man's meat, New York, 1938, The Macmillan Co.

284. Suter, Cary: Anomic aphasia, Journal of the American Medical Association **151**:462-468, 1953.

285. Sutherland, E. H.: Principles of criminology, Philadelphia, 1939, J. B. Lippincott Co.

286. Swinburne, A. C.: Selected poems of Algernon Charles Swinburne, New York, 1928, Dodd, Mead & Co., Inc.

287. Thigpen, C. H., and Cleckley, Hervey: Freudian psychodynamics—science or mirage? The New Physician (Journal of the Student American Medical Association) **10**:97-101, 1961.

288. Thompson, D. L.: Address at banquet meeting of the American Psychiatric Association, Montreal, 1949.

289. Thompson, G. N.: The psychopathic delinquent and criminal, Springfield, Ill., 1953, Charles C Thomas, Publisher.

290. Tindall, W. Y.: James Joyce, New York, 1950, Charles Scribner's Sons.

291. Tolstoy, Leo: Anna Karenina, New York, 1886, Thomas Y. Crowell Co.

292. Toomey, Regis: Gabriel blow that horn, The Reader's Digest, Jan., 1943.

293. Towne, Alfred: Sexual gentleman's agreement, Neurotica **6**:23-28, 1950.

294. Tredgold, A. F.: Mental deficiency, New York, 1929, William Wood & Co.

295. Verlaine, Paul: Confessions of a poet, New York, 1950, Philosophical Library.

296. Vidal, Gore: The city and the pillar, New York, 1948, E. P. Dutton & Co., Inc.

297. Wagner, Melinda: Psychiatrist at the drawing board, Today's Health, Aug. 1963, pp. 15-17.

298. Wall, James: A study of alcoholism in men, American Journal of Psychiatry **92**:1389-1401, 1936.

299. Waugh, Evelyn: Brideshead revisited, Boston, 1946, Little, Brown & Co.

300. Waugh, Evelyn: Vile bodies, Boston, 1946, Little, Brown & Co.

301. Waugh, Evelyn: A handful of dust, Boston, 1946, Little, Brown & Co.

302. Waugh, Evelyn: The loved one, Boston, 1948, Little, Brown & Co.

303. Wells, F. L.: Social maladjustment: adaptive regression (chap. 18). In A handbook of social psychology, Worcester, Mass., 1935, Clark University Press, pp. 845-915.

304. Wilde, Oscar: De profundis, New York, 1951, Philosophical Library.

305. Wilde, Oscar: Helas, from The ballad of Reading gaol and other poems, New York, Little Leather Library Corp.

306. Williams, Ben Ames: The strange woman, Boston, 1941, Houghton Mifflin Co.
307. Wilson, Angus: Hemlock and after, New York, 1952, The Viking Press.
308. Wilson, J. G., and Pescor, M. J.: Problems in prison psychiatry, Caldwell, Idaho, 1939, Caxton Printers, Ltd.
309. Wolf, M. L.: Introduction to Verlaine, Paul: Confessions of a poet, New York, 1950, Philosophical Library.
310. Woods, Andrew J.: Courtship and marriage. In Sladen, Frank J., editor: Psychiatry and the war, Springfield, Ill., 1943, Charles C Thomas, Publisher, p. 193.
311. Woolley, Lawrence F.: A dynamic approach to psychopathic personality, Southern Medical Journal 25:926-934, 1942.
312. Wylie, Philip: Opus 21, New York, 1950, Pocket Books, Inc.
313. Zilboorg, G.: The medical man and the witch during the Renaissance, Baltimore, 1935, The Johns Hopkins Press, pp. 26-28.
314. Zilboorg, G.: Mind, medicine and man, New York, 1943, Harcourt, Brace & Co., Inc.

Index

Stanford-Binet test, 470
State Department, homosexuality in, 304-305
Statistics, 34-37, 483-488
Stavrogin's Confession, 327
Stealing, 66, 76, 85-86, 93, 134, 136, 147, 152-153, 374-375
Stedman's Medical Dictionary, definition of psychopath, 28
Stigmata of degeneration, 84, 242-243, 248, 442
Story of Mrs. Murphy, The, 361
Strange Interlude, 356
Strange Woman, The, 357-358
Straus, Erwin, 325, 428, 432
Strecker, E. A., 346
Strindberg, A., 334
Subjective reactions, difficulty in appraising, 444-446
Substitutive reactions, 437-438
Suicide in psychopath, 119, 154, 173, 176, 182, 206, 262, 393, 440
  rarity of, 393
  social and spiritual, 440
Superego, 466
Superiority and vulnerability, 453-454
Superstition, 25
Supramarginal gyrus, 414, 421
Suter, Cary, 414
Svidrigailov, 356
Swift, Jonathan, 325, 430
Swinburne, A. C., 144, 329, 330-334
Symposium, The, 314
Syphilis, 48, 146

T

Test, objective, for semantic disorder, 422-423
Theft, 66, 76, 85, 93, 106, 122, 134, 136-137, 147, 153, 192, 374-375
Thénardier, 356
Therapy for psychopath, 455, 476-482
  electric shock, 478
  psychoanalytic, 477
  surgical, 478
Thompson, D. L., 454
Thompson, G. N., 453, 456
Throwing oneself away, 295
Tobacco Road, 358-359
Tolstoi, Leo, 324, 354
Tom, case history of, 84-91
Towne, Alfred, 316-318
Toynbee, A., 341
Traditions that obscure subject of psychopath, 27-33, 237-247

Transient episodes of semantic disorder, 284-286
Trélat, 405
Truancy, 67, 85, 134, 156, 162, 189, 214,
Turn of the Screw, The, 355

U

Unconscious, antisocial impulses, 444
  anxiety, 271
  conflict, 432, 442-443
  guilt, 249-250, 281-282, 322-323, 446-447
Unger, J. F., 422-423
Unity, 24-25
Unpredictability, 368-369
Unreliability, 368-369, 370-371
Unresponsiveness, 387-388
Untruthfulness, 370-371, 374

V

Value judgments, 57-58, 240-241, 462-466, 470
Van Gogh, V., 325
Verbal artifacts, 240-241, 306, 464-466
Verbal examination, misleading with psychopath, 377, 406, 419-420, 451, 466, 470
Verlaine, P., 325-326, 328
Veterans Administration Hospitals, 483-488
Violence, psychopath's threats of, 93, 95-96, 169, 211, 219

W

Wagner, Richard, 325
Walter, case history of, 161-171
Ward, Artemus, 25
Waugh, Evelyn, 429
Weininger, Otto, 335
Wells, F. L., 437-439
White, W. A., 173
Wiener, N., 341
Wilde, Oscar, 307-308, 319, 334, 344
Willard, Jim, 312
Williams, Ben Ames, 357-358
Witchcraft, 22, 456-457
Withdrawal, 437-440, 450, 453
Wolf, M. L., 326
Women's devotion to psychopath, 183, 207-208, 212
  styles, influence of homosexuality, 319-320
Woods, A. J., 398
Woodward, S. B., 238
Woodworth, R. S., 438